Euler at 300

An Appreciation

LEONH.ᴰ EULER
NAT. BASILEÆ   MDCCVII.
MORT. PETROP.   MDCCLXXXIII.

Leonhard Euler (1707–1783)
Courtesy of the Library of Congress collection.

Euler at 300

An Appreciation

Edited by

Robert E. Bradley, Lawrence A. D'Antonio
and C. Edward Sandifer

Published and Distributed by
The Mathematical Association of America

SPECTRUM SERIES

The Spectrum Series of the Mathematical Association of America was so named to reflect its purpose: to publish a broad range of books including biographies, accessible expositions of old or new mathematical ideas, reprints and revisions of excellent out-of-print books, popular works, and other monographs of high interest that will appeal to a broad range of readers, including students and teachers of mathematics, mathematical amateurs, and researchers.

MAA Service Center
P.O. Box 91112
Washington, DC 20090-1112
800-331-1622   FAX 301-206-9789

Introduction

When an important mathematician celebrates a landmark birthday, other mathematicians sometimes gather together to give papers in appreciation of the life and work of the great person. When a mathematician as influential and productive as Leonhard Euler celebrates an anniversary as important as the 300th, a single meeting isn't sufficient to contain all of the contributions. During the years leading up to Leonhard Euler's tercentenary in 2007, at more than a dozen academic meetings across the USA and Canada, mathematicians and historians of mathematics paid homage to Euler in presentations detailing his many achievements. This book collects together some of the most memorable of these papers.

Leonhard Euler (1707–1783) was the most important mathematician of the 18th century. His collected works, which number more than 800 books and articles, fill over 70 large volumes. Between 1910 and 1913, Swedish Mathematician Gustav Eneström published a comprehensive census of Euler's works. He enumerated 866 works, including books, journal articles, and some published items of correspondence. He assigned each of them a number, which are now referred to as "Eneström numbers." Much like the opus numbers of classical music composers, this gives scholars a quick way to identify Euler's writings. These numbers, in the form E9, E41, and E251, are used freely throughout this collection.

Leonhard Euler was born on April 15, 1707 in Basel, Switzerland, son of Paul Euler, a Protestant minister, and Margaret Brucker. He grew up in the suburban village of Riehen and at age 14 he enrolled at the University of Basel, expecting to follow his father into the clergy. At the University, though, he began taking Saturday lessons in mathematics from Johann Bernoulli, probably the best mathematical mind in Continental Europe at that time. Euler thrived under Bernoulli's tutelage, and his mentor soon persuaded the Eulers, father and son both, that Leonhard should pursue a career in mathematics.

Though Bernoulli's career advice eventually proved to be wise, in the short term it was not very practical, and in 1727 when Euler finished his studies in Basel, the only position he could find was at the newly-founded Academy of Peter the Great in St. Petersburg.

Czar Peter I died in 1725 and his wife, Empress Catherine I died in 1727, so when Euler arrived in St. Petersburg the country as a whole was in some disarray and the Academy suffered a severe absence of leadership and financial support. Most members of the Academy were almost entirely unproductive. Euler used the opportunity provided by the lack of supervision to pursue his own interests in mathematics and mathematical physics.

Many of Euler's best ideas have their beginnings in his first years in St. Petersburg. He established his fame among his contemporaries in 1735 when he solved the Basel problem, the best-known outstanding problem of the time. Several of our contributors, including Pengelley and Sandifer, describe aspects of this episode.

He also began his lifelong project of making the principles of physics mathematical, especially mechanics, using the new tool of calculus. He made his first large step in this program in 1731 with E33, *Tentamen novae theoriae musicae*, "Thoughts on a new theory of music," in which, among other things, he establishes the mathematical foundations of the evenly tempered musical scale, the scale to which most modern musical instruments are still tuned. Despite his popular connection with well tempered tuning of the clavier, Johann Sebastian Bach ultimately favored the even tempering that Euler described.

Influential though the *Music Theory* was, it took until 1739 to see publication, so it was not the first book that Euler published. That distinction goes to his *Mechanica*, E15 and E16, written in the years 1734 to 1736 and published in two volumes in 1736. This great treatise on the mechanics of point masses was only the first of a long series of important works in mathematical physics. It was followed in 1749 by *Scientia navalis*, E110 and E111, establishing new principles of fluid mechanics and their applications to ship-building. His *Theoria motus corporum solidorum seu rigidorum*, (Theory of the motion of solid or rigid bodies), E289, used calculus to explain the phenomena of rotating bodies, thus virtually completing the subject that the modern undergraduate physics curriculum calls "mechanics."

The mid 1730s brought some stability to Russia, and enough additional funding that Euler earned a salary increase. This gave him the resources to marry Katerina Gsell in January 1734, and their son, Johann Albrecht, was born in November of that year, the first of their 13 children.

The 1730s marked Euler's first work in a variety of other subjects as well. He had written a short paper on the calculus of variations, E9, in about 1727, and through the 1730s he systematized his study of the subject. In 1735 he wrote his paper on the Bridges of Königsberg, E53. This paper is often cited as the beginning of the field of topology.

Probably Euler's greatest impact on the day-to-day activities of today's mathematicians and physicists came from this era, the gradual standardization of the symbols π and e for the constants we use today.

In 1741 the death of Empress Elizabeth I again left Russia in political turmoil. Riots and mobs attacking foreigners made Euler fear for the safety of his young family. When the Prussian King Frederick II offered him a position in his new Academy in Berlin, Euler accepted and left Russia for 25 years.

Frederick II later became known as Frederick the Great for his many military conquests. For about half of the time Euler spent in Berlin, Frederick was away at war. As he had done in St. Petersburg, Euler used these relatively unsupervised intervals to great effect. He wrote the pioneering text on the calculus of variations, E65, the *Methodus inveniendi*, and what is regarded as one of the finest mathematics books ever written, the *Introductio in analysin infinitorum*, E101 and E102. Euler designed this two-volume work to help students make the difficult step from algebra to calculus.

While in Berlin, Euler also worked on celestial mechanics, number theory, ballistics, a differential calculus textbook, hydraulics, the theory of machines, differential equations and a dozen other topics, as well as discovering his polyhedral formula, $V - E + F = 2$. More about Euler's activities in Berlin and the intellectual backdrop of Europe in the Enlightenment can be found in Rüdiger Thiele's article on Euler in the 1750s.

When the Seven Years War ended in 1763, Frederick returned to Berlin and gave much of his attention to the Academy. Euler did not appreciate such close supervision from his King, so when he had the opportunity to return to the Academy in St. Petersburg in 1766, he and his family again transplanted themselves.

Euler was treated as a celebrity when he arrived in St. Petersburg, and his son Johann Albrecht was appointed Secretary of the Academy. He finished the three books he had been working on, *Letters to a German Princess*, E343, E344 and E417 in 1768 and 1772, his integral calculus textbook, *Institutionum calculi integralis*, E342, E366 and E385 in the years 1768 to 1770, and a textbook on the construction and sailing of ships, *Théorie complette de la construction et de la manoeuvre des vaisseaux*, E426 in 1773. With his life's plan for publishing books complete, he turned his attention to two final goals, to leave the St. Petersburg Academy a legacy of papers to publish for 20 years after his death and to train a generation of mathematicians to succeed him. Despite unsuccessful cataract surgery in 1771 that left him almost completely blind and a house fire that destroyed his library and many of his personal possessions, he was entirely successful in the first of these goals. The Academy continued publishing his papers regularly until 1830, almost 50 years after his death.

Euler was less successful at training the next generation. Though he worked closely with a group of successors and they showed good promise while they were under his wing, who today remembers the names Johann Albrecht Euler, Anders Lexell, Nicolaus Fuss, Mikhail Golovin, S. K. Kotelnikov, Stepan Rumovsky or Petr Inokhodtsev? Though they helped Euler write over 300 papers between 1766 and his death in 1783, they, unlike Euler, were not able to work effectively without the supervision of their teacher. After Euler's death, the Academy began a long and gradual decline into mediocrity.

In a very real sense, the celebration of Euler's tercentenary in the American mathematical community began with a Contributed Paper Session on January 11, 2001, at the Joint Mathematics Meetings in New Orleans, LA. The session, "Mathematics in the Age of Euler," was sponsored by the Mathematical Association of America (MAA) and organized by William Dunham and V. Frederick Rickey. Dunham is the author of the 1999 book *Euler: The Master of Us All* and Rickey was an organizer of the NSF-funded summer Institutes on the History of Mathematics and Its Use in Teaching. Well-known both for these achievements and for their outstanding abilities as speakers, Rickey and Dunham attracted an impressive array of speakers, who made presentations on the mathematics of Euler and his contemporaries. Four of the papers presented at that meeting are included in this volume: the pieces by Barnett, Heine, McKinzie ("The Formalist Argument") and Sandifer ("Euler's Fourteen Problems").

Less well-known, but just as important for the course of Euler studies, was the conversation that took place that evening among Ron Calinger, John Glaus and Ed Sandifer. Over dinner at Delmonico's, they conceived of an academic society devoted to the study of Euler's life, his achievements in mathematics and physics, and the broader historical issues related to his place in the European Enlightenment. Thus the Euler Society was founded, although it was not officially incorporated as a non-profit organization until 2003. The

Euler Society has held annual summer meetings since August 2002. The largest group of papers in this volume consists of those given at meetings of the Euler Society: the papers by D'Antonio, Godard, Klyve & Stemkoski, Langton ("Combinatorics"), Lathrop & Stemkoski, McKinzie ("Harmonic Series"), Pengelley, and Thiele ("The Decade 1750–60").

The Canadian Society for History and Philosophy of Mathematics (CSHPM), whose annual summer meetings are a crucial activity for North American historians of mathematics, has also played host to a large number of Euler-related talks in the years leading up to the Euler tercentenary. We have included four papers from CSHPM meetings: the pieces by Baltus, Bradley (both articles), and Sandifer ("Euler Rows the Boat").

Sectional meetings of the American Mathematical Society (AMS) sometimes include sessions on the history of mathematics. Papers in this volume by Jardine and Sandifer ("The Basel Problem") were first presented at AMS meetings in Boston, MA, in 2002 and New York, NY, in 2003, respectively.

To complete this volume, we have included two more papers from MAA-sponsored events. Langton's paper on lunes was given at the MAA Contributed Papers Session on "Mathematics in the Second Millennium" at the 2002 Joint Mathematics Meeting in San Diego, CA. Thiele's paper on the function concept was a special lecture sponsored by HOMSIGMAA (the MAA's History of Mathematics Special Interest Group) at the 2004 MathFest in Providence, RI.

Janet Heine Barnett's paper "Enter, Stage Center: The Early Drama of the Hyperbolic Functions" has previously appeared in *Mathematics Magazine*, February 2004, pp. 15–30. Otherwise, the papers in this collection have not appeared elsewhere in their present form. We would like to note that Carolyn Lathrop was an undergraduate and Lee Stemkoski was a graduate student when they co-authored "Parallels in the Work of Leonhard Euler and Thomas Clausen." Both Stemkoski and Dominic Klyve were graduate students when they wrote their paper "The Euler Archive: Giving Euler to the World."

This book is arranged thematically. It begins with three articles with a broad historical perspective. The rest of the chapters describe the details of many of Euler's mathematical discoveries. Results in pure mathematics come before those in applied mathematics. The mathematics papers begin with one article each on algebra and geometry. These are followed by eight chapters on analysis, the first four of which cover a variety of topics from the function concept to the theory of elliptic integrals, while the latter four are concerned with infinite series. These are followed by three pieces on combinatorial or probabilistic topics. The collection concludes with five papers on applied topics, from fluid mechanics to shipbuilding and mapmaking.

Many people contribute to the creation of a volume such as this one, and the editors wish to express their appreciation. We begin by thanking the fifteen authors, whose work the editors get three opportunities to enjoy: first of all when they made their presentations at the various meetings over the last several years, second in manuscript form as they worked with the authors to recast their spoken words as written ones, and finally they can enjoy their creative efforts in the form of this book for many years to come. We join our authors in extending thanks to the organizers of the many sessions and meetings that gave the authors venues to present their papers.

All of the authors—indeed, all Euler scholars—are grateful to Dominic Klyve and Lee Stemkoski for creating and maintaining the Euler Archive (www.eulerarchive.org).

They conceived of the archive, which they describe in chapter 3 of this book, at the first meeting of the Euler Society in 2002. With the assistance of Rachel Esselstein, Alison Setyadi, Erik Tou and a group of energetic Dartmouth undergraduates, Lee and Dominic have made more than 95% of Euler's original publications available on the worldwide web. Almost as important to scholars is the searchable data base of bibliographic information on Euler's writings. The archive is an efficient and powerful tool.

We thank the editors and staff at the MAA, especially Jerry Alexanderson, Bev Ruedi, Elaine Pedreira and Don Albers, for their hard work, insight and patience. To these we add special thanks to Theresa Sandifer. When the editorial work got particularly heavy for a while, she pitched in to help proofread and edit manuscripts. That help is greatly appreciated. We are also grateful to our wives and families (and cats) for their patience and support through the years it has taken to bring this book to fruition.

Robert E. Bradley   Lawrence A. D'Antonio
Adelphi University   Ramapo College of New Jersey
Garden City, NY   Mawah, NJ

C. Edward Sandifer
Western Connecticut State University
Danbury, CT

Contents

Leonhard Euler, the Decade 1750–1760[1]

Rüdiger Thiele

Introduction

I am delighted to have been invited to deliver The Euler Lecture at the Annual Meeting of our Society, however, I am not sure whether you will be delighted by my poor English.[2] In the Countdown to the Tercentenary, which the organizers drafted, I am obliged to deal with the decade from 1750 to 1760, and of course I will meet the obligation, at least in principle.

Let me start with a short overview of my lecture. First, I would like to embed the fifties into Euler's Berlin period and from this viewpoint I will say a few words about the situation in Berlin, especially the political, religious, and philosophical background of this time. Secondly, I will present a selection of important results Euler discovered in the 1750's to give you at least a glimpse of Euler's scientific activities in Berlin. Thirdly, I will briefly deal with the quarrel over the Principle of Least Action. Finally, I will describe one of the most important concepts in mathematics, essentially coined by Euler: the concept of function, in particular the analytical version.

On the historical background

The Enlightenment, although different in interests and appearance, changed the established ways of living. This movement of thought was concerned with the concept of reason, moreover it was convinced that each concern could be settled by rational thought and that is why each affair was dragged before the judgment seat of pure reason. Furthermore, the established ways of thinking and believing were attacked by the beginning of modern science and, as a by-product of science, anti-Christian Rationalism arose.

---

[1] Lecture delivered at the 2004 Euler Conference, August 8–11, Roger Williams University, Portsmouth, RI.

[2] I take this opportunity to express my thanks to the editors, who have improved my English. Furthermore, it is a pleasure to thank my colleague and friend Robert E. Bradley. We got to know each other when he invited me to speak at his Pohle Colloquium. Then I had repeated opportunities to take part in the life of The Euler Society and to become acquainted with many Eulerians in the United States thanks to the excellent hospitality afforded me by him and his wife Susan Petry.

In general culture the age of pure reason is often regarded as a time of philosophy alone (so called in honor of John Locke (1632–1704), François Marie de Voltaire (1694–1778) or other philosophers), however it was also a great time for the natural sciences too, a time that worked out a new frame of scientific thinking. As a well-known example, Isaac Newton (1643–1727) had explained the universe. It was the progress of the natural sciences that increasingly influenced the rise of industry and that, as a consequence, determined the human condition to this day.

Without any doubt the leading natural scientist of the 18th century was Leonhard Euler (1707–1783). About a century after Euler's death the German historian Hermann Hankel (1839–1873) properly remarked that Euler represented the scientific consciousness in the middle of the 18th century in the best way. In our day, the late Clifford Truesdell (1919–2000) estimated that in the 18th century Euler alone wrote about one third of the mathematical works (including mathematical physics). The whole life of this extraordinary man was determined by the natural sciences in the Enlightenment and by the Christian religion, as well as the relationship between the two.

Berlin

Frederick the Great (or Friedrich II of Prussia (1712–1786, king from 1740)) transformed Prussia into an efficient and prosperous European state. When his father, King Frederick William I (Friedrich Wilhelm I; 1688–1740, ruled from 1713) died, he left an army of about 83,000 soldiers from a population of about 2,000,000. Frederick II was a brilliant military campaigner; he made Prussia the foremost military power on the Continent enlarging Prussia's territory and undermining Austria's reign. Indeed, Frederick the Great was a strong military leader, but was guided by a strategy of power without regard for losses. However, Henry (Heinrich), Prince of Prussia (1726–1802), a younger brother of Frederick II, preferred a more modern type of warfare using tactical military maneuvers which minimized losses. These differences led to sharp discord with the King. Later on, in scientific matters, the King had a strained relationship with Euler.

Frederick William von Steuben (1730–1794), who served in the Prussian army under Prince Henry, knew these quarrels. When Steuben served the cause of U.S. independence he supported endeavors to install a constitution like the English, rather than a republican one. Moreover, in 1786 he tried to bring Henry to a leading position in America as a King or a Governor (letter to Henry from November 2, 1786) — but in vain (Henry's response from April 1787). [3]

Frederick II is often regarded as a philosopher on the throne who introduced new traits of absolutist reign. Indeed, the Francophile Frederick was also interested in the sciences, although more in art and philosophy. Voltaire rejoiced but boasted too soon: "Sciences and art mounted the throne." Indeed, among Frederick's first activities was an ambitious scientific aim: to transform the unimportant Society of Science founded by his father in Berlin in 1700 into a modern academy to rival that in Paris.[4] So, he invited top scholars

---

[3] Christian Graf von Krockow, *Die preußischen Brüder*. Stuttgart: Deutsche Verlags-Anstalt 1996, pp. 170f.

[4] The Prussian Academy is distinguished from those in Paris and London in at least two ways: i) the Berlin Academy was not financed by the King but by some privileges it had gotten (like the monopoly of the sales and marketing of calendars and geographical maps), ii) the Academy united natural sciences and humanities (as it is expressed in the name Académie Royale des Sciences et Belles Lettres) and was divided into four classes, one of which was the mathematical one.

Figure 1. Frederick II (1712–1786), King of Prussia from 1740. Courtesy of Sudhoff Institut, Leipzig.

Figure 2. Sans Souci (Carefree) was the summer residence of King Frederick II, erected from 1745–1747. The rotunda shown in the photo was the place where Frederick's Philosophical Circle met. Photograph by Rüdiger Thiele.

Figure 3. Prussian Academy in Berlin, in the Friedrichsstadt Quarter, 1752. Courtesy of the Archive of the Berlin-Brandenburgische Akademie Berlin.

to become members of his academy. However, when Leonhard Euler finally arrived in Berlin on July 25, 1741, the Prussian King was at war trying to conquer Silesia (Silesian Wars 1740–1742, 1744–1745, the Seven Years War, 1756–1763). At the time, Voltaire's judgment was "The prince takes off the philosopher's coat and takes out his sword if he recognizes an interesting province." Because of the war, the Prussian Academy was not reorganized until 1744 and formally opened in 1745.

In the 18th century, universities were not centers of mathematical research. Leadership was taken instead by a few royal academies. In Euler's case, the Academies of Berlin and St. Petersburg (founded in 1700 and 1725 respectively), which both owed their existence to the restless ambition of Gottfried Wilhelm Leibniz (1646–1716), gave Euler the chance to be the mathematician we know. Euler's friend Daniel Bernoulli (1700–1782) congratulated him from the bottom of his heart for the wonderful appointment in Berlin. Incidentally, it was above all these two academies, in addition to the academies in Paris and London, that made possible a full century of mathematical progress.

We are intimately acquainted with the music of the fifties: Johann Sebastian Bach (1685–1750) and Georg Friedrich Händel (1685–1759) died in this period, Wolfgang Amadeus Mozart (1756–1791) was born. But what did Euler do in those days 250 years ago? On 18 July 1754, in the *Registres*[5] of the Academy, we find the entry: "*L'académie est entrée dans les Feries Caniculaires*," i.e., it was closed until August 22 because of the Dog Days. Of course, the restless Euler carried on. On August 8 and 12 he got letters from his King hoping to bring Daniel Bernoulli to the University of Halle. On August 9 Euler got

[5]*Die Registres der Berliner Akademie der Wissenschaften*, 1746–1766, edited by E. Winter. Berlin: Akademie-Verlag 1957, p. 203; *Eulers Wirken an der Berliner Akademie der Wissenschaften*, 1741–1766. Spezialinventar. Ed. by W. Knobloch. Berlin: Akademie-Verlag 1984, pp. 149f.; *Euleri Opera Omnia*, ser. quarta A, vol. VI, ed. by P. Costabel et al. Basel: Birkhäuser 1986, p. 341; J.L. Lagrange, *Oeuvres*, ed. by J.A. Serret and G. Darboux, vol. 14. Paris 1892, pp. 135–138; the mentioned letters from Russia are preserved in the Petersburg Academy Archive.

Figure 4. Euler's house at Behrenstraße 21, now opposite the Comic Opera. The detail shows the memorial tablet from 1907, erected by the Berlin Mathematical Society. Photographs by Rüdiger Thiele.

galleys for an almanac and on August 10 he received a bill from a joiner for work he had done for the Botanical Garden, because Euler was responsible for seeing it was paid. On August 10 he got two letters from Petersburg, Russia, written by Gerhard Friedrich Müller (1705–1783) and Johann Daniel Schumacher (1690–1761) informing him that Georg Krafft (1701–1754), an old colleague from his Petersburg days, had died in Tübingen, Germany, on July 18. Even so long ago, they had an information network as quick and as complicated as our mail system. However the most important letter had already been on Euler's table for a few weeks: it was the first letter written on July 28 by the young Joseph Louis Lagrange (1736–1813), who reported an analogy between the binomial theorem $(a+b)^m$ and the product rule $d^m(xy)$ for higher differentials. Lagrange's second letter written one year later on August 12, 1755, was most important because it informed Euler of a new technique in the calculus of variations, the δ-formalism.[6]

Euler arrived in Berlin on 25 July 1741. At the beginning he was content. From the battlefield the King addressed a letter to Euler: "*A mon professeur Euler*" (To my professor Euler). Euler felt flattered and wrote enthusiastically: "In my research I can do just what I wish. [...] The King calls me his professor, and I think I am the happiest man in the world." Ultimately in 1746 Euler became director of the mathematical class of the newly founded Académie Royale des Sciences et Belles Lettres in Berlin and even substituted for the president Maupertuis when the latter was absent. Euler bought a house in the Bärenstraße 21 (now Behrenstraße, opposite the Comic Opera) for 2000 Thaler, and that house still

---

[6]See R. Thiele, Euler and the Calculus of Variations, in: *Leonhard Euler: Life, Work and Legacy*. Ed. by R. Bradley and E. Sandifer. Amsterdam: Elsevier 2007, 235–254, esp. pp. 249f.

Figure 5. Map of the east coast of North America from the *Atlas geographicus* (1760, 2nd ed.), edited by the Prussian Academy of Sciences and directed by Leonhard Euler. Courtesy of Leopoldina, Halle.

stands. Later he bought an estate and orchard for 6000 Thaler. His mother (Margaretha Euler, 1677–1761) arrived in Berlin in 1750 and stayed there until her death in 1761.

Euler's energy was inexhaustible. He supervised the library, the observatory, the botanical garden, the publication of scientific papers, selected the personnel, directed various financial matters including the publication of various calendars and geographical maps (the sale of which was a source of income to the Academy), and served the King as an advisor for example on state lotteries, insurance, pensions, salt mines, artillery, pumps for fountains in the royal summer residence, and correcting the level of a canal. Moreover, by submitting papers to the Prussian and to the Russian Academies, Euler *de facto* worked in both academies. Nevertheless, his endless stream of manuscripts overtaxed the publication capabilities of both. His busy pen left many manuscripts after his death, which the Petersburg Academy published during the half century that followed. Furthermore, he was a member of the parish council (*Gemeindeältester*) and it was precisely in the sense of his father that he reformed some of the affairs of the parish.[7] For example, he revised the instruction given to candidates for confirmation and he promoted the printing and repeating of sermons.

For all that, Euler was unpopular at Frederick's court. "*Nous avons ici un gros cyclope*

---

[7] See J. Glaus, Das Heilige und das Profane, in: *Euler-Gedenkband*, Braunschweig 2007.

Figure 6. Meeting of the Berlin Academy as imagined by the painter Adolph Menzel (1815–1905). Euler is seated on the left at the front and though Frederick II is at the head of the table, he never actually attended any meeting of his Academy (although his papers were read). Courtesy of Sudhoff Institut, Leipzig.

de géométrie (We have a great Cyclops of mathematics here)," Frederick II tastelessly wrote to Voltaire. In Greek mythology Cyclops are giants with one eye, and Euler was nearly blind in one eye. Euler's and the King's personalities were too different; these two important figures of the Enlightenment never became close friends. Frederick viewed science as the servant of the state—*his* state. The King exclusively judged science in view of its utilitarian aspects (not unlike the present arguments for cutting budgets). Frederick said that a country not supporting science would soon be a century behind its neighbors. Frederick appreciated Euler's scientific talents and he engaged him in a variety of practical problems. An example is the project to build up a hydraulic system of pumps and pipes at the royal summer residence. Unfortunately, the fountains never worked satisfactorily. The King interpreted this technical failure as a failure of Euler (who was not at all guilty), and as a failure of science itself.[8] He commented maliciously: "*Vanités des vanités! vanité de la Géométrie!*" (Vanities of vanities, vanity of geometry). On the other hand, in the Court, the discordant, ambivalent King appreciated good manners more than all the calculations of Newton. King Frederick and many others in Berlin were put out by Euler's penetrating attacks against free thinking ("the rabble of free thinkers (*die Rotte der Freygeister*)," "these wretched people (*diese elenden Leute*)").

Frederick preferred French high culture and its representatives, such as the atheist Voltaire or the Roman Catholic Pierre-Louis Moreau de Maupertuis (1698–1759); on the other hand Euler appreciated puppet shows. When Maupertuis died in 1759 (the year of the battle of Quebec that gave control of Canada to England) Euler continued to run the Academy, but Frederick never made him President. Euler safely managed the Academy in difficult days through Frederick's wars and successfully controlled its financial affairs. But Euler and the King differed more and more sharply, especially in financial affairs and personnel matters concerning the Academy. Calendars were a source of revenue for the

---

[8] See Eckart in *Euler: A Tercentenary Celebration*, ed. R. Baker, Kendrick Press, 2007.

Berlin Academy. On Euler's mathematically unconvincing accounts to the King regarding expected sales of calendars, Frederick responded arrogantly: "I, who do not know how to calculate, know that sixteen thousand écus [a French coin] of receipts are preferable to thirteen thousand." Euler felt unfairly discriminated against. His justified hopes were not realized, not even in the least.

For this and other reasons Euler began to think of leaving Berlin in 1762, and during the Seven Years War he contacted the enemy Russians where Catherine the Great (1729–1796, tsarina from 1762) had come to power. The war ended in 1763, the same year Canada was ceded to the British by the Treaty of Paris. On 2 February 1766, Euler pleaded for royal permission to leave Prussia, but the King, now becoming aware of the immense loss, declined the request. Euler insisted. Finally, on May 2, the King agreed with the following humiliating words, showing no gratitude for Euler's incomparable work: "*Je vous permets, sur votre lettre du trente d'avril dernier, de quitter pour aller en Russie.*"

Gotthold Ephraim Lessing (1729–1781), a contemporary German poet, remarked that the King does not pay someone who wants to be independent. So Euler, at 59, left Berlin on 9 June 1766. Joseph-Louis de Lagrange succeeded him in the same year and remained in Berlin until the death of Frederick II in 1786. At the same time James Cook (1728–1779) explored the seaways and coasts of Canada (1763–1767) and began to prepare his first circumnavigation of the world in 1768–1771.

The professor of French grammar Dieudonné Thiébault (1733–1807), arrived in Berlin in 1765 and his book *Mes souvenirs de vingt ans séjour Berlin* (My memories of a stay of twenty years in Berlin) is an early compendium of the well-known anecdotes and descriptions of Euler: Euler as a friendly man always ready to help, working amidst his playing children, but also Euler as stubborn enemy of botany, which as the science of dried grass he regarded as a trivial matter and completely unimportant ("*rien n'étoit moins important que la science botanique*"). Thiébault also describes Euler as an opinionated person as is often the habit of mathematicians. Euler once started a quarrel over a fence and took the affair to court; the legal costs were 100 Thaler. The fence would have cost only 5 Thaler. Where light is, there is shadow too.

A glimpse of Euler's research in the decade 1750–1760

In Berlin Euler's research was at the summit of his creative powers, and in the midst of this period he became an elected member of the Paris Academy (in 1755). He was the ninth foreign member although by its statutes only eight were permitted. Euler mainly devoted his energy to analysis and mathematical physics with a practical orientation. During the Berlin period Euler prepared about 380 works of which 275 were published in Berlin. He wrote and received about 1,000 letters. The papers included:

1750	"Sur la vibration des cordes" (E 140, OO II/10; 1748).[9] Wave equation.
1750	"Partitio numerorum" (E 191, OO I/2; 1750–51/1753).[10]
1751	"Recherches sur les racines imaginaires des équations" (E 170, OO I/6 ; 1749, 1751), Fundamental theorem of algebra: an algebraic polynomial of degree n

---

[9]OO is an abbreviation for *Opera Omnia Euleri*. Numbers such as E140 refer to Eneström's numbering of Euler's publications.

[10]In general Euler read a paper in the Academy and immediately submitted it to a journal, but the publication

with real coefficients can be resolved into linear and quadratic factors, i.e., it has n (complex) roots. The domain of complex numbers is "closed" under algebraic and transcendental operations (already in a letter to Goldbach in 1742).

1751   Version of the law of reciprocity in divisor theorems (E 164, OO I/2; 1744/46).

1752   "Découverte d'un nouveau principe de mécanique" (E 177, OO II/5; 1750), Law of angular momentum for rigid bodies: $L = dH/dt$ (L turning moment, H moment of momentum; addition to Newton's second law for point mechanics $F = dI/dt$; F force, I moment).

1753   *Theoria motus lunae* (E 187, OO II/23; written in 1751), first lunar theory.

1753   *Atlas geographicus* (Prefatio), 41 maps. (E 205, OO III/2 only Prefatio), new edition in 1760 with 44 maps.

1753–55   Analytical theory of hydrodynamics, turbine theory (E 179, 202, 203, 207, 208, 222, all in OO II/15).

1755   Euler read the proof of Fermat's theorem (E 262) at the Academy, printed in 1761.

1755   *Institutiones calculi differentialis* (E 212, OO I/10; completed about 1748).

1758   Polyhedral theorem (E 230, OO I/26). Equation for the motion of gyroscope.

1761   Power residues. "Theoremata circa residua ex divisione potestatum relicta." (E 262, OO I/2; 1758/59)

In his *Introductio* (E 101, OO I/8-9, §132; publ. in 1748) Euler gave the so-called de Moivre formula

$$e^{i\phi} = \cos\phi + i\sin\phi$$

which in a slightly different form had already been given by Roger Cotes (1682–1716) in 1714. A special case appears in the paper "De la controverse entre Messieurs Leibnitz et Bernoulli sur les logarithmes des nombres négatifs et imaginaires" (On the controversy between Messrs. Leibniz and John Bernoulli on the logarithms of negative and imaginary numbers) (E 168, OO I/17; 1749, 1751 printed): $\log(-1) = i\pi$ (already discovered in 1727), or in another form

$$e^{i\pi} + 1 = 0,$$

linking five important mathematical magnitudes in *one* equation.

Only a few mathematicians have invented more than two or three symbols which are universally accepted in modern mathematics. Euler is among them, because of his influential writings. Indeed he was a great notation builder. Some examples in analysis (with the year of print):

1734	$f(x)$	E 44, OO I, 22 (printed in 1740),
1736	e, π	*Mechanica*, vol. 1, pp. 68, 119 (E 15-16, OO II/1-2),
1748	$\sin x, \cos x$	E 101–102, OO I/8-9,
1755	$\sum, \Delta, \Delta^2$	E 212, OO I/10,
1794	$i = \sqrt{-1}$	E 671, OO I/19 (read in 1777).

---

was often delayed (even some years) so both dates are given: the year the volume was really planned for and the year it actually appeared.

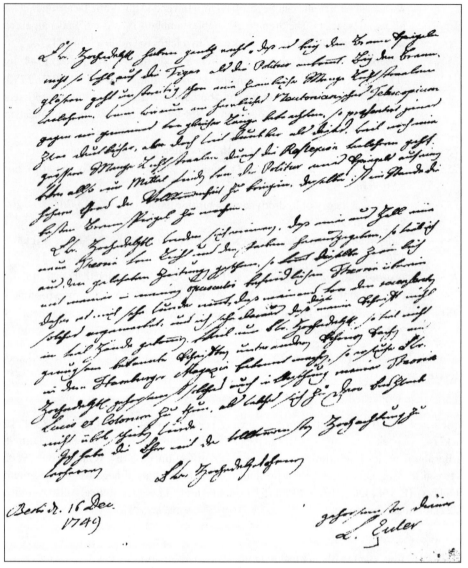

Figure 7. Last page of a letter from Euler to A.G. Kästner, Dec. 1749. Among other things Euler asked Kästner to review his paper "Conjectura physica" (E151, 1750). The review appeared in *Hamburgische Magazin* 8 (1751), pp. 271–287. Courtesy of Universitätsbibliotheken Leipzig and Göttingen.

Principle of Least Action

All in all, Euler led a peaceful life in Berlin for many years. However, Euler took part in several sharp philosophical-theological debates, the most famous of which was the controversial dispute on Maupertuis's principle of least action. Maupertuis published this principle in a paper entitled "Accord de différentes Loix de la Nature qui avoient jusq'ici paru incompatibles (Harmony between different laws of nature which have, up to now, appeared incompatible)" in 1744. Two years later he went on to state the "principe général" in a paper "Les Loix du Mouvement et du Repos déduites d'un Principe Métaphysique (On the

Figure 8. Voltaire, François-Marie Arouet de (1694–1778), French philosopher and temporary member of Frederick's Circle in Sans Souci. Courtesy of Sudhoff Institut, Leipzig.

Laws of Motion and of Rest Deduced by a Metaphysical Principle)." He expressed it in this way: "to produce some changes in nature the necessary quantity of action is the smallest that is possible." With this principle, Maupertuis hoped to unify the laws of physics and he even regarded the principle as a proof of the existence of God (*l'être suprême*). From a mathematical viewpoint, soon some scholars criticized the general principle. Among the first were the Gottsched Circle[11] in Leipzig in 1748, Patrick Comte d'Arcy (1725–1779) one year later, and in 1751 Samuel Koenig (1712–1757) even accused Maupertuis of plagiarizing Leibniz's work.

In the late 1740s and early 1750s this debate changed into a conflict and grew contentious; Voltaire and even Frederick II were involved. Euler supported Maupertuis, but Maupertuis was finally ruined. Because of his satire *Doctor Akakia*,[12] Voltaire fled and temporarily became a refugee in Leipzig. Here the Old Mocker even managed to insert a funny announcement into a newspaper saying Leipzig's authorities wanted Maupertuis and therefore would pay a reward of 1,000 Thaler for Maupertuis's capture to anybody who would bring him before the town walls.

Euler's attitude was ambiguous. Because he interpreted the principle as a theological one, he was compelled to defend religion against the hated ideology of free thought. On the other hand, as a mathematician he correctly formulated the principle for some cases in dynamics, and he believed that nature operates in this way. From his *Methodus inveniendi* (Calculus of Variations) (E 65, OO I/24; 1744):

---

[11] Johann Christoph Gottsched (1700–1766), fled from Prussia to Leipzig in 1724 because of military service obligations. He was an influential professor of poetry, later of logic and metaphysics, both at the University of Leipzig. For five years he held the position of the president (rector) of Leipzig's University. In 1740 Gottsched translated Bayle's *Dictionnaire historique et critique* (1695–1697) into German. From 1742 to 1750, he and his Circle modeled after the Académie Française and representing the ideas of the Enlightenment, edited the monthly journal *Neuer Büchersaal der schönen Wissenschaften und freyen Künste* (New books of the belles lettres and liberal arts), afterwards from 1751 to 1762 the journal *Das Neueste aus der anmuthigen Gelehrsamkeit* (The latest from the salon), which dealt with natural sciences as well as humanities.

[12] The Greek word *akakos* (α-$\kappa\alpha\kappa o\zeta$) means lighthearted or nonchalant, and in Berlin "Dr. Lighthearted" was Maupertuis's well-known nickname.

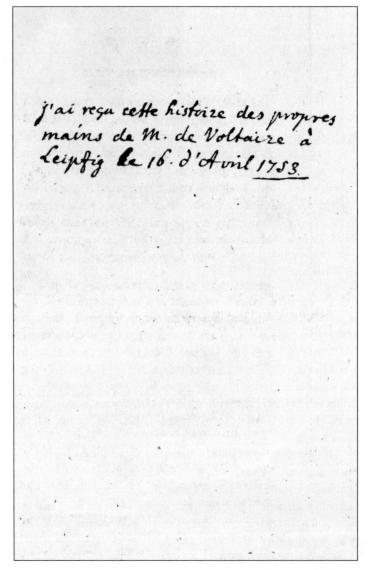

Figure 9. Title page of Voltaire's *Histoire du docteur Akakia*, 1753 (facing page). The inscription above (in an unknown hand) says Voltaire himself presented the book in Leipzig. Courtesy of Universitätsbibliothek Leipzig.

> For since the fabric of the Universe is most perfect and the work of a most wise
> Creator, nothing at all takes place in the Universe in which some rule of maximum
> or minimum does not appear.[13]

Euler had the strong belief that the basic physical principles can always be expressed by
some minimal or maximal properties. But mathematically, in his paper "On the motion
of bodies in a non-resisting medium, determined by the method of maxima and minima"
(Appendix II in *Methodus inveniendi*), he correctly limited himself to some particular ap-

---

[13] OO I/24, p. Add. I.

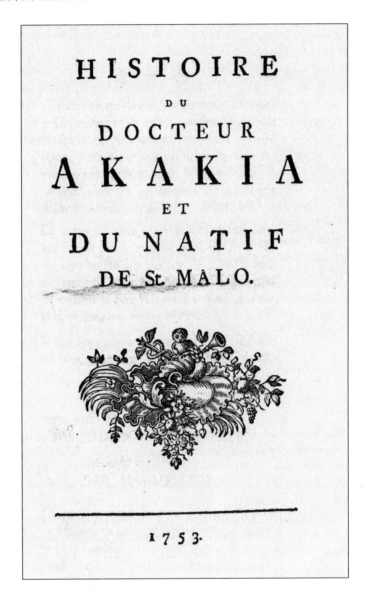

HISTOIRE

D U

DOCTEUR

AKAKIA

ET

DU NATIF

DE St. MALO.

1 7 5 3.

plications in dynamics and, *expressis verbis*, left the general case to Philosophers, and he did not use the principle to prove the existence of God mathematically. Although Euler was guided throughout by general teleological principles (by *a priori* conviction) his realistic view appears permanently (the *a posteriori* corroboration of the principles by true and sound dynamic methods).

Euler's physico-theological view clearly appeared in his defense of Maupertuis's principle, which stated that in all the changes that happen in nature, the cause that produces them is the least that can be. Maupertuis proclaimed his economic principle to be a *general law* of nature, most worthy of the Creator, whereas critics mocked Maupertuis for making the almighty God a stingy, or at least a parsimonious, Creator.[14] Moreover, Maupertuis regarded the principle as the first scientific proof of God's existence.

Euler saw a twofold way to describe the laws of nature, i.e., the corresponding differential equations. On the one hand, in mechanics we can follow Newton's laws, and on the other hand we can state an extremal principle as Maupertuis did. In natural sciences Euler was basically an experimentalist;[15] he tried to conjecture general laws and to prove them, but he was very impressed by the *a priori* view of Maupertuis. This admiration of setting *general* principles is one important reason for Euler's support of Maupertuis. Indeed, Maupertuis's principle contains many other widely known principles that hadn't been the case until then.

Let me mention here that for Euler the true foundation of human knowledge rests on three fundamentally distinct classes of information: the truth of the senses (experience), that of understanding (reasoning), and that of belief (history). Each of these three classes, of course, requires peculiar proofs of the trust placed in it:

> *I have seen or felt*, is the proof of the first class; *I can demonstrate it*, is that of the second: we likewise say, *I know it is so*. Finally, *I receive it on the testimony of persons worthy of credit*, or *I believe it on solid grounds*, is the proof of the third class. (*Lettres à une Princesse*, April 4, 1761; E 343–344, 417, OO III/11-12; 1768).

The concept of function

In any lecture on Euler, who is known as Analysis Incarnate (*l'analyse incarnée*, Domenique Arago, 1786–1853), we need to say something about his analysis. Incidentally, the status of analysis at that time is described by Voltaire (1694–1778) with his spiteful tongue in this way: "The art of numbering and measuring exactly a thing whose existence cannot be conceived,"[16] and Hermann Weyl (1885–1955) spoke of "Euler's era of happy-go-lucky analysis" in order to point out the carelessness rooted in good and reliable intuition.

It was Euler who established the concept of function at the heart of the new branch of mathematics called analysis. Furthermore, analysis was not only an application of algebra to geometry. It became a subject in its own right, above all by developing a formal theory of functions that had no need of geometrical conceptions. Therefore no figures are to be found in Euler's textbooks on analysis[17] as had been the case, for example, in Isaac Barrow's (1630–1677) *Lectiones geometricae* (1670) or in Guillaume François Antoine de l'Hospital's (1661–1704) *Analyse des infiniment petits* (1696) the first textbook on the subject matter.

---

[14] See footnote 11.

[15] Euler definitely made experiments, already for his early paper on the masting of ships ("Meditationes super problemate nautico," E4, OO II/20; 1727) he experimented. He even developed a mechanics of similarity which was used for models of bridges ("Regula facilis" (Simple Rule; E480, OO II/17, 1775, 1776)). And finally for years he made astronomical observations in St. Petersburg. André Weil saw Euler as an experimentalist in mathematics too. Euler "was very happy when he could conjecture a general law, and he was willing to spend a great deal of time to prove it; but if, instead of a proof, he had merely some really convincing evidence, that pleased him almost as well." (Two lectures on number theory, in: *Collected Papers*, vol. 3. New York: Springer 1980).

[16] "Lettres philsophiques." English translation "Philosophical letters. Or, Letters regarding the English nation," Indianapolis: Hackett 2007.

[17] There are two exceptions: the second volume of the *Introductio* deals with analytic geometry and therefore contains figures; the calculus of variations (*Methodus inveniendi*) partly resorts to old geometric methods, i.e., figures are necessary.

But what is a function? "Nobody can explain that," wrote Hermann Weyl in his book *Philosophy of Mathematics and Natural Sciences*, first published in 1928 and again in 1949. So, what is a function for Euler?

There is an unpublished Latin manuscript "Calculus differentialis" by Euler written in about 1727. In 30 pages he had briefly outlined the ideas that he gave in the *Introductio in analysin infinitorum* (1748, E 101) about 20 years later. Euler began the manuscript by introducing the concept of function:

> One quantity composed somehow from one or a greater number of quantities is called its or their function.[18]

This is a repetition of the definition given by his teacher John Bernoulli (1667–1748) in 1718.[19] Then Euler pointed out that functions may be composed by means of algebraic operations like addition, multiplication, etc., by inversion, by extraction of roots, by taking logarithms, or by combinations of these operations. In his *Introductio* he stressed the idea that analysis is a science of functions and presented this statement:

> §4. A function of one variable quantity is an analytic expression (analytic formula) composed in any way from this variable quantity and numbers or constant quantities.[20]

A function is an *analytic* (i.e., a calculating) *expression*, an algebraic formula. In the course of time gradually more operations were permitted. Then analytic expressions included transcendental functions or functions arrived at in the integral calculus or even functions only given implicitly. Euler classified functions: for example, he distinguished algebraic, transcendental, rational, irrational, explicit, implicit, odd, even, single or multivalued functions, etc. By the way, this simple classification of functions by Euler makes clear that functions were not only a tool for mathematics but had become objects themselves. However, we should not over-interpret Euler's classification and see them with the modern understanding as function spaces, i.e., as sets of functions with an algebraic and topological structure (because such concepts were not yet developed in Euler's time).

Analytic formulas were different to Euler from what they had been to his predecessors. For Euler, variable quantities represent numbers and not geometric quantities. Therefore his work marks a shift in the setting of analysis from geometry to algebra. Consequently, the idea of variable quantity assumed—at least implicitly—a concept of any domain of numbers. When Euler explained the difference between constant [a] and variable quantities [x], he took into account also such variables as infinitesimal quantities [dx] having the strange algebraic property that

$$a + dx = a; \tag{1}$$

in the words of his teacher John Bernoulli in 1691:

> A quantity, which is increased or decreased only by an infinitely small quantity, may be considered as remaining the same.[21]

---

[18] See A.P. Juškevič, Euler's unpublished manuscript *Calculi Differentialis*, in: *Leonhard Euler, Gedenkband des Kantons Basel-Stadt*. Ed. J.J. Burkhardt et al. Basel: Birkhäuser 1980, pp. 161–170.

[19] Remarques, *Mémoires de l'Académie Royale des Sciences*, Paris 1718, pp. 100–138.

[20] English translation of the *Introductio* by J. Blanton, *Introduction to Analysis of the Infinite*, 2 vols. New York: Springer 1988–1990.

[21] Johannis (I) Bernoulli, Lectiones de calculo differentialium, in: *Verhandlungen der Naturforschenden*

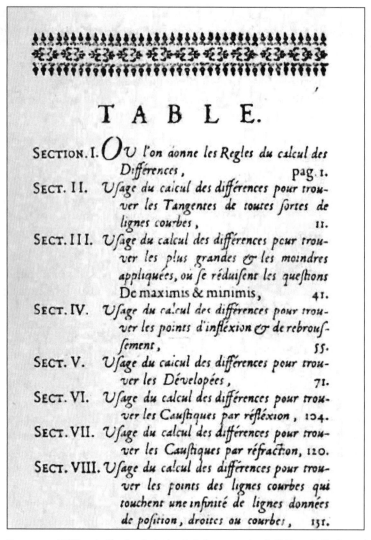

Figure 10. Contents of l'Hospital's *Analyse des infiniment petits* (1696) and (facing page) Euler's *Introductio* (E101, 1748). The comparison shows the rapid rise of the function concept which isn't to be found half a century earlier in l'Hospital. Courtesy: Universitätsbibliotheken Halle and Leipzig

Consequently, Euler even wrote "$dx\ revera\ =\ 0$ [equal zero]" (indeed equal zero)! In the differential calculus *Institutiones calculi differentialis* (published in 1755 but prepared about 1748; E 212; OO I./10) he elaborated the calculus of zeros, in which he distinguished between arithmetical and geometrical proportions of zeros. There are various interpretations of this concept. Three examples: the "classical" understanding of infinitesimals as variables tending to zero, the view of non-standard analysis regarding infinitesimals as elements of a non-Archimedean number field, and the "physical" intuition. Euler himself wrote:

Gesellschaft in Basel 34 (1922) 1–32, Postulatum 1, p. 3. In his *Analyse* l'Hospital wrote: "On demande...qu'une quantité qui n'est augmentée ou diminuée que d'une autre quantité infiniment moindre qu'elle, puisse être considérée comme demeurant la même...."

(xiv)

INDEX CAPITUM

TOMI PRIMI.

If a [nonnegative] quantity was so small that it is smaller than any given one, then it certainly could not be anything but zero; for if it were not $= 0$, then a quantity equal to it could be shown, which is against the hypothesis. To those who ask what the infinitely small quantity [differential] in mathematics is, we answer that it is actually zero. Hence there are not so many mysteries hidden in this concept as there are usually believed to be. The supposed mysteries have rendered the calculus of the infinitely small quite suspect to many people. Those doubts that remain we shall thoroughly remove in the following pages, where we shall explain this calculus [which only is a special case of the calculus of finite differences].[22]

What before in the calculus of finite differences was assumed arbitrary is now taken to

---

[22] *Institutiones calculi differentialis*, §83; English translation by J. Blanton, *Foundations of Differential Calculus*, New York: Springer 2000.

be infinitely small in the differential calculus; roughly speaking, for Euler analysis was just infinite algebra. Taking into account the specific properties of infinitesimal quantities Euler transformed the established rules of the calculus of finite differences into that of the differential calculus. A general principle is that in arithmetical comparison with finite quantities, infinitesimal quantities can be neglected (= zero), i.e., equation (1) is indeed valid. On the other hand, geometrical proportions of infinitesimal quantities led to the rules for differentiating functions. Euler's pragmatism here is most remarkable. Already in the early Latin manuscript *Calculus differentialis* he pointed out:

> It is evident that the differential calculus is a special case of the calculus which I have enunciated above [that is, the calculus of finite differences].[23]

Furthermore, in the beginning Euler believed that any analytic expression could be expressed as a power series (in Taylor's form), and he tried to extend the properties of a polynomial to an infinite series. This idea vaguely anticipates the theorem of Karl Weierstrass (1815–1897): the polynomials are dense in the continuous functions on a closed and bounded interval. His robust pragmatism may be illustrated by his remark:

> If anyone doubts that every function can be so expressed the doubt will be set aside by actually expanding functions.[24]

Obviously, this concept describes analytic functions. However, Euler extended the concept of Taylor series and regarded general power series including so-called Puiseux and Laurent series:

$$Az^\alpha + Bz^\beta + Cz^\gamma + Dz^\delta + \&c.^{25}$$

Working with power series is assessed variously: Detlef Laugwitz (1932–2000) interprets Euler from the viewpoint of non-standard analysis whereas Jean Dieudonné (1906–1992) resorts to the ring of formal power series.[26] In 1905 in a paper on functions "Sur les fonctions représentables analytiquement" (Functions which can be represented analytically) Henri Lebesgue (1875–1941) showed when infinite expressions such as infinite series and products and continuous fractions are allowed the resulting class of functions is equal to that of measurable Borel functions, which for R^n coincides with the class of all Baire functions. Let me quote from Hilbert's Paris talk in 1900:

> The proof that the power series permits the application of the four elementary arithmetical operations as well as the term by term differentiation and integration, and the recognition of the utility of the power series depending on this proof contributed materially to the simplification of all analysis.[27]

In later years Euler laid less stress on the need for any particular kind of the analytical form. He had noticed that the known functions (analytic expressions) were insufficient for the requirements of analysis, especially in the debate on the vibrating string (for

---

[23] See footnote 18.

[24] *Introductio,* §59.

[25] α, β, γ, δ, etc., are powers of a fixed rational number and integer numbers for Puiseux and Laurent series respectively; Chap. 4, §59. Such special power series are used by Euler for investigating singularities.

[26] D. Laugwitz, *Zahlen und Kontinuum.* Mannheim: Bibliographisches Institut 1981; J. Dieudonné, "Formal vs. convergent power series," in: *Mechanics, Analysis, and Geometry,* Amsterdam: North Holland 1991, pp. 549–558.

[27] English translation by M. Newsome in *Bull. Amer. Math. Soc.* 8 (1901/02) 437–479, reprinted in the same *Bulletin* 37 (2000) 407–436.

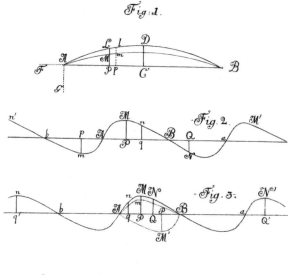

Figure 11. Figures from Euler's paper on vibrating strings (E140, 1750), showing how to construct the solution for arbitrary initial values in a geometrical way. Courtesy of Leopoldina, Halle.

1747). Some boundary conditions of the problem lead to *nonanalytic* functions, for example a plucked string (triangular shape) and more general any arbitrary hand-drawn curve. Furthermore, analytic functions are completely determined on an arbitrary small interval whereas the initial state of a string obviously is not. The debate on the new class of functions continued for another 20 years and involved prominent mathematicians, among them, above all, Leonhard Euler, Jean le Rond d'Alembert (1717–1783), and Daniel Bernoulli.

To summarize the complicated debate, what is the general solution of the problem of the vibrating string? I mention central points of disagreement. Euler and d'Alembert disagreed as to which kinds of functions were admitted. Euler gave up the idea of *one* law (formula) describing the whole function and allowed what he called *discontinuous* functions (that is, piecewise composed functions of analytic expressions). Daniel Bernoulli suggested *trigonometric series* to solve the wave equation. Euler rejected this possibility because the character of the trigonometric functions imposes certain restrictions on the form of solution that therefore cannot be fully general. This is an important question playing a crucial role in further development: Can an arbitrary function be given by a particular type of series representation? Incidentally, Euler gave cursory attention to trigonometric series and on this occasion, curiously, he unconsciously did reasonable work to determine the coefficients in a trigonometric expansion.[28] It was Gustav Peter Lejeune Dirichlet (1805–1859) in 1837 who showed that Fourier series represent a broad class of arbitrary functions; among them are all functions of classical physics or "empirical functions" as Hermann Amandus Schwarz (1843–1921) called them.

---

[28]"Disquisitio ulterior super seriebus …," (E704) in *Nova Acta Academiae Scientarum Imperialis Petropolitanae* 11 (1793) 114–132 (printed in 1798). Here Euler dealt with a totally different problem of astronomy and that's why he missed the consequence of his result in the theory of series; see R. Thiele "What is a function?" later in this volume.

In his *Institutiones calculi differentialis* (1755) one important result of the controversy appeared. In the Preface, Euler gave a general definition of a function as a quantity whose values somehow change with the changes of the independent variables:

> If, therefore, x denotes a variable quantity, all quantities which depend in some way on x or are determined by it, are called functions of this variable.

Here we have a new aspect: Euler formulates the dependence between quantities and does not speak of the composition of the analytic expression. The crucial words for an interpretation, however, are "depend in some way" and "are determined." In the actual forming of such functions Euler cannot help but use the known kinds of determining; i.e., he must use the standard algebraic and transcendental operations. In other words, in his *Introductio* (1748) he had already dealt with the same concept; more or less his definitions given in 1748 and 1755 are also to be regarded as being more or less equivalent.[29] Functionality was for Euler a matter of formal representation by calculable expressions and not so much as a description of relations by concepts.[30] By the way, he never used the new definition in the *Institutiones* or in his other analysis books and also ignored it when discussing the function $y = (-1)^x$. Therefore any attempt to interpret the 1755 definition in modern terms does not at all reflect Euler's vision of the concept. Incidentally, the *Institutiones* was written about 1748, the year the *Introductio* was published. Of course, the preface which contains the definition mentioned above could have been added later, especially in view of the controversy over the vibrating string and the involved evolution of the function concept. However, Euler repeated in 1766 that the calculus "as it has been treated until now can only be applied to curves, whose nature can be contained in one analytical equation."[31]

Such a modern interpretation is also often falsely attributed to the definitions of Nikolai I. Lobachevsky (1793–1856) and Lejeune Dirichlet given in 1834 and 1837 respectively. However, like Euler in his analytic expression, both regarded continuous changes of functions only and therefore dealt not with modern functionality, but were guided by "mechanical" motions. Lobachevsky spoke of "*postepenno insmenjajetsja*" (gradual change), so did Dirichlet ("*allmählich*"—gradually) and furthermore Dirichlet demanded only that the graph of a function can be imagined "*gesetzlos gezeichnet*" (drawn without any particular rule). The famous nowhere continuous function appears not as an illustration of the definition but more as a counterexample. A one-to-one correspondence between arbitrary sets appears in 1887 in the famous paper "Was sind und was sollen die Zahlen?" (What are numbers and what are they for?) by Richard Dedekind (1831–1916) (sets = systems in Dedekind). In order to define a continuous function on such sets for numbers a topology is given by intuition. However for arbitrary sets the topology had not yet been developed. To paraphrase Neil Armstrong's (born in 1930) famous 1969 quotation, just a third of a century old: That's one small step for a modern mathematician, one giant leap for the 19th-century mathematician.

Furthermore, Euler stated that there was no need for the relation between the quantities

---

[29] Euler always considered number quantities, and imaginary numbers are regarded as such quantities too (although they lack a concept of distance, see *Vollständige Anleitung zur Algebra*, part I, chap. 13, §143, part II, chap. 9, §140, E 387–388, OO I/1).

[30] Euler demanded laws for the number magnitudes in order to be able to deal with them (*Vollständige Anleitung zur Algebra*, part I, chap. 13, §§141f.).

[31] "Éclaircissements sur le mouvement des cordes vibrantes," (E317) *Mélanges de philosophie et de mathématique de la Société Royale de Turin*, 3 (1762/65) 1766, 1–26.

to be given by the same law throughout an interval, nor was it necessary that the relation be given by mathematical formulas (and such functions he called *discontinuous*).[32] He therefore regarded curves freely drawn by hand (*cum libero manus ductu*) as functions. These are the so-called mechanical curves. As I mentioned, Euler even discussed the graph of $y(x) = (-1)^x$. Written while still in Berlin in about 1763, but not published until during the Second Petersburg period, Euler's treatise on the integral calculus was not available for a long time but the existence of the manuscript was a widely circulated rumor. A Swiss furrier and amateur mathematician, Christoph Jetzler (1734–1791), wished to copy the manuscript and arrived in the spring of 1763 to ask Euler for permission. The request was granted, and Jetzler made a copy of 1,000 pages which he finished in autumn of the same year.

Euler did all things as easily as he could. Therefore he fitted his concepts to the problems (not the other way round), and he did this in the case of functions too. When he built up analysis the analytic expression was permanently extended. It is very remarkable that in the end Euler gave up his favored calculating concept linked with power series and considered trigonometric series as the appropriate means to represent arbitrary functions. We see it as openness that characterizes Euler's concept of function. Finally, Euler classified functions as continuous and discontinuous. Continuous functions in the sense of Euler are identical with the functions he used in the *Introductio* (1748) and the *Institutiones calculi differentialis* (1755), i.e., with power series that have a common analytic expression. Note that Euler's notion differs from the modern concept. Discontinuous functions, on the other hand, cannot be expressed by such a single analytic expression, but they can be piecewise composed of finitely many continuous functions and they can even be represented by hand-drawn curves.

In 1787, four years after Euler's death, the Petersburg Academy proposed the question on the nature of arbitrary functions for its prize competition. The paper "Sur la nature des fonctions arbitraire" (On the nature of arbitrary functions) by Antoine Arbogast (1759–1803) was awarded the prize in 1790. In this paper Arbogast summarized Euler's view of an extended concept of functions in this way:

> Euler had the daring idea not to subject these curves to any laws [i.e., to regard arbitrary curves], and it was he who said for the first time that curves may be any line, that is, irregular and discontinuous, or composed of different parts of curves [*functiones mixtas*] and drawn by hand in a free movement [*cum libero manus ductu*], with no spatial restrictions.

The tendency to render mathematics in arithmetical terms has continued since the days of Euler. I need only remind you of Lagrange's book *Théorie des fonctions analytiques* (Theory of analytic functions, 1797) or of the book *Vorlesungen über reelle Funktionen* (Lectures on real functions, 1918) by Constantin Carathéodory (1873–1950). Felix Klein (1849–1925) spoke of the arithmetization, however he (who "saw" the things) was not pleased by these abstract arithmetizing tendencies. The analytic expression that shifted the setting of analysis from geometry to arithmetic arose in the isoperimetric problems of the calculus of variations posed in 1697 and their solutions. This tendency, however, was not straightforward, but that is another story.

Let me end with a few words on Leonhard Euler himself. One of his most admirable qualities was a willingness to explain how he did mathematics, how he made discoveries.

---

[32] De usu functionum discontinuarum (E 322, OO I/23; read in 1762, printed in 1767).

His extraordinary memory enabled him to make detailed calculations in his head (like the Austrian composer Wolfgang Amadeus Mozart, a younger contemporary, who had every composition in his head before he started writing). He never wanted to have the last word. On the contrary, in his papers he gave readers many things to complete in order to encourage and to involve them. Dirk Struik (1894–2000) once said he would not like to have a cup of coffee with the quarrelsome and envious mathematicians of the 18th century. No doubt, Euler is to be excluded. On a memorial tablet in the Swiss village of Riehen we find a concise characterization of nine words by Otto Spiess (1878–1966): "He was a great scholar and a kind-hearted person (*Er war ein großer Gelehrter und ein gütiger Mensch*)."

Each volume of Euler's *Opera omnia* provides important texts. Thirty entries in the index of a Japanese *Encyclopedic Dictionary of Mathematics* and 53 articles of the German *Mathematisches Wörterbuch* (Mathematical Dictionary) confirm Euler's influence over the two and a half centuries from his death in 1783 until modern times. Clifford A. Truesdell estimated that in the 18th century Euler wrote about one third of the mathematical papers (including those of mathematical physics). This outstanding contribution to mathematical sciences may be an essential reason that the esteem in which Leonhard Euler is held has not diminished in the last 250 years. Johann Heinrich Lambert (1728–1777), Euler's colleague during the Berlin period, regarded Euler and d'Alembert as the first mathematicians among his contemporaries followed by himself. Euler was "the most prolific mathematician in history" and the "major figure in the development of analysis in the eighteenth century," to quote a modern historian of mathematics (Victor Katz, born in 1942). One and a half centuries ago the *princeps mathematicorum*, Carl Friedrich Gauss (1777–1855), said of Euler's mathematical lifework:

> The study of Euler's work will remain the best school for the different fields of mathematics and nothing else can replace it.

In his *Disquisitiones arithmeticae* (1801) Gauss spoke of "*summus* Euler" using an epithet he attributed to no other scholar with the unique exception of Isaac Newton. Finally, Carl Gustav Jacob Jacobi remarked: "It is today quite impossible to swallow a single line of d'Alembert, while most writings of Euler can still be read with delight."

It has been impossible to summarize all of Euler's important contributions to mathematics, and I did not try to do so. At best one can only present his work in a qualified sense. In this spirit, let me quote in conclusion from Johannes Scheffler (1624–1677) better known as Angelus Silesius:

> Friend, it is really enough. In case you wish to read more, go and become yourself the report and the essence.[33]

References

[1] Bernoulli, Johann, "Lectiones de calculo differentialium," in *Verhandlungen der Naturforschenden Gesellschaft in Basel*, 34(1922), 1–32.

[2] Biermann, Kurt-R., "Wurde Euler durch Lambert aus Berlin vertrieben?" *Festakt und Wissenschaftliche Konferenz aus Anlaß des 200. Todestages von Leonhard Euler.* W. Engel, ed. Berlin: Akademie-Verlag 1985, pp. 91–99.

---

[33] Freund, es ist auch genug. Im Fall du willst mehr lesen,/ So geh und werde selbst die Schrift und selbst das Wesen. (Cherubinische Wandersmann, 1674).

[3] Dieudonné, Jean, "Formal vs. convergent power series," in *Mechanics, analysis and geometry: 200 years after Lagrange*, ed. M. Francaviglia, North Holland Press, Amsterdam, 1991, 549–558.

[4] Euler, Leonhard, *Opera omnia*, 4 series since 1911. Leipzig, Teubner, later Zürich, Basel; at present 76 vols.

[5] ——, *Introductio in analysin infinitorum*, Lausanne, Bousquet, 1748 = *Opera omnia* I/8-9.

[6] ——, "Remarques sur les mémoires précédens de M. Bernoulli," *Mémoires de l'Académie Royale des Sciences et Belles Lettres*, Berlin 9 (1753) 196–222 = *Opera omnia* II/10, pp. 233–54.

[7] ——, "Sur la vibration des cordes," *Mémoires de l'Académie Royale des Sciences et Belles Lettres*, Berlin 4 (1748) 69–85 = *Opera omnia* II/10, pp. 63–67.

[8] ——, *Institutiones calculi differentialis*, St. Peterburg Academy, 1755 = *Opera omnia* I/10.

[9] Glaus, John, "Das Profane und das Heilige," *Begleitband zur Euler-Ausstellung in Braunschweig*, Braunschweig, Mayer-Verlag, in press.

[10] Harnack, Adolf, *Geschichte der Königlich-Preußischen Akademie der Wissenschaften*, 3 vols., Berlin, 1900.

[11] Hartweg, F.G., "Eulers Tätigkeit in der französisch-reformierten Kirche von Berlin," *Die Hugenottenkirche* 32, 4 (1979) 14–15; 32, 5 (1979) 17–18.

[12] Juškevič (Juschkewitsch, Youshkevitch, Yushkevich), A. P. and Eduard Winter, eds., *Die Berliner und Petersburger Akademie im Briefwechsel Leonhard Eulers*, 3 vols., with the collaboration of P. Hoffmann, Berlin, Akademie-Verlag, 1959–1976.

[13] Knobloch, Wolfgang, *Leonhard Eulers Wirken an der Berliner Akademie der Wissenschaften, 1741–1766*, Berlin: Akademie-Verlag, 1984.

[14] Laugwitz, Detlef, *Zahlen und Kontinuum: eine Einführung in die Infinitesimalmathematik*, Bibliographisches Institut, 1986.

[15] Thiebault, Dieudonné, *Mes souvenirs de vingt ans de séjour à Berlin*, Paris: Buisson 1803–04.

[16] Thiele, Rüdiger, "… unsere Mathematiker können es mit denen alles Akademien aufnehmen," *Leonhard Eulers Wirken an der Berliner Akademie. Begleitband zur Euler-Ausstellung in Braunschweig*. Braunschweig, Mayer-Verlag, in press.

[17] Valentin, G., "Leonhard Euler in Berlin," *Festschrift zur Feier des 200. Geburtstages Leonhard Eulers*. Edited by the Berliner Mathematische Gesellschaft, Leipzig, Teubner, 1907, pp. 1–20.

[18] Voltaire, *Mémoires pour servir à la vie de M. de Voltaire*, J. Brenner, ed. Paris 1965.

[19] Weil, André, "Two lectures on number theory, past and present," *L'Enseignement mathématique, IIe série*, 20 (1974), 87–110. In *Collected Papers*, vol. 3, Springer Verlag, New York, 1980.

[20] Winter, Eduard, *Die Registres der Berliner Akadmie der Wissenschaften, 1746–1766*, Berlin, Akademie-Verlag, 1957.

Euler's Fourteen Problems[1]

C. Edward Sandifer

Introduction

The role of problems in promoting and guiding progress in mathematics is well known. Over the centuries, the mathematical community has chosen its problems in different ways. I admit to a gross simplification of a considerably more complex situation as I try to condense the last five centuries of this evolution into just a few sentences.

In the 16th century, the times of Tartaglia and Cardano, there were the problem contests by which people won and kept their academic positions. The next century brought problems like Debeaune's problem of inverse tangents, the Brachistochrone Problem, the Basel Problem and Fermat's Last Theorem. These problems were posed by individuals, sometimes to bring an unresolved issue to the attention of the mathematical community, and sometimes as personal challenges to specific people.

The 18th and 19th centuries saw the spread of academic societies and their prize competitions. The best known is probably the Paris Prize, won so many times by Euler. It seems, though, that prizes were offered by almost all the important academic societies, including St. Petersburg, Leipzig, Madrid, Copenhagen, among others. Prize problems were sometimes rather general. One of the Paris competitions that Euler won was to explain the nature of fire [E34]. As time went on, academy problems became more specific. In 1862, the Danish Academy offered a gold bar for explaining the breeding behavior of the hagfish [G]. *The New York Times* reports (01/02/2001) that the prize is still unclaimed.

In the 20th century, it can be said, mathematicians got to pose their own problems. That, essentially, is how a grant proposal works. The applicant poses a problem and offers to work on it, and the granting agency sends money.

In the 20th century people occasionally posed lists of problems. Hilbert's 23 Problems are probably the most famous. The seven Clay Mathematical Institute Millennium Prize Problems, each backed with a million dollar prize, may prove to be significant, though it can be argued that those problems had already been posed and named, and that CMI has only anthologized the problems, rather than posing them.

---

[1] An earlier version of this paper was first presented at the Joint Mathematics Meetings in New Orleans in January 2001.

Erdős, of course, published more lists than you can count. Most were in number theory and combinatorial mathematics, and he attached monetary prizes up to $1000 to many of these.

Long before Clay or Erdős or Hilbert, Leonhard Euler also posed lists of problems. Moreover, Euler posed not just one, but at least five lists!

Euler read his first list before the *Klassensitzung* in Berlin, essentially the weekly seminar of the Mathematics Department, on September 6, 1742 [W p. 23]. It is short, just seven problems he thought were important and that he was working on. He isn't challenging other mathematicians to work on them.

Euler's list of 1742

1. Determination of the orbit of the comet that was observed in the month of March in the year 1742.

2. Theorems about the reduction of integral formulas to the quadrature of circles.

3. On finding integrals which, if after integration the value for the determined variable quantity is assigned.[2]

4. On the sum of series of reciprocals arising from the powers of natural numbers.

5. On the integration of differential equations of higher degrees.

6. On the properties that certain conic sections have in common with infinitely many other curved lines.

7. On the resolution of the equations $dy + ayy\,dx = bx^m dx$.

To put a context to these problems, in 1742, Euler had been in Berlin for just over a year. His solution to the Basel Problem, about the sum of the reciprocals of the squares [E41], had been published in 1740 (after a six year publication delay) and Euler's fame was spreading rapidly. In June of 1742, he had received the letter from Goldbach posing his famous conjecture about even numbers always being the sum of two primes. A couple of years ago, a publishing company offered a million dollars for a solution to the Goldbach Conjecture. [D] Their prize went unclaimed.

Most of these problems became Euler's published papers in the next couple of years, and he wasn't really challenging the rest of the mathematical community to join him in working on the problems.

The two "Quaestiones Physicae" lists

Euler's next two lists were two drafts of "Quaestiones Physicae." The first version of 17 problems was included in a letter from Euler in Berlin to Schumacher in Petersburg dated

---

[2]This is a rather cryptic choice of words. The original Latin reads "De inventione integralium, si post integrationem variabili quantitati determinatus valor tribuatur." In 1743, Euler published an article, E60, with exactly this title, dealing with the resolution of certain integrals into infinite products.

August 13/24, 1751. [W], [J+W 1961, pp. 251–252.] In that letter, Euler specifically recommended that the Petersburg Academy use the questions as prize problems.

Euler sent a second draft of "Quaestiones Physicae" to the Petersburg Academy on November 18/29, 1755. [J+W 1961, pp. 437–439.] These 18 questions were read before the Petersburg Academy almost two years later, on July 7, 1757. Among them were:

2. What is the cause of the fluidity of water?

4. What is the physical explanation of how metal is dissolved in certain materials, and yet precipitated from others?

13. What is the cause of the shape of snow?

14. Why does mercury descend in a barometer when a rainstorm is coming and rise when fair weather is coming?

15. What is the physical cause of the aurora borealis?

18. What is the cause of the variation of the magnetic needle in different regions of the earth?

These problems were clearly intended to motivate and guide scientific research for the next several years, the same motives claimed by Hilbert and by the Clay Mathematical Institute. But they are "Questions of Physics," and we are interested in mathematics.

The Fourteen "Quaestiones Mathematicae"

Euler's fourth list of problems, the fourteen "Quaestiones Mathematicae," are on the back side of the same sheet of paper that contain the second draft of the "Quaestiones Physicae." They, too, were read before the Petersburg Academy two years later and were intended as potential problems for the Academy's prize.

Quaestiones Mathematicae

1. A theory is sought for the rising of water by the screw of Archimedes. Even if this machine is used most frequently, still its theory is desired.

2. A theory is sought for the friction of fluids while they are moved through tubes, and how much of the motion of a fluid through channels is diminished by friction.

3. A true theory of sound is sought about how it is propagated through air.

4. An explanation is sought about how sound is perceived in the hearing organ and whether or not it is in a similar means as light.

5. An explanation is sought for the formation of voice, and in what way all kinds of sound are articulated by the organ of speech.

6. A complete theory is sought for the motion of waves derived directly from Newton.

7. The surface of water contained in a vessel is not perfectly horizontal, but at the edges the water either curves up or curves down. A cause for this phenomenon is sought and at the same time a determination of the location and motion of bodies which are floating on those surfaces.

8. A theory is sought about the position where a moving body will float in the sea when the sea itself is driven by flux.

9. A theory is sought for the pressure of the atmosphere and to what extent it is filled with vapors of all kinds.

10. It is asked how the motion of a machine such as a clock can be restored to even motion even if it is subjected to a force whose action is irregular or variable.

11. A determination of the motion of three bodies is sought if they are attracting each other with a force proportional to the square of the reciprocal of the distance between them, but if this determination is expressed not just as a simple algebraic formula, what about that motion can be determined.

12. It is asked about the motion of a body spinning on a plane, such as a hoop, when its motion is disturbed by friction.

13. Since a telescope composed just of glass lenses suffers several flaws, such as large magnifications require excessively long tubes, and besides that, a small blending at the opening of the lens and a breaking up at different distances from the center, which even happens in those catoptrical telescopes which are called Newtonian or Gregorian, it is asked whether or not these telescopes are capable of greater perfection, and finally a complete theory of dioptrical telescopes is sought whence these instruments may be brought to the highest grade of perfection.

14. It is noted that common microscopes work with the annoying property that the object is either very much blended together or very darkly represented. What is desired is an absolute theory of these instruments, the benefits of which would free it from these annoying properties and bring them to the highest perfection.

I have not yet been able to determine how many of these problems were actually used as prize problems, though some of them, numbers 6 and 8 for example, certainly were, and others, number 12, for example, were probably pre-empted by Euler's own work before they could be used as prize problems.

As we take a closer look at the problems, we ask, "Where's the math!" There is no number theory, no differential equations, no infinite series.

The answer lies in the meaning of the word "Mathematics." To Euler, mathematics included what we now call mathematical physics and mathematical modeling. Topics we call "pure mathematics" now, he called geometry, arithmetic or analysis.

Now that we've accepted the idea that "Quaestiones Mathematicae" means applied mathematics, not pure mathematics, let's look at some of the questions themselves.

1. A theory is sought for the rising of water by the screw of Archimedes. Even if this machine is used most frequently, still its theory is desired.

The problem here doesn't seem very interesting, but the comment, "Even if this machine is used most frequently, still its theory is desired," is very illuminating. It tells us that, to Euler, applied mathematics was more than just a design tool. It was a key to understanding. Even after a machine has worked well for thousands of years, it is important to know why it works. I think that Euler would agree with R. W. Hamming, who wrote 200 years later [H2] that "The purpose of computing is insight, not numbers."

2. A theory is sought for the friction of fluids while they are moved through tubes, and how much of the motion of a fluid through channels is diminished by friction.

Euler worked on problems of fluids for much of his career. This question, along with questions 6, 7 and 8, all reflect that continuing interest. Fluid flow still presents major mathematical problems. The Clay Mathematical Institute problem about the Navier-Stokes equations [F], is a modern version of Euler's questions 2, 6, 7 and 8. The second word in Charles Fefferman's official explanation of the Clay problem is "Euler."

3. A true theory of sound is sought about how it is propagated through air.

4. An explanation is sought about how sound is perceived in the hearing organ and whether or not it is in a similar means as light.

5. An explanation is sought for the formation of voice, and in what way all kinds of sound are articulated by the organ of speech.

Euler had published *Tentamen novae theoriae musicae* in 1739, (E33) about 15 years earlier. These questions show Euler's continued interest in subjects of acoustics. Moreover, the great scientific controversies of the times were based on the different world views of the Newtonians and the so-called Wolffians, the disciples of Descartes and Leibniz. The main points of their disputes were the nature of light and the action of gravity. I believe that Euler felt that if he could establish a similarity between the nature of light and the nature of sound, then he might be able to make some progress on the fundamental questions of the nature of light [H1]. For example, does light require a medium for its propagation?

6. A complete theory is sought for the motion of waves derived directly from Newton.

Euler also worked a good deal on this problem [S1] and made real progress. However, he did not discover the principle of superposition, and that left the way open for Fourier, in the next century, to win a prize with his solution to the problem.

7. The surface of water contained in a vessel is not perfectly horizontal, but at the edges the water either curves up or curves down. A cause for this phenomenon is sought and at the same time a determination of the location and motion of bodies which are floating on those surfaces.

This is the question of the meniscus, which we now understand to be caused by surface tension. In Euler's time, questions of the meniscus were near the center of the Wolffian-Newtonian controversies. Like gravity, the meniscus seemed to be a mysterious force capable of action at a distance. Thus, this apparently innocuous little question lies at the heart of one of the day's greatest issues.

The second part of Euler's question suggests that he suspected that the meniscus is somehow related to the surface of the fluid.

I would caution against misreading Euler's remarks here. When he wrote of the "motion of bodies which are floating on those surfaces," far sighted though he was, he was not speaking of Brownian motion. Instead, he was asking for an explanation of the phenomenon that small objects floating near a concave meniscus will seem to float "up hill" to the edge of the container. A dual phenomenon occurs near a convex meniscus, where objects float up hill away from the edge.

8. A theory is sought about the position where a moving body will float in the sea when the sea itself is driven by flux.

Euler is asking that the results of his then-recent 1749 book *Scientia navalis* (E110) be extended. Indeed, they were, and he published them again in 1773 as *Théorie complète de la construction et de la manoeuvre des vaisseaux* (E426).

9. A theory is sought for the pressure of the atmosphere and to what extent it is filled with vapors of all kinds.

It is not clear what Euler expected from this problem. Does he want a differential equation that explains the decrease in air pressure with altitude? That seems too simple. Is it a chemistry question? Is it a meteorology question? Perhaps it is related to the Berlin Academy's 1746 problem "on the general cause of the winds." In Euler's time, chemists were just letting go of the old Aristotelian idea of just four elements, Earth, Air, Fire and Water. When Euler asks about "vapors of all kinds," is he siding with the faction that believes in more than four elements? I am afraid that I do not understand the question.

10. It is asked how the motion of a machine such as a clock can be restored to even motion even if it is subjected to a force whose action is irregular or variable.

11. A determination of the motion of three bodies is sought if they are attracting each other with a force proportional to the square of the reciprocal of the distance between them, but if this determination is expressed not just as a simple algebraic formula, what about that motion can be determined.

Both of these questions have the same practical objective, the measurement of time and, from that, the measurement of longitude for navigation. [S2] With these two questions, Euler was promoting both of the leading programs seeking practical methods for the determination of longitude. The clock would keep a standard time, like Greenwich Mean Time, and the traveler would use astronomical observations to determine latitude and local time. The difference between the two times would determine longitude, and the navigator would know where he was.

A solution to question 11, the three body problem would allow the calculation of a standard time from almanac data about the position of the Moon or of the moons of Jupiter. The almanac data required the accurate solution of a three-body problem, either a Sun-Earth-Moon system or a Sun-Jupiter-Moon system. The solutions given in his 1753 *Theoria motus lunae* (*Theory of the motion of the moon*, E187) were too complicated to be useful, but by 1772, in *Theoria motuum lunae*, (*Theory of the motions of the moon*, E418), the techniques were almost practical.

Such questions of navigation motivated much of Euler's other mathematics. For example, when he wrote a paper about using infinite series to evaluate sines or tangents or logarithms of trigonometric functions, he probably had navigational applications in mind.

12. It is asked about the motion of a body spinning on a plane, such as a hoop, when its motion is disturbed by friction.

This is the "spinning quarter" or "spinning hoop" problem. Why does the hoop seem to hover there instead of falling down flat? A toy demonstrating this phenomenon was marketed a couple of years ago in the "educational toy" stores under the name "Euler Disk."

It is a little surprising to see this problem on this list, prepared in 1755, read to the Academy in 1757, since Euler's well-known paper on the subject, E257 "De frictione corporum rotantium," was mailed to Schumacher in St. Petersburg 23 Aug/3 Sept 1754. It almost seems that Euler posed the problem after he himself had solved it. Perhaps he was dissatisfied with his solution, or perhaps he had prepared the list before 1755.

13. Since a telescope composed just of glass lenses suffers several flaws, such as large magnifications require excessively long tubes, and besides that a small blending at the opening of the lens and a breaking up at different distances from the center, which even happens in those catoptrical telescopes which are called Newtonian or Gregorian, it is asked whether or not these telescopes are capable of greater perfection, and finally a complete theory of dioptrical telescopes is sought whence these instruments may be brought to the highest grade of perfection

14. It is noted that common microscopes work with the annoying property that the object is either very much blended together or very darkly represented. It is desired therefore an absolute theory of these instruments, the benefits of which would free it from these annoying properties and bring them to the highest perfection.

In these last two problems, Euler poses practical problems in optics, questions which he himself addressed over and over again in several important papers and in his three-volume *Dioptricae*, published in 1769.

Twenty-two scientific problems from 1765

In 1765, the year he Euler returned to St. Petersburg after 25 years in Berlin, Euler sent a letter to Stählin, the Director of the St. Petersburg Academy containing a list of twenty-two "Preisfragen," or "Prize-questions." [J+W 1976, pp. 236-239] These problems are even less mathematical than the 1755 list had been. In the interests of brevity, we simply quote a few representative examples, without further discussion:

I. A complete theory of friction is desired, explaining how, when one body is moved upon another, the quantity of friction and its relation to speed can be described.

XIV. An explanation is desired of the force by which metals or other substances can be dissolved in certain fluids, and then be recovered from the resulting solutions.

XIX. What is the cause of motion in muscles?

Conclusions

It seems that the fourteen problems that Euler sent to the Petersburg Academy in 1755 were, like Hilbert's, intended to motivate progress in mathematics, particularly applied mathematics, for the next several decades. Some of them became problems for the Academy's prize. Others remained on Euler's own research agenda and became some of his own important contributions. A form of Euler's second problem has been reformulated into whether the Navier-Stokes equation has a unique solution, which remains a major unsolved problem today. [C, F]

References

[B]   Burckhardt, J. J., E. A. Fellmann and W. Habicht, eds., *Leonhard Euler: Beiträge zu leben und Werk*, Birkhäuser, Basel, 1983.

[C]   Clay Mathematics Institute, www.claymath.org.

[D]   Doxiadis, Apostolos K., *Uncle Petros and Goldbach's Conjecture*, Bloomsbury, NY, 2000.

[E41]   Euler, L., De summis serierum reciprocarum, *Commentarii academie scientarum Petropolitanae*, 7, (1734/5) 1740, pp. 123–143. Reprinted in *Opera Omnia*, Series I vol. 14 pp. 73–86. Available online at EulerArchive.org.

[E34]   Euler, L., RP Lozeran de Fiesc, Comte de Créquy, Émilie du Châtelet and Voltaire, *De la nature et de la propagation de feu, cinq mémoires couronnés par l'Académie Royale des Sciences Paris 1738*, Association pour la Sauvegarde et la Promotion du Patrimoine Métallurgique Haut-Marnais, France, 1994. Available in its original Latin original in *Opera Omnia* Series 3 vol. 10 pp. 1–14 and online at EulerArchive.org.

[F]   Fefferman, Charles, "Existence and Smoothness of the Navier-Stokes Equation," www.claymath.org/millennium/Navier-Stokes_Equations/, as of January 21, 2007.

[G]   Goldberg, Carey, "Students Pursue One of the Ocean's Slimy Mysteries", *The New York Times*, p. F4, January 2, 2000.

[H1]   Hakfoort, Casper, *Optics in the Age of Euler: Conceptions of the nature of light, 1700–1795*, Cambridge University Press, 1995.

[H2]   Hamming, R. W., *Numerical Methods for Scientists and Engineers*, 2ed., McGraw-Hill, 1973.

[J+W]   Juškevič, A. P., and E. Winter, eds., *Die Berliner und die Petersburger Akademie der Wissenschaften in Briefwechsel Leonhard Eulers*, 3 vols., Akademie-Verlag, 1959, 1961, 1976.

[S1]   Schot, Steven, "Vibrating Strings, Functions and Distributions", unpublished manuscript distributed at the Institute for the History of Mathematics and Its Uses in Teaching, summer, 1996.

[S2]   Sobol, Dava, and William J. H. Andrews, *The Illustrated Longitude*, Walker and Company, NY, 1998.

[W]   Winter, Eduard, *Die Registres der Berliner Akademie der Wissenschaften 1746–1766*, Dokumente für das Wirken Leonhard Eulers in Berlin Zum 250. Geburtstag, Akademie-Verlag, Berlin, 1957.

The Euler Archive
Giving Euler to the World

Dominic Klyve and Lee Stemkoski

Euler Scholarship in the Twentieth Century

Suppose that all the mathematicians who have ever lived could be ranked according to their importance in the development of mathematics. Then let them be ranked again according to the amount of scholarly study that has been devoted to them. If the ratio between the two values was computed, then the person with the highest ratio—the mathematician with the profound impact to whom disproportionately little attention has been paid—would be Leonhard Euler. Indeed, as of the writing of this article, although there are many biographical sketches and accounts of Euler's scholarship (see [3] and [12]), no full length biography exists in any language. The longest published to date are Thiele [10], Fellmann [6], and Du Pasquier [9], none of which cover more than 150 pages. With a few notable exceptions (e.g., Truesdell [11] and Calinger [1] and [2]), Euler has been largely ignored in American scholarship during this past century.

Several reasons have been suggested for the lack of attention paid to Euler. The two most notable have been:

1. The volume and diversity of Euler's work means that a complete study is an enormous undertaking, one which very few people have the time and breadth of expertise to undertake.

2. Accessing Euler's original sources is extremely difficult. Birkhäuser has continued to publish the *Opera Omnia* [6], which by the end of the century included almost all of Euler's works. Unfortunately, the $17,000 (USD) price is prohibitively expensive to all but the largest libraries. Furthermore, modern typesetting often hides details in notation and symbology which could give scholars additional insight.

The need for an Archive

The difficulties presented to one individual trying to study the voluminous works of Euler were neatly solved in 2002 with the formation of the Euler Society. This group, through its newsletter and annual conferences, brought together people from around the world studying Euler in a variety of contexts. Their collective work, some of which is featured in this volume, accelerated the growth of Eulerian scholarship in America far beyond that which would have otherwise been achieved.

We came into contact with the Euler Society in 2002 at their first annual meeting. Two things quickly became apparent. First, they are clearly a passionate and dedicated group of scholars. Second, the majority of participants had no access to the works of Euler in any format—not even the *Opera Omnia*. At that time we both were graduate students at Dartmouth College, whose library includes fairly extensive holdings of old journals, including many of Euler's original publications. The copyrights for these materials had long since passed into the public domain, and we decided shortly after the conference to collect them and put them on the internet in a format which would be free and accessible to not only the Euler Society, but the world at large.

The technology needed to build the Euler Archive arrived with such perfect timing as to seem foreordained. Inexpensive machines which could rapidly copy and scan large numbers of pages and save the images in convenient computerized format had only recently become available—and at the very time when the world needed an easy way to access the works of Euler. Thus the Euler Archive could be built and could solve problem (2), completing the process necessary to bring Euler to 21st century American scholarship.

Euler Archive Version 1.0—Just the Facts

Having decided to build an Euler Archive, we next needed to consider its structure and organization. After lengthy consideration and discussion with members of the Euler Society (notably Ed Sandifer, Ron Calinger, Rob Bradley, and John Glaus), we decided on a minimal website which could be easily set up yet which left ample room for additional information and future developments. At the beginning of the 20th century, Eneström [6] numbered and cataloged 866 of Euler's published works; this catalog also included information on the dates that Euler wrote, presented (to a scientific academy), and published these works. More recently, Ed Sandifer had completed the heroic task of entering this and other data (e.g., source of original publication and location in the *Opera Omnia*) for all 866 works into a large database. Building on this work, we used Sandifer's database to create a web page for every work of Euler. Each page was designed to eventually contain the following information:

1. the index number and title of the work,

2. a translation of that title,

3. a summary or description,

4. information on all known publications and editions,

5. a link to a scanned copy of the original publication,

6. links to translations available on the Archive,

7. a list of modern resources which cite or discuss the work.

Naturally, most of this information was not available at the time the Archive was first constructed. Although many of our pages were fairly sparse for some time, the framework had been constructed.

Having created the web pages, we turned our attention to the problem of organizing them. The freedom allowed to us by a web-based archive gave us flexibility in dealing with Euler's works that previous publishers have not enjoyed, e.g., the material need not be presented according to a single linear ordering. We initially decided to allow the pages to be searched in three ways: by subject, date, and Eneström number.

Subject   The Archive first cataloged each of Euler's works as pertaining to a given subject and specialty (e.g., "Astronomy"/"Eclipses and Parallax") loosely following the structure of the *Opera Omnia*. However, unlike the *Opera Omnia*, which necessarily had to assign each of Euler's works to a single subject, we are able to classify works under multiple headings.

Date   As mentioned before, Euler's papers (and to a lesser extent his books) can all reasonably be assigned any one of three dates:

1. **The date of composition.** This is an important piece of information for reconstructing Euler's thought process as he moved through his career. Because these dates are not always documented, we have relied on the work of Eneström, who included his best estimate as to the date of composition in his catalog. We anticipate modifying and improving some of these estimates as scholars of the 21st century come to a better understanding of Euler's life.

2. **The date Euler read the paper to an academy.** Both in Saint Petersburg and Berlin, reading one's paper was the standard mode of announcing one's research, and this date tells us when the rest of the world could reasonably expect to know Euler's new results. This date is useful when comparing Euler's works with others published at about the same time, particularly by those in the same scientific academy as Euler. For Euler's works, this date could be anywhere between a month and ten years after the date of composition.

3. **The publication date.** Significant publication delays were common in Euler's time, especially in Saint Petersburg. During Euler's life, some of his papers were not published until ten years or more after he first presented them. Complicating the situation even further, almost 300 of Euler's numbered works were published posthumously, including a collection (the *Opera Postuma* [5]) of 59 never-before published papers which appeared in 1862—seventy-nine years after Euler's death.

Eneström Number   For the scholar who knows precisely which paper she is looking for, the list of Euler's works by Eneström Number is usually the fastest way to access it.

This version of the website, which we internally referred to as the Euler Archive 1.0, was presented to the Euler Society at their second annual meeting (August 2003), at which point the Archive contained 63 of Euler's works—7.2% of Eneström's numbered total.

Version 2.0—Euler in Context

Having built the frame of the Euler Archive, we moved forward in two directions. The first and most essential direction was to dramatically increase the number of Euler's works online—an archive that is not at least mostly complete is of very little use. The second direction was to expand the site to include more commentary and information, thus placing Euler's works in context.

Increasing the number of Euler's works online was a daunting task. The 800+ works remaining to be scanned and posted comprised over 30,000 pages of printed material, and at the time, we were a pair of students copying and scanning articles during spare evenings. By a happy coincidence, at the time we were in need of additional assistance, Marianne Gerber, then Deputy Consul and Deputy Director of the Swiss House for Advanced Research and Education (SHARE) in Cambridge, Massachusetts, attended the annual Euler Society meeting in 2003. A joint operation of the State Secretariat for Education and Research and the Swiss Department of Foreign Affairs, SHARE is dedicated to promoting science, research, and education, especially as applied to Swiss-American interaction. An annual American conference dedicated to Switzerland's greatest scientist naturally attracted their interest.

Consul Gerber invited us to visit the SHARE office in Cambridge to present our work to the consular staff. SHARE took great interest in our project, and subsequently arranged a small grant for us from a sister organization (Présence Switzerland) to facilitate our efforts. This money allowed us to employ a team of undergraduates at Dartmouth College, who put in hundreds of hours over the next year systematically copying, scanning, and posting Euler's works.

In our efforts to include more information and commentary, we were fortunate at this point to be joined in our efforts by three dedicated and enthusiastic individuals, also then graduate students: Rachel Esselstein, Alison Setyadi, and Erik Tou. Their efforts were of crucial importance, as without their help in locating additional information and documents, supervising our team of undergraduates, writing historical notes and article summaries, and helping with general website maintenance, the Archive would never have grown as large or as quickly as it did. In addition to their help, a wealth of new material from Ed Sandifer, John Glaus, and diverse scholars from around the world allowed us to supplement the Euler Archive with a significant amount of contextual information.

Version 2.0 of the Archive, presented to the Euler Society in 2004, was significantly expanded and improved over the version of one year earlier. It included:

- Hundreds of summaries and descriptions of articles,

- Over 1000 references to modern articles and scholarship about Euler and his works,

- A considerable "Euler Historica" section, with information about the historical context of Euler's time, as well as the cities and academies in which Euler worked,

- A keyword search, allowing users greater freedom in finding articles and information on the Archive,

- A "search by publication" feature, which allows a user to find all of Euler's works that appeared in a given journal, along with information about the journal, its publication, and often tables of contents, giving more context to Euler's writings,

- 669 original works available (77% of the total),
- More than 20 translations of Euler's works.

Version 3.0—Beyond Archiving

As we entered 2005, we were increasingly motivated by the tercentennial of Euler's birth in 2007. We had two goals we wanted to accomplish by that year. First, we wanted to expand our holdings to include at least 95% of Euler's works. During 2004 we had added over 600 works to our Archive, including some of Euler's books. The remaining 200, however, were more difficult to obtain. Sometimes this was due to restricted access or circulation; other times, original works could not be located at all. Happily, a dedicated effort involving the Archive staff and several collaborators, along with another pair of grants (these from SHARE and Switzerland's State Secretariat for Education and Research) allowed us to reach and pass the 95% mark by September 2005. At this point the Euler Archive had made 824 of Euler's works available online, including all but one of his major books, the exception being the *Scientia Navalis*, which appeared on the Archive during the summer of 2006. At this point, while our original goals were nearing completion, the Archive continued to evolve beyond what its creators had initially envisioned.

The Euler Archive by this time had achieved a fairly large internet presence, and ever larger numbers of people were "stumbling across" the Archive while looking into questions involving Euler in particular, and the history of science in general. November 2005, for example, saw almost 10,000 unique visits to our site from over fifty countries. It was perhaps natural, then, that we would begin to serve as a communications hub for Eulerian studies.

To facilitate a community-driven communication network for scholars of Euler and the history of science, the Euler Forums were created. This part of the website consisted of a system of bulletin boards, where any individual could sign up for an account and post information of interest to the users of the Archive directly to the website. Upcoming meetings were listed, topics of current research were discussed, and questions from the public were asked and answered. However, it was inevitable that as traffic to the Archive increased, some of the visitors would disrupt the intellectual atmosphere of the Euler Forums. In the interests of being all-inclusive, potential forum users were not screened for academic integrity. As a result, some users posted advertisements or linked to highly off-topic websites, presumably in the hopes of making some form of profit. While irritating, these posts could be deleted on a case-by-case basis by Archive staff members, and the offending users were removed from the system. The difficulties came to a climax one day when an unknown assailant was able to hack into the network hosting the Euler Archive (through the program running the Euler Forums) and temporarily hijack the server for their own purposes. Since the bulletin board software had been developed by a third party, the Archive staff was unaware of this security hole at the time of installation. The Euler Archive went offline for a few days, during which the Euler Forums were removed out of necessity. We hope that a new version of the Euler Forums will appear online in the future.

On a more positive note, the knowledge that the Euler Archive was being frequently used led several scholars and students to contribute their own writings and translations to the Archive for electronic publication. The biggest success story along these lines is the number of new translations now available. Three years ago, the total number of Euler's

The Euler Archive

Main Page
Quick Start
Archive Tour
FAQs

Search archive by:
  Subject
  Date
  Publication
  Index Number
  Keyword Search
  What's Available

Historical Information:
  18th Century Europe
  The Life of Euler
  Contemporaries
  Important Locations

Archive features:
  Archive Blog
  Translations
  Correspondence
  Resources

Documents Needed
Contact Us
Archive Staff

View Enestrom Number:

| | Go |

The works of Leonhard Euler online

The Euler Archive is an online resource for Leonhard Euler's original works and modern Euler scholarship. This dynamic library and database provides access to original publications, and references to available translations and current research.

The Archive is built around "E-pages." There is one of these pages for each of work written by Leonhard Euler (all 866 of them!).
Each page includes:

- The title of the work (and an English translation of the title)
- A summary of the work
- A description of where the work was originally published
- A description of where the work is published in the **Opera Omnia**
- A scanned pdf version of Euler's original publication
- A brief list of modern research papers which discuss or cite the work

(Click here if links do not appear to the left)

Be sure to visit the website for **The Leonhard Euler Tercentenary - Basel 2007**!

The Euler Archive would like to thank the following institutions for their support:

| PRS - Presence Switzerland | SHARE - The Swiss House for Advanced Research and Education | State Secretariat for Education and Research | The Euler Society | Dartmouth College |

The Euler Archive home page as of June 2007.

works fully translated into English was less than twenty. Today, seventy-four translations are available on the Archive, over half of which have been published nowhere else. While this number represents a fairly small fraction of Euler's work, the dramatic increase in the amount of Euler's work available to English speakers has been extremely satisfying.

We have also had a great deal of success in electronically publishing Euler's correspondence. While most has never been published, a fairly significant portion was in print in the late nineteenth and early twentieth centuries. These letters are now available in the Archive, as is a searchable version of the catalog of Euler's correspondence put together by the Euler Commission [8]. We are also proud to publish a unique synergy of translation and correspondence. In particular, John Glaus has translated and written commentary for a significant body of Euler's correspondence, and his collection serves as a unique, first-rate introduction to Euler as a man and as a scholar.

We have every hope and confidence that these trends will continue: that both amateur and professional historians will continue to translate and write commentaries on Euler's works. In fact, it is quite possible that the next twenty-five years will see a complete edition of Euler in English, opening up many new opportunities in Eulerian scholarship.

Looking to the Future

In the last three years, the Euler Archive has more than succeeded in achieving its original goals. As these have been met, we continue to look to the future, setting new goals to keep us moving forward. Over the next few years, we hope to convert the images of Euler's works into searchable full-text documents. With the help of our current and future contributors, we will continue to increase the number of translations of Euler into modern languages, and to add new summaries of his works. We plan to solicit commentaries on Euler's contributions to entire disciplines—another enterprise that will greatly increase the usability of the Archive for non-specialists. With these improvements, we will continue to serve the scientific and historical communities by preserving and promoting the legacy of Leonhard Euler.

References

[1] R. Calinger. Leonhard Euler: The First St. Petersburg Years (1727–1741), *Historia Mathematica*, May 1996, vol. 23, no. 2, 121–166.

[2] ——. Euler's "Letters to a princess of Germany" as an expression of his mature scientific outlook. *Archive for History of Exact Sciences*, 1976, vol. 15(3), 211–233.

[3] W. Dunham. *Euler: The Master of Us All*. Mathematical Association of America, Washington, DC, 1999.

[4] G. Eneström, Die Schriften Eulers chronologisch nach den Jahren geordnet, in denen sie verfasst worden sind, *Jahresbericht der Deutschen Mathematiker-Vereinigung*, 1913.

[5] L. Euler, *Opera Postuma*, Petropoli: St. Petersburg Academy, 1862.

[6] E.A. Fellmann, *Leonhard Euler*. Birkhäuser: Hamburg, 1983.

[7] A. Juškevič et al., eds. *Opera Omnia*.

[8] A. Juškevič et al., eds. Leonhardi Euleri Commercium Epistolicum. *Opera Omnia, Series Quarta*, Volume 1. Birkhäuser, 1975.

[9] G. du Pasquier, *Euler et Ses Amis*. Paris, 1927.

[10] R. Thiele, *Leonhard Euler*. Leipzig: Teubner, 1982.

[11] C. Truesdell. *An Idiot's Fugitive Essays on Science — Methods, Criticism, Training, Circumstances*. New York: Springer-Verlag, 1984.

[12] A. Youskevich, "Euler." *The Dictionary of Scientific Biography*, New York: Scribner, 1975.

The Euler-Bernoulli Proof of the Fundamental Theorem of Algebra

Christopher Baltus

In 11 letters, from 1742 to 1745, which Nicolaus Bernoulli exchanged with Leonhard Euler, a proof of the fundamental theorem of algebra emerged which includes the essential components of Euler's 1751 proof. That process is examined here, together with shortcomings of the proof. Of particular interest is the symmetric function concept, rudimentary in 1744, more developed in 1751, but only completed by Lagrange in 1771–72.

Introduction

Nicolaus Bernoulli (1687–1759), son of Nicolaus and nephew of Johann and Jacob, studied mathematics under his uncles in Basel; at the same time he studied law.

Encouraged by Jacob, young Nicolaus became a master in the emerging field of probability. His 1709 dissertation for Doctor of Jurisprudence, *De usu artis conjectandi in jure,* applied concepts of Jacob's *Ars Conjectandi,* incomplete at Jacob's death in 1705. His work from 1710 to 1713, time spent largely in travel, solidified Nicolaus's leading position. With Leibniz, he saw to the publication, in 1713, of *Ars Conjectandi,* for which Nicolaus wrote an introduction. In the same year, his exposition of probability was included, as correspondence, in the second edition, 1713, of *Essai d'analyse sur les jeux de hazard* by his friend Pierre Rémond de Montmort [6, p. 462].

Guided by Johann, Nicolaus also took up analysis. He did important work on series convergence and orthogonal trajectories [5] and he is credited with the first claim for the interchangeability of mixed partial derivatives, 1719 [5, p. 58].

Nicolaus had a brief mathematics professorship at Padua, 1716–1719. We know he disliked Italy, but he left us no further explanation for the turn he then took. He left Italy and he left mathematics; he returned to Basel to marry, in 1720, and to take a chair of Logic during 1722–1731, followed by a chair of Law.

Thus one of the most promising mathematicians of Europe resigned himself to mathematics as a hobby. Some fifteen years later, however, the question of the sum of the reciprocal squares piqued his interest and he produced a paper. That paper, through Johann, with a recommendation from his cousin Daniel, reached Euler in 1738.

Leonhard Euler (1707–1783) had also studied under Johann Bernoulli. He had been, in 1735 [8], the first to find the sum, $\pi^2/6$, of the reciprocal squares

$$\frac{1}{1^2} + \frac{1}{2^2} + \frac{1}{3^2} + \frac{1}{4^2} + \cdots.$$

This achievement marked Euler as the foremost mathematician of Europe and it soon brought him into contact with Nicolaus Bernoulli.

Euler wrote to Nicolaus in January 1742 to discuss the reciprocal squares and related sums and the publication of Bernoulli's paper in the Petersburg *Commentaries*. [Volume 10, for 1738, which contained Bernoulli's paper, appeared only in 1747.] With that letter began a rich and unexpected exchange of eleven letters, ending in 1745. They ranged over several topics, including the "sum" of divergent series; by their third letter, the fundamental theorem of algebra (FTA) appeared. [All quotations from the correspondence, and the numbering of the letters, are from [6].]

The fundamental theorem of algebra is the claim that every real polynomial of positive degree has real or complex roots. That every such polynomial has roots of some form had long been accepted, but that the roots must be complex was essentially an eighteenth century idea, first clearly articulated by Euler in a letter to Johann Bernoulli in 1739 [11, p. 447] and in print in 1743 [9]. [[14] gives this history.] Euler delivered a proof of the FTA to the Berlin Academy in November 1746. That proof, titled "Theoremata de radicibus aequationum imaginariis," lost in its original form, served as a draft for [10]. The first published proof was by Jean le Rond d'Alembert; his manuscript reached Berlin in December of 1746 and appeared, in 1748, in the *Mémoire* for 1746 [3]. And in 1751, the proof by Euler, in French, appeared in the Berlin Academy *Mémoires* for 1749 [10].

The proofs of both Euler and of d'Alembert [see [1]] included significant gaps. Still, it is worth establishing the order. D'Alembert's was the first to see print. However, by examining Euler's correspondence with Nicolaus Bernoulli, we see that Euler's 1751 proof had been essentially worked out, jointly with Bernoulli, by early 1744. The one development of note between 1744 and 1751 was in Euler's handling of symmetric functions.

Background: Descartes

Nicolaus Bernoulli brought to his discussion of the FTA Descartes's development of the roots of the fourth degree equation, from the *Geometry*, 1637, Book III. Since Descartes's ideas lay behind the approach of Bernoulli and Euler, a presentation of Descartes's work is in order.

Descartes worked with the *depressed* quartic (cubic term is missing):

$$x^4 + px^2 + qx + r = 0 \quad \text{[Descartes's} \pm \text{is replaced here by} +\text{]}$$

is to be factored into

$$x^2 - yx + \frac{1}{2}y^2 + \frac{1}{2}p + \frac{q}{2y} = 0 \quad \text{and} \quad x^2 + yx + \frac{1}{2}y^2 + \frac{1}{2}p - \frac{q}{2y} = 0.$$

Multiplying and equating coefficients gives just one equation:

$$y^6 + 2py^4 + (p^2 - 4r)y^2 - q^2 = 0.$$

Jean le Rond d'Alembert
Drawn by N. R. Jollain and engraved by B. I. Henriquez.

If p, q, r are real and $q \neq 0$, then there is a positive root y^2, and so a real root y. Note that the coefficients of the proposed factors are rational in the root y and the original coefficients p, q, and r.

Letter 3. Euler to Bernoulli   1 Sept. 1742

The FTA was first mentioned in the context of integration of rational expressions by partial-fraction decomposition. Euler wrote:

> ... which proposition seems to me quite true but for which I do not have a general proof. The theorem runs thus: that every algebraic expression
>
> $$\alpha + \beta x + \gamma x^2 + \delta x^3 + \text{ etc.},$$
>
> of whatever dimension, if it cannot be resolved into simple real factors $p + qx$ then always can be resolved into trinomial factors $p + qx + rxx$, which are all real.

Letter 4. Bernoulli to Euler   24 Oct. 1742

In what the editor of the N. Bernoulli - L. Euler correspondence calls Bernoulli's one "blunder," Bernoulli answered Euler's claim with a counterexample:

> But in this I do not accept what you believe, ... For example, this quantity
>
> $$x^4 - 4x^3 + 2xx + 4x + 4$$
>
> cannot be given two real factors of dimension two, nor can the four roots of the equation $x^4 - 4x^3 \ldots$, namely,
>
> $$x = 1 + \sqrt{2 + \sqrt{-3}}, \qquad x = 1 - \sqrt{2 + \sqrt{-3}}$$
> $$x = 1 + \sqrt{2 - \sqrt{-3}}, \qquad x = 1 - \sqrt{2 - \sqrt{-3}},$$
>
> be paired so the product of two is real.

Bernoulli's error is ironic since many years earlier, in 1719, he had produced the real factorization of $x^4 + a^4$, the expression which Leibniz claimed in 1702 had no such factorization [16, p. 412].

Letter 5. Euler to Bernoulli 10 Nov. 1742

Euler pointed out Bernoulli's error, and asserted a general claim in the quartic case:

> As I wrote to you earlier, Most Celebrated Man, [about the factorization into real simple and trinomial factors] ... I expressly added that I had not composed a complete proof, but it is so certain that its truth cannot be doubted. However, I have a rigorous proof if the highest power does not exceed the fourth, wherefore with the example $x^4 - 4x^3 + 2xx + 4x + 4$ I am *a priori* certain that it can

be resolved into two quadratic factors, which are from the roots of that equation $x^4 - 4x^3 + 2xx + 4x + 4 = 0$, which are found

$$\text{I. } x = 1 + \sqrt{2 + \sqrt{-3}}, \qquad\qquad \text{II. } x = 1 - \sqrt{2 + \sqrt{-3}},$$

$$\text{III. } x = 1 + \sqrt{2 - \sqrt{-3}}, \qquad\qquad \text{IV. } x = 1 - \sqrt{2 - \sqrt{-3}},$$

for with I. and III. and also with II. and IV. paired, both the sum and the product are real.

$$\text{I} + \text{III} = \cdots = 2 + \sqrt{4 + 2\sqrt{7}}$$

$$\cdots$$

and so the expression $x^4 - 4x^3 + 2xx + 4x + 4$ has two real factors....

Letter 6. Bernoulli to Euler   6 April 1743

In his next letter, Bernoulli admitted his error, essentially conceding that he had not reviewed Descartes's work before his letter of October 1742.

> Now I erred in my last letter.... The occasion of the error was: I knew that Descartes taught a method of resolution of the biquadratic $x^4 + px^3 + qxx + rx + s = 0$ into two quadratics by means of a cubic or by means of a sixth degree equation lacking coefficients for odd powers of y, and I knew further that the cubic had at least one real root, that is y^2, which I believed could be negative, from which I concluded that y could be imaginary; ....

Then Bernoulli started down the path that led many of his contemporaries astray, namely, the idea that polynomial roots should all be expressible in terms of square roots, cube roots, etc., of real and complex expressions. Thus, he continued in his letter to show that the square and cube root of a complex expression are complex, saying

> Now with my opinion changed, I affirm that your assertion can be proved, provided (which no one will deny) every imaginary quantity is formed of one or several functions of one or several quantities of the form $b \pm \sqrt{-a}$; now truly all powers, roots, and functions of the binomial $b \pm \sqrt{-a}$ can be reduced to a similar binomial $B \pm \sqrt{-A}$....

Letter 7. Euler to Bernoulli   14 May 1743

Euler is divided over the question of whether arithmetic operations and root extraction suffice to express all polynomial roots; he expects it to be true but knows there is, as yet, no proof. However, he can solve the quartic equation in a way he thinks will apply to any polynomial equation:

> I concede with the greatest pleasure what you claim, that every imaginary root ..., although its form is unknown, can be considered some function of this type of expression $a \pm \sqrt{-b}$. However, for the moment, if some doubt the truth of this,

I admit that I do not see in what way to prove what you assert. However, I am indeed confirmed not a little by a singular mode of resolving equations, similar to the Cartesian. Let the given equation be

$$x^4 + px^3 + qxx + rx + s = 0,$$

which to resolve I put into factors

$$xx + \alpha x + \beta = 0 \quad \text{and} \quad xx + \gamma x + \delta = 0.$$

Euler then replaced $q = \alpha\gamma + (\beta + \delta)$ by $t + u$,

$$\text{where we let} \quad u = \alpha\gamma \quad \text{and} \quad t = \beta + \delta. \tag{1}$$

Since

$$q = t + u, \quad p = \alpha + \gamma, \quad \text{and} \quad s = \beta\delta, \tag{2}$$

then a value for t leads to values for u, and then α, γ, β, and δ.

By equating coefficients, etc., we reach a cubic in t, [as corrected by Bernoulli in Letter 8]:

$$t^3 - qtt + (pr - 4s)t - rr - pps + 4qs = 0. \tag{3}$$

As (3) is cubic, it has a real root t.

"If we let a, b, c, d be the four roots, then t $[= \beta + \delta]$ has these three values: $ab + cd$; $ac + bd$; $ad + bc$."

And a sixth degree equation, Euler continued, would factor into three quadratics:

$$xx + \alpha x + \beta, \quad xx + \gamma x + \delta, \quad xx + \varepsilon x + \xi.$$

Further, $\alpha\gamma\varepsilon$, the product of the middle coefficients, takes as values all the permutations of

$$-(a + b)(c + d)(e + f),$$

which number $5 \cdot 3 \cdot 1$. So it satisfies an equation of odd degree, and so can be assumed real.

"The truth has not yet been truly won; however the road to a conclusive demonstration can perhaps be seen."

Letter 8. Bernoulli to Euler   29 Nov. 1743

Here Bernoulli's remarkable insight shines. He corrected Euler's computational error, with (3). Then he pointed out a crucial oversight by Euler and went on to suggest a better way.

Although t and u, therefore, have a real value, it does not follow that the roots ... α, γ, β, and δ are real....

The resolution of equations of higher degree into quadratic equations depends, on the whole, on the resolution of equations

$$x^{2^n} + px^{2^n-1} + qx^{2^n-2} + \text{etc.} = 0. \tag{4}$$

[When the second term is removed, the equation] can be resolved into

$$x^{2^{n-1}} + \alpha x^{2^{n-1}-1} + \text{etc.} = 0 \quad \text{and} \quad x^{2^{n-1}} - \alpha x^{2^{n-1}-1} + \text{etc.} = 0 \quad (5)$$

where $\alpha\alpha$ is always determined by an equation of odd degree; so the difficulty of the demonstration ... is reduced to demonstrating that $\alpha\alpha$ is always positive. Thus the resolution of an equation of degree eight into two biquadratics, and from there, further, into quadratic equations, will be performed by finding a root of an equation of degree 35, and not by an equation of degree $1 \cdot 3 \cdot 5 \cdot 7 = 105$. But who among mortals wants to resolve equations in this manner? For I believe that speculation on this is more curious than useful.

[Note: $\binom{8}{4} = 70$ is the number of values of α, which values occur in opposite pairs.]

Letter 9. Euler to Bernoulli   4 Feb. 1744

Euler, in this letter, thanked Bernoulli for his corrections and went on to highlight the issue before them and to acknowledge the superiority of Bernoulli's approach.

If it is conceded that the imaginary roots of equations can be considered functions of numbers $a + \sqrt{-b}$, then it necessarily also follows that equations of odd degree always have at least one real root, just as the number of imaginary roots must always be even. Nevertheless, it is not yet seen how if the latter is conceded, then the first, in turn, follows; for I do not see how this is to be demonstrated with respect to the form of the imaginary roots....

Moreover, as you correctly showed, the real character of the trinomial factors is much more easily reached by the method of Descartes, in that one removes the second term, and so you have brought to perfection my intention in this proof.

Euler then turned the discussion to the character of the equation whose roots are the values of α. It is crucial that this equation be of oddly-even degree—*impariter parem*, meaning twice an odd number. Referring to (4), with the second term removed, and the factorization (5),

since α is the sum of 2^{n-1} roots of the earlier equation, α is defined by an equation of degree equal in number to [$\binom{2^n}{2^{n-1}}$, oddly-even.]....

... the constant term [of this *resolvent* equation], since it is the product of all the values of α, which are in pairs of opposites, will be a negative square, whose [square] root can be assigned by q, r, s, etc.

This is the core argument which Euler later presented in his 1751 *Recherches sur les racines imaginaires des équations* [10]. We can agree with the conclusion of Christian Gilain [14, p. 109] that the essential elements of Euler's 1751 proof of the FTA had already been developed, by 1744, in correspondence with Nicolaus Bernoulli. However, the last part of Euler's argument above is revealing and differs in emphasis from the 1751 version [10, Art. 33] .

In 1744, Euler seems to have believed for all numbers what is true only for reals, namely, that the product of opposites is negative. He apparently understood, moreover, without citing a theorem, that expressions symmetric in the roots of an equation are (rationally) expressible in the coefficients of the equation, but he applies this idea only to claim that the constant term of the *resolvent* equation is expressible in those coefficients.

When Euler returned to this argument in Article 33 of [10], he openly addressed the difficulty. He let a, b, c, d denote the roots of the given equation

$$x^4 + Bx^2 + Cx + D = 0,$$

and $x^2 - ux + \beta$ a proposed factor. The six values of u are $\pm p, q, r$, where

$$p = a + b, \quad q = a + c, \quad \text{and} \quad r = a + d.$$

Euler noted that

> one will object that I have here supposed that the quantitiy pqr is real, and $ppqqrr$ is positive; this is doubtful for, since the roots a, b, c, d may be imaginary, it can happen that the square of the quantity pqr may be negative. But I respond that this case will never occur ....

> ... $pqr = (a + b)(a + c)(a + d)$ is determinable, as one knows, by the quantities B, C, D, and will be, consequently, real; as we have seen, it is effectively $pqr = -C$ and $ppqqrr = CC$. One easily recognizes, likewise, that in higher degree equations the same circumstances will occur....

Thus, by 1751, still without a statement of a theorem, Euler clearly based his claim that pqr is real on its symmetric expression in the roots of the [real] equation.

[Note: This equation whose root is u, or α, would now be called a *resolvent*. A decade earlier [7], Euler had given that name to a related, but somewhat different auxiliary equation; he did not use *resolvent* in his correspondence with Bernoulli nor in his 1751 paper. Lagrange used *réduite* for this equation in 1770–1771 [18, p. 213]. Euler used no technical name for *symmetric* functions and Lagrange, in [18], used the larger class of functions that he called *similar* to derive the property we now express in terms of *symmetric* functions. *Symmetric* was, it seems, introduced in 1797 by S. F. Lacroix [17, p. 277] .]

Afterward: Lagrange, 1771, 1772

Several shortcomings of Euler's argument were addressed by Lagrange in 1771 and 1772.

The first was a superficial repair. In *Sur la forme des racines imaginaires des équations* [19], 1772, Article 21, Lagrange provided a general argument, by the change of variable

$$u := (sum\ of\ all\ roots) - 2\alpha$$

that when $-C^2$ denotes the resulting constant term, then C is, as we now say, a *symmetric function* of the roots: "the permutations which one might make among the roots produce no change in the function."

Second, Euler had assumed, without proof and without a clear theorem, that when a real value was found for coefficient α of the proposed factor $x^n + \alpha x^{n-1} + \cdots$, then all other coefficients would be real. Lagrange stated the precise theorem in *Réflections sur la résolution algébriques des équations* [18], 1771:

Joseph-Louis Lagrange
Engraved by Robert Hart from a bust in the library of the Institut de France.

it follows from our solution that if the value of the supposed known coefficient [of the supposed factor] is a simple root of the equation on which depends the determination of the coefficient, all the others will be expressible rationally by that one; but if the value of the known coefficient is a double or triple root, etc., of the same equation, then each of the other coefficients can only be given in terms of that one by means of an equation of degree 2 or 3, etc. [Article 102]

Finally, in [19], 1772, Articles 24-30, Lagrange corrected the critical shortcoming that is apparent in the above theorem: If 0 is among the possible values of α, then the constant term $-C^2$ is 0 and there need be no positive root α^2 and the real root $\alpha = 0$ is of even multiplicity. Article 102 of [18] cannot then guarantee that the desired factor is real.

This difficulty is avoided by an elaborate change of variable. We suppose that the given equation has real coefficients, has degree $m = 2n$ that is a power of 2, and that

$$x^{(1)}, x^{(2)}, x^{(3)}, \ldots, x^{(n)}, x^{(n+1)}, \ldots, x^{(2n)}$$

denote the roots. We let

$$x^n - Mx^{n-1} + Nx^{n-2} - Px^{n-3} + \quad - \cdots$$

and

$$x^n - M'x^{n-1} + N'x^{n-2} - P'x^{n-3} + \quad - \cdots$$

be the proposed factors, where

$$M = x^{(1)} + x^{(2)} + x^{(3)} + \cdots + x^{(n)}$$

and

$$M' = x^{(n+1)} + x^{(n+2)} + \cdots + x^{(2n)}.$$

Then

$$N = x^{(1)}x^{(2)} + x^{(1)}x^{(3)} + x^{(2)}x^{(3)} + \cdots + x^{(n-1)}x^{(n)},$$

and

$$N' = x^{(n+1)}x^{(n+2)} + x^{(n+1)}x^{(n+3)} + x^{(n+2)}x^{(n+3)} + \cdots + x^{(2n-1)}x^{(2n)}, \text{ etc.}$$

We let

$$\mu = M - M', \quad \nu = N - N', \quad \omega = P - P', \text{ etc.}$$

and let $u = a\mu + b\nu + c\omega + \cdots$, where a, b, c, etc. are constants to be determined. [Lagrange, in fact, described the system of equations by which an equation in unknown u can be found.]

We now consider two cases [Article 30]. If for some partition of the roots

$$x^{(1)}, x^{(2)}, x^{(3)}, \ldots, x^{(2n)}$$

between the two sums of roots M and M', we should have $\mu = 0$ (so $M = M'$) and $\nu = 0$ and $\omega = 0$, etc., then we can see that M is real, and therefore that N is real, etc., so we have a real factorization. On the other hand, if every partition of the roots into two sets of n roots leaves at least one of $\mu, \nu, \omega, \ldots$ not 0, then, since there are a finite number of such partitions, we can find real values for $a, b, c, \ldots$, so that u is 0 for no partition of the roots. There are, in modern notation, $\binom{2n}{n}$ partitions of the n roots producing distinct values for M, M', N, N', etc. $\binom{2n}{n}$ is oddly-even; moreover, a partition producing particular values $\mu, \nu, \omega, \ldots$ is matched with one producing $-\mu, -\nu, -\omega, \ldots$. Therefore, the equation whose roots are the possible values of u is of odd degree in u^2 and has a negative constant term. As argued above, there is a positive root u^2, from which follows real u and then real values for $\mu, \nu, \omega, \ldots$ and for $\alpha = M + M', \beta = N + N'$, etc., from which, finally, follow real coefficients M, M', N, N', P, P', etc., in the factors.

This result follows from Lagrange's theorem of Article 104 of [18], which generalized that of Article 102.

[Suppose t and y are functions of the roots of]

$$x^k + mx^{k-1} + nx^{k-2} + \cdots = 0,$$

and that the functions are such that every permutation among the roots $x^{(1)}, x^{(2)}, x^{(3)}, \ldots$, which makes y vary also makes t vary at the same time. Then one can, generally speaking, have the value of y in t and in $m, n, p, \ldots$ by a rational expression, ... if it happens that t is found as a double or triple root, etc., of the equation in t, then the corresponding value of y will depend on a quadratic, cubic, etc., equation....

[See the proof in [21], p. 190–193.]

Final Note

Two remaining foundational issues took a century for resolution.

As is well known, even with the corrections of Lagrange, Gauss, in his 1799 proof of the FTA, did not accept the validity of Euler's proof. As Gauss pointed out, Euler and Lagrange had accepted without argument the existence of polynomial roots, of indeterminant form, which could be involved in ordinary arithmetic, and then set out to prove that those "imaginary" roots were complex [12]. Gauss wrote that such reasoning was circular in that the existence of roots was assumed. His second proof of the FTA, of 1816 [13], avoided the need for such a *splitting field* which contained the roots of a polynomial.

The second issue was the claim that any real equation of odd degree has a real root. Even Gauss, in his second proof of the FTA, in 1816, felt there was no need of a proof: "It is evident (*constat*) that such an equation of odd degree is solvable, indeed by a real root,...." [Article 20] Just the next year, the work of Bernard Bolzano appeared, pointing out the need for justification by what is now called the *Intermediate Value Theorem*, deduced from a *Greatest Lower Bound Property* of real quantities [2]. However, Bolzano's was an isolated call that few heard.

It was only in the latter half of the nineteenth century, in the work of Kronecker and Dedekind, that the existence of a *Splitting Field* and the *Intermediate Value Theorem* were set on a firm basis [15]. The algebraic proof of the FTA, begun in the correspondence of Leonhard Euler and Nicolaus Bernoulli, and developed alongside a growing understanding of symmetric functions, was finally complete.

Note Thanks to Professors J. Caramalho Domingues and R. Bradley for information on Lacroix and the Berlin Academy, respectively.

References

[1] Christopher Baltus, d'Alembert's proof of the fundamental theorem of algebra, *Historia Mathematica* **31** (2004) 414–428.

[2] Bernard Bolzano, Rein analytischer Beweis des Lehrsatzes, dass zwischen je zwey Werthen, die ein entgegengesetzes Resultat gewähren, wenigstens eine reelle Wurzel der Gleichung liege, Prague, 1817, translation by S. B. Russ, *Historia Mathematica* **7** (1980) 156–185.

[3] Jean d'Alembert, Recherches sur le calcul intégral, *Mem. Berlin* 1746 (1748) 182–224.

[4] René Descartes, *La Géométrie*, 1637, translated and edited by D. E. Smith and M. L. Latham, Dover Publications, New York, 1954.

[5] Steven Engelsman, *Families of Curves and the Origins of Partial Differentiation,* North Holland, Amsterdam and New York, 1984.

[6]   Leonhard Euler, *Commercium Epistolicum, cum Johanne (I) Bernoulli et Nicolao (I) Bernoulli,*
      edited by E. Fellmann and G. Mikhajlov, in *Leonhardi Euleri Opera Omnia,* sub ausp. Soc.
      Scient, Nat. Helv. 1911– , Series 4A vol. 2, Birkhäuser, Basel, 1998.

[7]   ——, De formis radicum aequationum cuiusque ordinis coniectatio, (E30) *Comm. Acad. Sci.*
      Petrop. 6 1732–33 (1738) 216–231, in *Euler Opera Omnia* Series 1 vol. 6, 1–19.

[8]   ——, De summis serierum reciprocarum, (E41) *Comm. Acad. Sci. Petrop.* 7 1734–35 (1740)
      123–134, in *Euler Opera Omnia* Series 1 vol. 14, 73–86.

[9]   ——, De integratione aequationum differentialium altiorum gradium, (E62) *Miscellanea Bero-*
      linensia VII (1743) 193–242, in *Euler Opera Omnia* Series 1 vol. 22, 108–149.

[10] ——, Recherches sur les racines imaginaires des équations, (E170) *Mem. Berlin* 1749 (1751),
      in *Opera Omnia* Series 1 vol. 6, 78–147.

[11] J. Fauvel, and J. Gray (editors), *The History of Mathematics: A Reader,* Macmillan Press with
      the Open University. In North America, The Mathematical Association of America, Washing-
      ton, D.C., 1987.

[12] C. F. Gauss, Demonstratio nova theorematis omnem functionem algebraicam rationalem inte-
      gram unius variabilis in factores reales primi vel secundi gradus resolvi posse, 1799, in *Carl*
      Friedrich Gauss Werke, Leipzig, 1863–1933, vol. 3, 1–30.

[13] ——, Demonstratio nova altera theorematis omnem functionem algebraicam rationalem inte-
      gram unius variabilis in factores reales primi vel secundi gradus resolvi posse, 1816, in *Carl*
      Friedrich Gauss Werke, vol. 3, 31–56.

[14] Christian Gilain, Sur l'histoire du théorème fondamental de l'algèbre: théorie des équations et
      calcul intégral, *Archive for the History of Exact Sciences* **42** (1991), 91–136.

[15] Melvin Kiernan, The development of Galois Theory from Lagrange to Artin, *Archive for the*
      History of Exact Sciences **8** (1971), 40–154.

[16] Morris Kline, *Mathematical Thought from Ancient to Modern Times,* Oxford University Press,
      New York, 1972.

[17] Silvestre François Lacroix, *Traité du Calcul Différential et du Calcul Intégral,* vol. 1, Duprat,
      Paris, [An V] 1797.

[18] J. L. Lagrange, Réflexions sur la résolution algébrique des équations, *N. Mem. Berlin* 1770–71
      (1771–72), in *Oeuvres de Lagrange,* 14 volumes, Gauthiers-Villars, Paris 1867–1892, vol. 3,
      205–421.

[19] ——, Sur la forme des racines imaginaires des équations, *N. Mem. Berlin* 1772 (1774), in
      Oeuvres de Lagrange, vol. 3, 479–516.

[20] Ferdinand Rudio, *Foreword* to *Leonhardi Euleri Opera Omnia,* sub ausp. Soc. Scient, Nat.
      Helv. 1911- , Series 1 vol. 6 (1921), Teubner, Leipsig and Berlin, *vii–xxvi.*

[21] Jean-Pierre Tignol, *Galois' Theory of Algebraic Equations* (English version), Longman Scien-
      tific; in the US by John Wiley, New York, 1988.

The Quadrature of Lunes, from Hippocrates to Euler

Stacy G. Langton

Abstract. A lune is a figure formed by two intersecting circular arcs. In the 5th century B.C., Hippocrates of Chios found examples of lunes which could be squared by straight-edge and compasses. Euler took up this question around 1770. Expressing the condition for squarability in the form of a polynomial equation, he found additional examples of squarable lunes which could be constructed by straightedge and compasses (because the equation was quadratic, or reducible to a quadratic), as well as examples which he was able to show could not be constructed. This paper will consider the algebraic and analytic techniques which Euler brought to bear on this problem.

A *lune* is a figure formed by two intersecting circular arcs which lie on the same side of their common chord.[1] The story of lunes begins with the Greek mathematician Hippocrates of Chios (an island in the Aegean) in the 5th century B.C. (not to be confused with the contemporary Greek physician, Hippocrates of Cos). Hippocrates considered an isosceles right triangle inscribed in a semicircle, together with a segment of a circle cut off by the diameter of the semicircle at a 45° angle (Figure 1). Since the areas of similar segments are proportional to the squares of their chords (by Euclid's *Elements*, XII.2), it follows by the Pythagorean theorem that the area of the segment on the base of the triangle is equal to the sum of the areas of the two segments on its legs. Adding to both sides of this equation the area of the part of the triangle outside the larger segment, it follows that the area of the lune is the same as the area of the triangle.[2]

---

[1] In "The Problem of Squarable Lunes," Abe Shenitzer considers also "convex lunes," formed by arcs which lie on opposite sides of their common chord. I have not found any other references to this type of "lune." (The Greek word for lune, *mēniskos*, means "crescent.")

[2] The work of Hippocrates was described in the History of Geometry written by Aristotle's pupil, Eudemus of Rhodes (4th century B.C.). Eudemus's history is lost, but the section which describes the work of Hippocrates on lunes is quoted in a commentary on Aristotle's *Physics* by the 6th century A.D. commentator Simplicius. Thus, Eudemus wrote a century after the time of Hippocrates, and Simplicius 1000 years after that time. The texts are available in the first volume of *Greek Mathematical Works* in the Loeb Classical Library (pp. 234–253), edited and translated by Ivor Thomas. A recent treatment of the quadrature of Hippocrates is found in William Dunham's *Journey through Genius*, chapter 1.

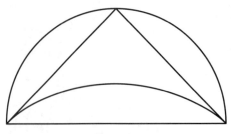

Figure 1.

Using analogous arguments, Hippocrates found two other "squarable" lunes, one having its outer arc greater than a semicircle, the other having outer arc less than a semicircle. He also found a lune which, together with a certain rectilineal region, has the same area as a circle.

As far as we know, this was the first time in Greek mathematics that anyone had proved that a region bounded by curved lines was equal in area to a rectilineal region. There is disagreement among the commentators about whether Hippocrates was trying to "square the circle," or whether he thought that he had succeeded.

Before going further, let's consider the general setting which includes Hippocrates's three quadratures. Let the central angles subtended by the circular arcs which form the lune be $2m_1$ and $2m_2$, and let the corresponding radii be r_1 and r_2. (See Figure 2.) Now Daniel Bernoulli observed in 1724 that if we adjust these angles and radii so that the two *sectors* have equal area, namely by taking $r_1^2 m_1 = r_2^2 m_2$, then

$$0 = \text{area}(\text{sector}\, AC_2 B) - \text{area}(\text{sector}\, AC_1 B)$$
$$= \text{area}(\text{lune}\, AB) - \text{area}(\text{quadrilateral}\, AC_1 B C_2),$$

so that the lune will have the same area as the quadrilateral, and hence will be squarable.[3]

Most of the authors who have considered the problem of squarable lunes have made the assumption that the angles m_1 and m_2 are *commensurable*, in other words that the ratio $(m_1 : m_2)$ is *rational*. In this case, we can generalize the argument of Hippocrates

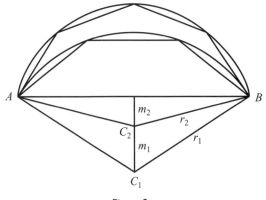

Figure 2.

[3]"Problema aliquod geometricum," *Exercitationes quœdam mathematicœ*, Venice, 1724; reprinted in *Die Werke von Daniel Bernoulli*, vol. 1, pp. 353–362.

as follows. Say, for example, that $2m_1 = \mu_1\omega$ and $2m_2 = \mu_2\omega$, where μ_1 and μ_2 are integers. Suppose that the arc subtended by $2m_1$ is divided into μ_1 arcs, each of angle ω, and the other arc similarly. Since all the circular segments so produced are subtended by the same angle ω, they are all similar, so that their areas are proportional to the squares of their radii. From Daniel Bernoulli's condition $r_1^2 m_1 = r_2^2 m_2$, we have $\frac{1}{2}r_1^2\mu_1\omega = \frac{1}{2}r_2^2\mu_2\omega$, so that $\mu_1 r_1^2 = \mu_2 r_2^2$, whence it is clear that the sum of the areas of the μ_1 circular segments on the inner arc is equal to the sum of the areas of the μ_2 circular segments on the outer arc. Adding to both sums the area enclosed between the inner arc and the chords to the segments along the outer arc, we see that the area of the lune is equal to the area of the polygonal region enclosed by all the chords.

In terms of this framework, then, we can say that the cases studied by Hippocrates were those in which the ratio $(m_1 : m_2)$ was $(1 : 2)$ (the original quadrature, described above), $(1 : 3)$ (the lune having its outer arc greater than a semicircle), and $(2 : 3)$ (the lune having outer arc less than a semicircle).

From the point of view of modern mathematics, however, we might ask what it is that is special about "squarable" lunes. After all, we now know how to assign areas to any "integrable" region of the plane —in particular, to any lune at all.

It is sometimes suggested that Greek mathematicians had a special preference for constructions by straightedge and compasses. It is not quite clear where this idea comes from, though of course these are the only constructions found in Euclid's *Elements*.[4] Certainly, Greek mathematicians solved many problems by means other than straightedge and compasses.[5] The 4th-century A.D. mathematician Pappus of Alexandria classified geometric problems into *plane* problems, which can be solved with straightedge and compasses, *solid* problems, which can be solved by means of conic sections, and *linear* problems, which require higher-order curves. Pappus considered it a fault to use conics or higher-order curves to solve a plane problem.[6] Obviously, this view does not restrict geometric constructions to the use of straightedge and compasses. It is the same aesthetic sense which leads modern mathematicians, for example, to look for "elementary" proofs of the prime number theorem.

Nevertheless, it happens that the three squarable lunes of Hippocrates can all be constructed by straightedge and compasses, although this point is not noted by Eudemus-Simplicius. (It appears that Hippocrates himself constructed his third lune —the one whose outer arc is less than a semicircle— by means of a "*neusis*" construction: roughly, a construction in which a straightedge with a given length marked on it is slid into place between given lines.) But once the lune itself has been constructed by straightedge and compasses, it is easy to see that the corresponding rectilineal region having area equal to that of the lune has also been constructed.

This, then, is the problem that Hippocrates left to later generations of mathematicians: to find additional lunes which can be constructed by straightedge and compasses, and which are *squarable*, in the sense that they have the same area as a certain polygonal region, which can also be constructed by straightedge and compasses.

---

[4]For a thorough study of the subject of straightedge-and-compass constructions, see Arthur Donald Steele, "Über die Rolle von Zirkel und Lineal in der griechischen Mathematik." It was Steele's article that first led me to Euler's "Considerationes cyclometricae."

[5]Many examples are given in Chapter IX of Thomas's *Greek Mathematical Works*.

[6]Thomas, *Greek Mathematical Works*, vol. 1, pp. 346–353.

I now pass quickly over some 2000 years of mathematical history, mentioning only a couple of high points. The Egyptian mathematician Ibn al-Haytham (Alhazen; 965–1040) wrote two treatises on lunes.[7] The French mathematician François Viète (1540–1603) rediscovered the lune of Hippocrates having ratio of angles $(m_1 : m_2) = (1 : 3)$ and also constructed a new lune corresponding to the ratio $(m_1 : m_2) = (1 : 4)$.[8] Viète constructed the lune with ratio $(m_1 : m_2) = (1 : 4)$ by solving a cubic equation —or rather, by inserting two mean proportionals between two given lengths; the lune is not constructible by straightedge and compasses.

In 1727, when the young Euler arrived in St. Petersburg, lunes had already been a subject of discussion among Nicholas II and Daniel Bernoulli and Christian Goldbach.[9] In a letter to Goldbach of October 7, 1722, Nicholas suggested the problem of finding squarable lunes in addition to the lune of Hippocrates.[10] According to Nicholas, his father Johann had found the problem in a book by John Craig and had suggested it to Nicholas's brother Daniel.[11] Goldbach responded to Nicholas (October 17, 1722)[12] with a sketch of a solution, and then (October 22)[13] with a problem of his own concerning lunes.[14] Daniel Bernoulli published his own solution of Goldbach's problem and his work on the problem of squarable lunes in his *Exercitationes Mathematicae* of 1724. Euler's first paper on lunes, "Solutio problematis geometrici circa lunulas a circulis formatas" (E73) gave another solution to Goldbach's problem.

Euler returned to the problem of squarable lunes in his paper "Considerationes cyclometricae" (E423), presented to the St. Petersburg Academy on July 4, 1771. Taking up the program that Daniel Bernoulli in his work of 1724 had sketched, but not carried out explicitly, Euler showed that each constructible squarable lune corresponds to a solution of a certain polynomial equation. By studying these equations, Euler was able to show the non-existence of constructible lunes for certain angle-ratios $(m_1 : m_2)$ (in particular, for the case $(m_1 : m_2) = (1 : 4)$ of Viète) and to find two new cases of constructible lunes which were not known to Hippocrates.[15]

---

[7] See the article on Ibn al-Haytham by A. I. Sabra in the *Dictionary of Scientific Biography*.

[8] In *Variorum de rebus mathematicis responsorum, liber VIII*, pp. 379–381. Viète knew only the first of the lunes of Hippocrates. He quotes the tenth-century Byzantine encyclopedia, the *Suda*, which evidently did not mention the other two. The fact that Hippocrates had also constructed the cases $(m_1 : m_2) = (1 : 3)$ and $(m_1 : m_2) = (2 : 3)$ was not recognized until the nineteenth century.

[9] For a description of the circumstances, see Bottazzini's introduction to Daniel Bernoulli's *Exercitationes mathematicae* in volume 1 of Bernoulli's *Werke*. The problem of lunes had also attracted the attention of Tschirnhaus, David Gregory, Wallis, L'Hôpital, John Craig (1663–1731), Jacob Bernoulli, and Johann Bernoulli. Several of the letters in Fuss's *Correspondance Mathématique et Physique* refer to the subject of lunes. Bottazzini gives a table: *op. cit.*, pp. 195–196.

[10] Fuss, *Correspondance Mathématique et Physique*, vol. 2, pp. 155–156. In this letter and another letter to Goldbach of April 11, 1723 (*op. cit.*, p. 163), Nicholas refers to the "lunes" of Hippocrates in the plural. There is no indication that Nicholas knew any of Hippocrates's lunes other than the one with ratio $(m_1 : m_2) = (1 : 2)$. Perhaps he was referring to the infinitely many lunes of different sizes or positions having this ratio.

[11] Nicholas does not identify the book. According to Bottazzini, *op. cit.*, p. 188, it was probably *De calculo fluentium*, London, 1718.

[12] Fuss, *op. cit.*, pp. 157–158.

[13] Fuss, pp. 159–161.

[14] For a description of this problem, see Andreas Speiser's introduction to volume I.26 of Euler's *Opera Omnia*, pp. VIII–XII.

[15] These two new cases, having $(m_1 : m_2) = (1 : 5)$ and $(3 : 5)$, had in fact already been found in a 1766 dissertation by the Finnish mathematician Daniel Wijnquist. Though printed in Åbo (now Turku), this work was not widely known. For a description of Wijnquist's work, see Christoph J. Scriba, "Welche Kreismonde sind

Euler begins (§1) by observing that, in order for a squarable lune to exist with angle-ratio $(m_1 : m_2)$, it must be the case that

$$\frac{m_1}{\sin^2 m_1} = \frac{m_2}{\sin^2 m_2}. \tag{1}$$

Though Euler gives no reference here, this condition had been found by Daniel Bernoulli in his work of 1724. We can derive this condition easily as follows. (Bernoulli's own derivation was slightly different.) Because the two circular arcs forming the lune must have a common chord, we have $r_1 \sin m_1 = r_2 \sin m_2$ (see Figure 2), whence $r_1^2 \sin^2 m_1 = r_2^2 \sin^2 m_2$. Then the result follows immediately from Bernoulli's condition $r_1^2 m_1 = r_2^2 m_2$.[16]

To find pairs of angles m_1, m_2 satisfying equation (1), Euler considers (§§3–6) the behavior of the function[17]

$$f(m) = \frac{m}{\sin^2 m},$$

for $0 \leq m \leq \pi$. A good calculus student today should be able to see that the graph of this function is "concave up," with vertical asymptotes at $m = 0$ and $m = \pi$ (Figure 3). Thus, f has a unique minimum, at $m = a \approx 0.371\pi$. Though Euler does not draw the graph of f (nor does he apply the "second-derivative test"), he describes its variation in words and computes the minimum $f(a) \approx 1.38$.

Thus, for any $c > f(a)$, there is a pair of values $m_1 < m_2$ such that $m_1/\sin^2 m_1 = m_2/\sin^2 m_2 = c$. Since $m_1 \to 0$ and $m_2 \to \pi$ as $c \to \infty$, we can find a lune satisfying Daniel Bernoulli's condition for any angle-ratio $(m_1 : m_2) < 1$. (Of course, the corresponding lune need not be constructible by straightedge and compasses.) Though Euler does not explicitly state this argument by continuity, it is presumably clear to him.

If, however, we choose $m_1 < a$, then m_2 will be determined by Bernoulli's condition. Euler studies the dependence of m_2 on m_1, first (§8) when m_1 is near 0, and then (§9) when m_1 is near a. In both cases, he uses an infinite-series approximation to express this dependence. The case in which m_1 is near 0 is particularly interesting, in that the series Euler gets is a so-called "Puiseux series," that is, a power series in a fractional power of the variable, in this case the $\frac{1}{2}$-power. Though Euler does not say here how he computed this series, he would presumably have had to use the method discovered by Isaac Newton and sketched in Newton's two letters to Leibniz, through Oldenburg, using the "Newton polygon."[18]

---

elementar quadrierbar? Die 2400jährige Geschichte eines Problems bis zur endgültigen Lösung in den Jahren 1933/1947," pp. 528–529.

[16] Bernoulli stated his condition $r_1^2 m_1 = r_2^2 m_2$ as a necessary and sufficient condition for a lune to be squarable (*sc.*, and constructible by straightedge and compasses), but his argument for the converse was not correct. Landau proved the converse in 1902, under the assumption that $(m_1 : m_2)$ is *algebraic*, using the Lindemann-Weierstrass theorem. See "Über quadrierbare Kreisbogenzweiecke." A description of Landau's argument is given in Scriba, *op. cit.*, pp. 532–533. See also Shenitzer, "The Problem of Squarable Lunes" (containing a translation from M. M. Postnikov's *Galois Theory*), pp. 646–647; but the reader should beware that the two formulas for the areas of lunes at the bottom of p. 646 are incorrect.

[17] Euler refers to it as an "expression."

[18] The letters are dated June 13 and October 24, 1676. See H. W. Turnbull, ed., *Correspondence of Isaac Newton*, vol. 2, pp. 20–47 and 110–161. I don't know whether anyone has tried to trace the reception of Newton's method within the mathematical community. I haven't been able to find anything about it in the *Introductio in Analysin Infinitorum* (1748). According to Jean Guérindon and Jean Dieudonné, Newton's method was extended by Cramer in his *Introduction à l'analyse des lignes courbes*, 1750. (See their "L'Algèbre et la géométrie jusqu'en 1840," chapter II of *Abrégé d'histoire des mathématiques, 1700–1900*, vol. 1, p. 78.) Victor Puiseux (1820–1883) applied

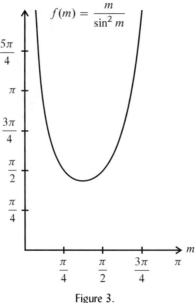

Figure 3.

Euler recognizes, next (§16), that, if the lune with angles $2m_1$ and $2m_2$ is to be constructible by straightedge and compasses, the angles m_1 and m_2 must be constructible. It would suffice, in fact, for their cosines to be constructible. Assuming that we have $m_1 = \frac{1}{2}\mu_1\omega$ and $m_2 = \frac{1}{2}\mu_2\omega$, where μ_1 and μ_2 are integers, Euler writes the condition $m_1/\sin^2 m_1 = m_2/\sin^2 m_2$ in the form $\mu_1(1 - \cos\mu_2\omega) = \mu_2(1 - \cos\mu_1\omega)$. Now write $z = \cos\omega$, so that $\cos\mu\omega = \cos(\mu\arccos z) = T_\mu(z)$. As Euler knew, the function $T_\mu(z)$ is a *polynomial* in z with integer coefficients, now known as a *Chebyshev polynomial*.[19] Euler writes down the first several Chebyshev polynomials explicitly. Thus, the equation $\mu_1(1 - \cos\mu_2\omega) = \mu_2(1 - \cos\mu_1\omega)$ becomes a polynomial equation in z with integer coefficients. If a solution z of this equation can be constructed with straightedge and compasses, then the angle ω can be constructed, and hence so can the lune with angles $2m_1$ and $2m_2$.

Furthermore, Euler knows that constructions with straightedge and compasses correspond to solutions of *quadratic* equations.[20] Thus, the problem of squarable lunes reduces to the question of whether the equation for z can be reduced to quadratic equations.

Newton's method in the context of complex variable theory in "Recherches sur les fonctions algébriques" (1850). Newton's method is the foundation of the modern subject of "resolution of singularities"; see, for example, Steven Dale Cutkosky, *Resolution of Singularities*, 2004.

[19]These polynomials arise implicitly in Chebyshev's work on the approximation of functions; see "Sur les questions de minima qui se rattachent à la représentation approximative des fonctions," 1859, p. 310. Chebyshev does not write the polynomials down explicitly.

[20]Descartes showed that a length obtained by straightedge-and-compass construction must satisfy a quadratic equation (*La Géométrie*, Book I, p. 302), and, conversely, that a length which satisfies a quadratic equation can be constructed by straightedge and compasses (p. 313). In addition, Descartes claims that if a length satisfies an irreducible polynomial equation of degree greater than 2, then it is "certain" that the length cannot be constructed by straightedge and compasses (Book III, p. 383). Of course, Descartes gives no proof of this claim. The first rigorous proof that a length which satisfies an irreducible cubic is not constructible by straightedge and compasses is generally credited to Pierre Laurent Wantzel, 1837. See Cajori, "Pierre Laurent Wantzel," and Richard L. Francis, "Did Gauss discover that, too?"

At this point (§17), Euler examines the polynomial equations for z which result from taking μ_1 and μ_2 to have small integer values. (Note that $z = 1$, corresponding to the angle $\omega = 0$, is always a solution of the equation, so that we can always reduce the equation by dividing out $z - 1$.)

The values $\mu_1 = 1$ and $\mu_2 = 2$ give the equation $z = 0$, whence $\omega = 90°$ and $m_1 = 45°$, $m_2 = 90°$. This is, as Euler points out, the lune that was squared by Hippocrates. The values $(\mu_1, \mu_2) = (1, 3)$ and $(\mu_1, \mu_2) = (2, 3)$ lead to quadratic equations in z. They correspond to the other two quadratures of Hippocrates (a fact of which Euler is unaware). Euler refers to these cases as "plane problems," using the terminology of Pappus.

Euler next looks at the case $(\mu_1, \mu_2) = (1, 4)$ which had been studied by Viète. Since this case leads to an irreducible cubic equation in z, Euler classifies it as a "solid" problem.[21] Similarly, the case $(\mu_1, \mu_2) = (3, 4)$ is a solid problem.[22]

The cases $(\mu_1, \mu_2) = (1, 5)$ and $(\mu_1, \mu_2) = (3, 5)$ lead to fourth-degree equations in z; however, in both cases the resolvent cubic equation has a rational root, so that the solution z can be expressed in terms of square roots only, and ω is constructible: these are plane problems. In this way, Euler has found two new squarable lunes, constructible with straightedge and compasses, which were unknown to Hippocrates.[23]

Finally, the cases $(\mu_1, \mu_2) = (2, 5)$ and $(\mu_1, \mu_2) = (4, 5)$ also lead to quartic equations in z, but in these two cases the resolvent cubic is irreducible, so that the expression for the solution z requires cube roots. Euler pronounces both cases "solid problems" without further explanation.

In the last section of the paper, Euler makes some general remarks, the meaning of which is perhaps not quite as clear as we could wish. He first suggests that the construction of lunes for other ratios $(m_1 : m_2)$ will require "higher geometric loci." I take this to mean that they will not be constructible by straightedge and compasses. In other words, Euler appears here to be stating the conjecture that the five cases of "plane" problems he has just exhibited are the only cases of squarable lunes which can be constructed by straightedge and compasses. As we will see, this conjecture is true, though the proof would not be completed for another 175 years.

Euler goes on to remark that constructions based on these "higher loci" were no less "geometric" than those which could be done with straightedge and compasses. Thus (in agreement with Pappus), the "solid" problems were no less "geometric" than those which could be done by the methods of Euclid. But then Euler remarks, "But whether except for these cases there could be any other lunules which could be determined geometrically, or not, appears to remain in doubt." If the "higher loci" produce lunes which are "determined

---

[21] By Cardano's formula, the solution to the cubic equation can be expressed in terms of square roots and cube roots. Since cube roots can be constructed geometrically by means of conic sections, this really is a solid problem in the sense of Pappus. Like Descartes, Euler takes it for granted that the root of an irreducible cubic cannot be constructed by straightedge and compasses.

[22] There is a logical question here which Euler does not address. Even if we know that the angle ω is not constructible by straightedge and compasses, we cannot in general conclude that the angles $2m_1$ and $2m_2$ are not constructible. Thus, in the present case, we have $2m_1 = 3\omega$, and 3ω might be constructible even though ω itself is not. On the other hand, $2m_2 = 4\omega$, so that ω must be constructible if $2m_2$ is. A similar argument shows that at least one of $2m_1$ and $2m_2$ is not constructible in each of the cases that Euler classifies as "solid" problems.

[23] Although, unbeknownst to Euler, they had already been found by Wijnquist; see fn. 15. Euler gives two methods of solving quartic equations—the second invented by himself—in his *Vollständige Anleitung zur Algebra* of 1770; see the English translation by John Hewlett, *Elements of Algebra*, pp. 272–288.

geometrically," what does the phrase "these cases" refer to? Could Euler be wondering whether polynomial equations of degree higher than 4 can always be solved by radicals? Evidently not, for in the summary of the article in the *Novi commentarii* (undoubtedly written by Euler himself) it says, "If some other ratio between μ and ν is taken, the construction of the lunules rises to higher Geometric loci, which nevertheless should always be considered to be Geometric, so long as μ and ν are mutually commensurable." It would appear, then, that the "other cases" that Euler is referring to are those in which the angles of the lunes are not commensurable.

The title of Euler's article suggests that it will deal with the quadrature of the circle, a topic which Euler now finally brings up. He alludes to a "commonly adduced" argument that if (some? many? those with incommensurable angles?) lunes could be squared, then the quadrature of the circle would follow. Euler points out that this argument is fallacious, then remarks, "Although it may indeed have been adequately established that the ratio of the circumference to the diameter could not be expressed by rational numbers, still less has it so far been possible to see that even irrational numbers could not be used for this purpose." Indeed, the irrationality of π was proved in 1761 by Euler's then colleague at Berlin, Johann Heinrich Lambert, using Euler's own work on continued fractions[24] (and of course Lindemann would not succeed in proving that π is transcendental until 1882).[25]

I now briefly outline the development of the theory of lunes following Euler. The two new constructible lunes with angle-ratios $(m_1 : m_2) = (1 : 5)$ and $(3 : 5)$ discovered by Wijnquist and Euler are sometimes attributed in the literature to Thomas Clausen (1801–1885).[26] Not knowing of the work of Wijnquist or Euler (nor of any but the first of the quadratures of Hippocrates), Clausen published in *Crelle's Journal* in 1840 a 2-page paper in which he recovered the four constructible lunes with $(m_1 : m_2) = (1 : 3), (2 : 3), (1 : 5)$, and $(3 : 5)$.[27] Clausen also conjectured that there were no other constructible lunes than these five. (This conjecture was called "Clausen's conjecture" by Chebotarev,[28] although, as we have seen, Euler had previously stated the same conjecture, however obscurely.)

In 1902, the Euler-Clausen conjecture was taken up by Landau, who proved the nonexistence of constuctible lunes with ratio $(m_1 : m_2) = (1 : p)$, where p is a prime other than a Fermat prime.[29] The Bulgarian mathematician Liubomir Chakalov (1886–1963) ruled out the cases $(m_1 : m_2) = (n : p)$ where p is a Fermat prime. Building on the work of Chakalov, the Ukrainian mathematician Nikolai Chebotarev ruled out the remaining cases in which m_1 and m_2 were both odd. Finally, in 1947, Chebotarev's student Ana-

---

[24]"Mémoire sur quelques propriétés remarquable des quantités transcendantes circulaires et logarithmiques," 1761 (1768). For the difficult relations between Euler and Lambert, see Kurt-Reinhard Biermann, "Vertrieb J. H. Lambert L. Euler aus Berlin?," 1985.

[25]Euler goes on to discuss questions involving the *rectification* of the circle —that is, the computation of its arc-length. He observes that questions involving the nature of π involve the *whole* circumference, and that it is obviously possible to have *partial* circular arcs with rational lengths. I think that Euler may be alluding in this paragraph to Daniel Bernoulli's incorrect proof of the converse of his condition for squarability; see fn. 16.

[26]For example, in Shenitzer, "The Problem of Squarable Lunes," pp. 649, 650.

[27]"Vier neue mondförmige Flächen, deren Inhalt quadrirbar ist." On Clausen, see now J. Schönbeck, "Thomas Clausen und die quadrierbaren Kreisbogenzweiecke"; Clausen's work on lunes is described on pp. 219–221. Schönbeck suggests (p. 219) that Clausen went further than Euler in that he actually computed the angles of the five constructible lunes. In fact, however, Euler computed explicitly the value $z = \cos \omega$ for each of these lunes; to get the angle ω itself then requires nothing more than a trig table.

[28]Schönbeck, p. 221.

[29]For this part of the history of lunes, see especially Scriba, "Welche Kreismonde sind elementar quadrierbar?"

tolii Vasilievich Dorodnov took care of the cases in which one of m_1, m_2 was even. Thus, after more than 175 years, the conjecture was finally proved.

Euler's "Considerationes cyclometricae" stands in the middle of the long history of lunes. And it contains in itself a crossroads of the mathematics of the 18th century.

This paper is based on a talk given at the MAA Session on the History of Mathematics in the Second Millennium, AMS-MAA Joint Meetings, San Diego, California, 6 January 2002. Una Bray of Skidmore College gave a talk at the same session on "The crescents of Hippocrates from the second millennium BCE to the second millennium CE."

References

[1] Daniel Bernoulli, "Problema aliquod geometricum," in *Exercitationes quædam mathematicæ*, Venice, 1724; reprinted in *Die Werke von Daniel Bernoulli*, vol. 1, ed. Volker Zimmermann, Umberto Bottazzini, and Mario Howald-Haller, Birkhäuser, Basel, 1996, pp. 353–362.

[2] Kurt-Reinhard Biermann, "Vertrieb J. H. Lambert L. Euler aus Berlin?," *Ceremony and scientific conference on the occasion of the 200th anniversary of the death of Leonhard Euler*, Berlin, 1985, pp. 91–99. Russian translation: «Был ли Леонард Эйлер изгнан из Берлина И. Г. Ламбертом?», in Развитие идей Леонарда Эйлера и современная наука, Moscow, 1988.

[3] Umberto Bottazzini, Editor's introduction to *Die Werke von Daniel Bernoulli*, Birkhäuser, Basel, 1996, pp. 129–197.

[4] Florian Cajori, "Pierre Laurent Wantzel," *Bulletin of the American Mathematical Society*, **24**, 1918, pp. 339–47.

[5] Pafnuty Lvovich Chebyshev, "Sur les questions de minima qui se rattachent à la représentation approximative des fonctions," *Mémoires de l'académie Impériale des sciences de St.-Pétersbourg*, Sixième série, Sciences mathématiques et physiques, **7**, 1859, pp. 199–291; reprinted in *Oeuvres de P. L. Tchebycheff*, ed. A. Markoff and N. Sonin, reprinted by Chelsea Publishing Company, New York, n.d., vol. 1, pp. 271–378.

[6] Thomas Clausen, "Vier neue mondförmige Flächen, deren Inhalt quadrirbar ist," *Journal für die reine und angewandte Mathematik*, **4** (1840), pp. 375–376.

[7] Steven Dale Cutkosky, *Resolution of Singularities*, American Mathematical Society, 2004.

[8] René Descartes, *La Géométrie*, Leiden, 1637; photographically reproduced with an English translation by David Eugene Smith and Marcia L. Latham, Open Court, 1925; reprinted by Dover Publications, 1954.

[9] Jean Dieudonné, *Abrégé d'histoire des mathématiques, 1700–1900*, Hermann, Paris, 1978.

[10] William Dunham, *Journey through Genius: the great theorems of mathematics*, Wiley, 1990.

[11] Leonhard Euler, "Solutio problematis geometrici circa lunulas a circulis formatas" (E73), *Commentarii academiae scientiarum Petropolitanae* **9** (1737), 1744, pp. 207–221; reprinted in *Opera Omnia*, vol. I.26, pp. 1–14.

[12] ——, *Introductio in Analysin Infinitorum* (E101/102), Lausanne, 1748; reprinted in *Opera Omnia*, vol. I.8 and I.9. English translation by John D. Blanton, *Introduction to Analysis of the Infinite*, Springer-Verlag, 1988 and 1990.

[13] ——, *Vollständige Anleitung zur Algebra* (E387/388), St. Petersburg, 1770–1771; reprinted in *Opera Omnia*, vol. I.1. English translation by John Hewlett, *Elements of Algebra*, London, 1840; reprinted by Springer-Verlag, 1984.

[14] ——, "Considerationes cyclometricae" (E423), *Novi commentarii academiae scientiarum Petropolitanae* (**16**) (1771), 1772, pp. 160–170; reprinted in *Opera Omnia*, vol. I.28, pp. 205–214.

[15] Richard L. Francis, "Did Gauss discover that, too," *Mathematics Teacher* **89**, 1986, pp. 288–93. Reprinted in Frank J. Swetz, ed., *From Five Fingers to Infinity*, Open Court, 1994, pp. 584–89.

[16] P.-H. Fuss, *Correspondance Mathématique et Physique de quelques célèbres géomètres du XVIIIème siècle*, St.-Pétersbourg, 1843, vol. 2; reprinted by Johnson Reprint Corporation, New York and London, 1968.

[17] Charles Coulston Gillispie, ed., *Dictionary of Scientific Biography*, Scribner, New York, 1970–1980.

[18] Johann Heinrich Lambert, "Mémoire sur quelques propriétés remarquable des quantités transcendantes circulaires et logarithmiques," *Histoire de l'Académie Royale des Sciences et des Belles-Lettres de Berlin*, 1761 (1768), pp. 265–322; reprinted in Andreas Speiser, ed., *Johannis Henrici Lamberti opera mathematica*, vol. 2, Zürich, 1948, pp. 112–159.

[19] Edmund Landau, "Über quadrierbare Kreisbogenzweiecke," *Sitzungsberichte der Berliner Mathematischen Gesellschaft* **2** (1903), pp. 1–6.

[20] Victor Puiseux, "Recherches sur les fonctions algébriques," *Journal de Mathématique*, **15** (1850), pp. 365–480.

[21] J. Schönbeck, "Thomas Clausen und die quadrierbaren Kreisbogenzweiecke," *Centaurus*, **46** (2004), pp. 208–229.

[22] Christoph J. Scriba, "Welche Kreismonde sind elementar quadrierbar? Die 2400jährige Geschichte eines Problems bis zur endgültigen Lösung in den Jahren 1933/1947," *Mitteilungen der Mathematischen Gesellschaft in Hamburg*, **11** 1988, pp. 517–539.

[23] Abe Shenitzer, "The Problem of Squarable Lunes," *American Mathematical Monthly*, **107** (2000), pp. 645–651.

[24] Andreas Speiser, Editor's introduction to *Leonhardi Euleri Opera Omnia*, vol. I.26, Lausanne, 1953, pp. VIII–XXXVI.

[25] Arthur Donald Steele, "Über die Rolle von Zirkel und Lineal in der griechischen Mathematik," *Quellen und Studien*, B, **3** (1936), pp. 287–369.

[26] Ivor Thomas, *Greek Mathematical Works*, Harvard University Press, vol. 1, 1939.

[27] H. W. Turnbull, ed., *Correspondence of Isaac Newton*, Cambridge University Press, vol. 2, 1960.

[28] François Viète, *Variorum de rebus mathematicis responsorum, liber VIII*, reprinted in *Francisci Vietæ Opera Mathematica*, edited by Frans van Schooten, Leiden, 1646, pp. 379–381 (reprinted by Georg Olms Verlag, Hildesheim, 1970).

What is a function?[1]

Rüdiger Thiele

Introduction

Can you imagine attending a mathematics meeting without hearing the word function (or the synonymous words mapping, transformation, relation)? Obviously, the concept of function seems to be the sort of concept that has never come into being—it appears to be an eternal Platonic idea existing from eternity to eternity or, at least, it must have been present since the birth of mathematics. Again, can you imagine being invited to any Greek symposium in Antiquity and listening to Plato (427–348 BC) or Archimedes (287?–212 BC) talking about functions? Furthermore, do you think Isaac Newton (1643–1727), Leonhard Euler (1707–1783), Carl Friedrich Gauss (1777–1855), William Rowan Hamilton (1805–1865) or Bernhard Riemann (1826–1866) would understand this concept of a function?

> For a subset G of the Cartesian product $X \times Y$, the triple $\Gamma = (G, X, Y)$ is called a correspondence from X to Y. If to any x belonging to the domain X of Γ there corresponds one and only one y belonging to Y, then Γ is called a univalent correspondence. (Patrick Suppes, *Axiomatic set theory*, 1960)

I hope my introduction was successful in convincing you that the concept of function is historical; it is not an eternal idea, the same forever, but a growing, developing one. If I am right, since when have we had such concepts? In the 18th century an English-speaking reader who opened his *Britannica* (first edition, 1781) would be disappointed: there is no entry for "mathematical function"; function is defined as "the act of fulfilling the duties of any employment." But there is hope. Just one century later David Hilbert (1862–1943) told his audience:

> Besides the concept of number, the concept of function is the most important in mathematics. (Lecture "Functionentheorie," 1893)

Today a mathematician would probably complete this statement by including the concept of set. So let us look at two of Hilbert's disciples and their very different uses of the

---

[1]Lecture delivered at the MAA MathFest in Providence, RI, August 13, 2004; revised version at the Courant Institute, January 5, 2005.

Figure 1. The "Allegory of Bathos," engraving by William Hogarth (1697–1764).
Courtesy Niedersächsische Universitäts und Landesbibliothek, Kunstsammlung.

fundamental concept of a function. In 1891 Hilbert delivered his first lecture on analytic functions and that lecture was attended by only one student, the American Fabian Franklin (1853-1939), an important figure in invariant theory. Hermann Weyl (1885-1955), another disciple of Hilbert, declared in a book on the philosophy of mathematics in 1928, "Nobody can explain what a function is." But in the 1948 English edition of the book, published during his American exile, he added "but this is what really matters." If nobody can explain the function concept, does that mean the last trumpet has already sounded and I can end my lecture here by showing you this engraving "Allegory of Bathos"?

This is not what I have in mind. On the contrary, I shall support Weyl's opinion only insofar as I will try to convince you of the various historical aspects of the concept that change in time, but in the end each of the concepts will contain and maintain necessary openness. In doing so, I will avoid arguing strictly along mathematical lines.

Antiquity

The concept of function arose as a result of a long process, in which special functions were considered first, before the development of any general theory of functions. The roots of the modern function concept cannot be found explicitly in Greek mathematics. Instead of the well-known algebraic formulas we see magnitudes (quantities) and proportions, which are used instead of functions and variables, and finally the role of the real number field is played by the Eudoxian theory of proportions. Of course, we could project our familiar modern views onto those of the Greeks, for example, by interpreting the chords of a circle worked out by Ptolemy (83?–161? AD) in tabular form as trigonometric functions. But this does not correspond to the Greek view of the matter.

The central Greek concept is that of a *magnitude*, which is characterized by the property of being able to increase and decrease. Euclid (365?–300? BC) deals with magnitudes throughout the *Elements*. Magnitudes of the same kind can be compared and composed (added and multiplied). The Greeks distinguished strictly between numerical magnitudes (natural numbers) and *geometrical magnitudes* (continuous quantities). The operation which changes a geometrical magnitude is the *construction*, generally executed by ruler and compass. Geometrical constructions can be regarded as the geometrical aspect of the function concept. Towards the end of Antiquity the concept of motion arose: a point generates a line, a line a surface, and so on. By this idea, which contradicts Plato's philosophy, *variables* were introduced and they became very effective in the hands of Bonaventura Cavalieri (1598?–1647), Isaac Barrow (1630–1677), and Isaac Newton (but was later again criticized in the logical school by Gottlob Frege (1848–1925) and others who would have preferred the first definition of a function I gave above).

Algebra

Most of ancient and Arabic arithmetic—or I might even say algebra—was rhetorical. The Renaissance mathematicians, inspired by Arabic mathematics, developed an efficient symbolic notation. Above all this development of algebraic symbolism was due to the needs of commercial arithmetic and it was the work of many people.

This finally culminated in Viète's *Logistica speciosa*, the technique of operating with letters, in which François Viète (1540–1603) systematically used letters to represent unknown and undetermined magnitudes when he wrote equations. Before Viète, there was no universal scheme which immediately showed the dependence of an expression on a magnitude as is shown today by the symbols of powers. Viète's algebra had a firm geometrical foundation which is reflected in the requirement that all equations be homogeneous (i.e., geometrically interpretable). His ideas on the use of algebra in geometry were reformulated by Descartes and Fermat.

Descartes

There is no doubt about the essential content of René Descartes's (1596-1650) *Géométrie* of 1637: curves have equations and, conversely, equations define curves. We read in Pierre Fermat's (1601–1655) "Ad locos planos..." written in 1629, but first published in 1679: "As soon as two unknown quantities appear in a final equation, there is a locus, and the end point of one of the two quantities describes a straight line." Therefore we can study a curve by algebraic means (by its equation) and on the other hand interpret an equation geometrically by means of the corresponding curve—curve and equation, formula and figure, are linked with the help of a Cartesian rectangular coordinate system. They are more or less equivalent notions. "The arithmetical symbols are written diagrams and the geometrical figures are graphic formulas," Hilbert told his audience in Paris in 1900. (p. 443).

A deeper historical investigation, however, shows that the story is more complicated and, at least from a modern viewpoint, the statements just mentioned appear more as side issues and are overshadowed by much algebraic theory, which we would find misplaced today. Only once can the equation of a straight line be found and, at a first glance, it is difficult to see any coordinate system, let alone a rectangular one.

From our point of view, however, such confusing details are not of interest. Let us look at the opening sentence of the *Geometry*:

> Any problem in geometry can easily be reduced to such terms that a knowledge of the length of certain straight lines is sufficient for its construction. (*La Géométrie*, p. 297)

What did Descartes do? He referred line segments given in a certain order by a rule to line segments of a fixed line, an axis, and he said "*appliquée par ordre*" (which means drawn by a certain rule or applied in order to another line) and that's why he spoke of "applicates" (now ordinates). The dependence of the line segments was determined by a corresponding construction and could be represented by algebraic expressions. That means we have to deal with algebraic equations (in coordinates along straight axes). Such equations are built up by the four basic operations of arithmetic plus the extraction of roots. Of course, any geometric construction by ruler and compass delivers such an algebraic equation. But conversely, we can ask which algebraic curves (named then geometric curves) are constructible with ruler and compass? Are there curves in geometry which cannot be accepted under such restrictions? And if so, how then should constructions be done when ruler and compass are insufficient? Think of the duplication of the cube, where ruler and compass alone are indeed insufficient. Besides ruler and compass, therefore, Descartes was forced to accept constructions of curves by drawing instruments other than circles and straight lines, which means geometrically he had also to accept other, more sophisticated instruments than ruler and compass.

In this way, guided by the new branch of algebra, he extended the realm of classical geometry by displacing the line separating geometrical and mechanical curves. Curves that can be described by some "regular" motion could now be accepted in geometry. Let me quote from Hilbert's Paris speech in 1900 on the range and importance of transcendental tools: "The theory of algebraic curves experienced a considerable simplification and attained greater unity by ... the consistent introduction of transcendental devices." (p. 441)

Descartes dealt extensively with curves that have algebraic equations in two geometrical magnitudes. Here, as before, curves like spirals and cycloids were excluded from geometry because to Descartes the involved motions have no exact and measurable relation. In geometry no conclusions which are based upon such curves can be accepted as exact and rigorous (*exact et assuré*). This belief is due to Descartes's philosophical *Ignorabimus*, of which we read in his *Geometry*:

> The ratio between straight line and curved lines is not known and I believe cannot be discovered by the human mind.   (*Géom.*, p. 340)

Predictions are always dangerous. Only one generation later mathematicians dealt in the calculus with this ratio successfully.

Aprés cela ie fais K I eſgale & parallele a B A, en ſorte qu'elle couppe de B C la partie B K eſgale à *m*, à cauſe qu'il y a icy + *m*; & ie l'aurois adiouſtée en tirant cete ligne I K de l'autre coſté, s'il y auoit eu -- *m*; & ie ne l'au-rois point du tout tirée, ſi la quantité *m* euſt eſté nulle. Puis ie tire auſſy I L, en ſorte que la ligne I K eſt a K L, comme Z eſt a *n*. c'eſt a dire que I K eſtant *x*, K L eſt

$\frac{n}{z}x$. Et par meſme moyen ie connois auſſy la proportion

qui

qui eſt entre K L, & I L, que ie poſe comme entre *n* & *a*: ſibienque K L eſtant $\frac{n}{z}x$, I L eſt $\frac{a}{z}x$; Et ie fais que le point K ſoit entre L & C, a cauſe qu'il y a icy -- $\frac{n}{z}x$; au lieu que i'aurois mis L entre K & C, ſi i'euſſe eu + $\frac{n}{z}x$;

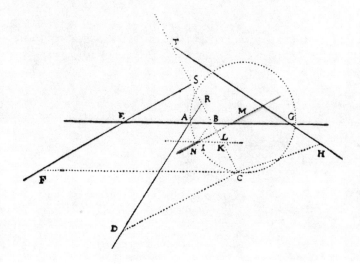

Figure 2. Cartesian coordinate lines for solving a geometrical problem (problem of four-line locus), *Géométrie*, 1637. *EABG* is the fixed line (*x*-axis) and *TLC* one applicate (ordinate) related to the fixed line. Here Descartes infers the equation of the line *I L*. Courtesy of Sudhoff-Institut, Leipzig.

Of course, from a modern viewpoint in analysis the distinction between geometrical and mechanical (or as Gottfried Wilhelm Leibniz (1646–1716) would say transcendental) curves is mathematically unjustified because the class of algebraic functions is not closed under the operation of integration. For its completion the class of transcendental functions is required.

Figure 3. Gottfried Wilhelm Leibniz (1646–1716). Courtesy of Sudhoff-Institut, Leipzig.

Leibniz

After Descartes, mathematicians were confronted with the problem of how to represent curves analytically. Many of the problems arose from mechanical questions and often a representation by algebraic equations was impossible, as for example for the important cycloids and isochrones. The representation by the method of analytic geometry was rather

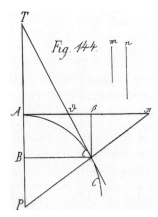

Figure 4. The function concept in Leibniz is geometric. The ordinate, tangent, subtangent, normal etc. of a point P on a curve are "functions" of P. De linea ex lineis, *Acta eruditorum* 1692. Courtesy of Leopoldina, Halle.

new and therefore did not convince some mathematicians. Furthermore, in this period of transition from geometry to analysis no universally accepted standards existed.

Let me mention the notable contributions by Leibniz. He coined the term *function* which, however, differs completely from our modern understanding and denotes various geometric quantities associated with a curve, such as ordinate, tangent, normal, subtangent, and subnormal. Quoting from his 1673 manuscript *Methodus tangentium inversa*: "... Other kinds of lines which, in a given figure, perform some function." Whereas Newton considered variables as flowing quantities depending on time, Leibniz thought in terms of sequences of infinitesimally close values. His calculus enabled him to discuss many unsolved problems elegantly: such as evolutes, involutes, roulettes, catenaries, loxodromes, isochrones, and others. That means he successfully crossed the separating line between geometrical and mechanical (i.e., transcendental) curves, which was still dogmatically drawn by Descartes. We find this awareness of pulling down a demarcation in Leibniz as early as in 1673. Here is a relevant quotation from his famous *Nova methodus* which inaugurated the differential calculus in 1684: "It is clear that our method also includes transcendental curves—those that cannot be reduced by algebraic computation, or have no particular degree."[2]

Now Christiaan Huygens (1629–1695) comes into our story, through his correspondence with Leibniz in 1690. Leibniz dealt with mechanical problems, especially with a falling body in a medium with resistance proportional to the square of velocity v. For Huygens, who thought strictly geometrically, Leibniz's solution was perplexing. Huygens had expected some proportions or at least manipulated proportions, that is, something like this:

$$A : B = C : D.$$

Instead, what he got was:

$$B^t = a^{gt} = (1 + av) : (1 - av), \qquad \text{(g is the constant of acceleration).}$$

Huygens responded:

---

[2]Translation from D.J Struik, *A Source Book for Mathematics*, Harvard U. Press, 1969, p. 276.

I must confess that the nature of that sort of supertranscendental lines, in which the unknowns enter the exponent, seems to me so obscure that I would not think about introducing them into geometry (Bos, p. 23),

and he demanded a geometrical, i.e., a pointwise construction of the curve under consideration. We know that for an exponential equation, such a construction by ruler and compass is impossible. To our surprise, however, we read in Huygens's next letter:

I have looked at your construction of the exponential curve which is **very good.** Still I do not see that this expression …is a great help for that: I knew the curve [*Logarithmica*, i.e, the logarithmic curve] already for a long time.   (Bos, p. 25)

For Huygens—as we clearly see—the *Logarithmica*, that is the transcendental curve representing the relation between an arithmetical progression on the x-axis and a geometrical progression of the corresponding ordinates, was already acceptable. Nevertheless, Huygens still preferred the geometric representation to the analytic one.

Bernoulli

The next cornerstone is a by-product of the quarrel between John Bernoulli (1667—1748) and his brother and former teacher James (1654–1705). Challenged in 1696 by John's problem of the brachistochrone, one year later James posed the isoperimetric problems, and there is no doubt: one of James's intentions was to discredit his brother and former disciple thoroughly.

The simplest case of the challenge is an old problem of geometry: the problem of queen Dido. In a plane, let there be given a string with fixed endpoints B and N, the endpoints of an axis BN; it is required to find the curve, representing the shape of the string, such that the area under the string with respect to the axis is a maximum.

Here is James's generalization: do not consider the area under the string, but rather that under another curve, the ordinates PZ of which depend on the string's ordinates PF.

In which way can PZ depend on PF? In Descartes' extended understanding of geometry, we can admit constructions involving powers and roots. It is precisely in this sense that

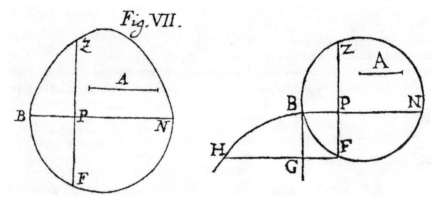

Figure 5. Isoperimetric problem as posed by Jakob Bernoulli (left) and as extended by Johann Bernoulli (right). The curve BH is arbitrary. *Acta eruditorum*, May 1697; *Histoire des Ouvrages des Savans*, June 1697. Courtesy of Leopoldina, Halle.

James posed the problem. However, in order to compromise James, John remarked boastfully he would solve a much more general problem (*mille fois plus général*); specifically, he would regard the dependence of the ordinate *PZ* on the ordinate *PF* as *arbitrary*. What did he mean by an arbitrary dependence? At this time they did not yet have transcendental representations. Instead, John found a loophole by returning to geometrical representations, i.e., to a curve drawn freely by hand.

Here we have an interesting methodological aspect: by what rule is such an arbitrary curve determined in the end? The arbitrariness of a mathematical object is expressed by means of physiology or, at least, of mechanics. In geometry such an answer is curious, for why should the capabilities of the hand be a criterion for acceptable curves? The arguments are taken from completely different branches of knowledge: physiology and mathematics!

Let me ask a question to elucidate the fact that we have a contradictory pair: arbitrariness and rule. For you, what is an arbitrary function? How arbitrary is an arbitrary function? How far can you define an arbitrary function without using any rules?

Let me return to John Bernoulli. James offered him 50 Thaler as a reward, rather embarrassing for the ambitious John who, at least publicly, always emphasized that glory, not money, was the solver's aim. Although John extended the function concept he failed to give a corresponding solution. However, this line is due to John (1706):

> *ou généralement telle que les fonctions quelconques de ces appliquées* (Thiele, p. 163)

> "...or generally such a curve as the arbitrary functions of these applicates (i.e., ordinates)."

This is why B. de Fontenelle (1657–1757), secretary of the Paris Academy, remarked in 1706 in the journal of the Academy, *Histoire de l'Académie Royale*:

> He [John] changed the powers of the applicates into such things he called functions. Powers are but a special kind of functions. In this way Mr. Bernoulli delivers for all kinds of functions of applicates you can imagine the equations of a required curve. (Thiele, p. 164)

John's boasting

> *Je n'ai employé en tout que trois minutes de tems pour tenter,*

i.e., for the problem he would have needed only three minutes, because of the falseness of John's solution it was spitefully commented on by his brother

> John should have taken six minutes because this loss of time would not have reduced John's inventions essentially.

After the death of his brother in 1705 John did not publish on this subject, though Taylor's well-known book *Methodus incrementorum* (1715) came into his hands. Brook Taylor (1685–1731) also dealt with the isoperimetric problem and dared not to mention the brothers. This is not quite true, because Taylor actually gave them credit, but only in an abstract in the *Transactions of the Royal Society*, written in English, which John did not or could not read.

So John became furious and we have a paper *Remarques* in 1718 with this analytic definition:

On appelle ici Fonction d'une grandeur variable, une quantité composée de quelque manière que ce soit de cette grandeur variable & de constante.

A quantity composed in any way of a variable quantity and constants is called a function of a variable quantity.

What did John have in mind when he wrote "*quelque manière*" (composed in any way)? Obviously nothing other than the basic operations of arithmetic applied to geometric quantities; the expression "*grandeur variable*" (variable quantity) still refers to continuous geometrical magnitudes and not yet to real numbers. In the end it will be John's famous disciple Leonhard Euler (1707–1783) who will not only pick up the arithmetical form but make the analytic aspect the guiding principle: any magnitude can be measured by a number, the values of magnitudes are numerical quantities, and from the very beginning functions are functions of variable number quantities and the subject of the analysis of the infinite is these functions.

Leonhard Euler

So it was Euler, known as "analysis incarnate," who took up the mathematical challenges of his time and, by establishing the concept of a function at the heart of his research, completely eliminated the geometrical point of view and created a new branch of mathematics: analysis. Euler's attention was focused on the arithmetical symbols themselves and their rules of calculation. His analytic trilogy is well known: the *Introductio in analysin infinitorum*, a prerequisite course published in 1748, the *Institutiones calculi differentialis*, written in the same year but published in 1755, and finally the *Institutionum calculi integralis*, written about 1763 and published from 1768 through 1770.

As a matter of fact Euler's work started as early as 1727, when he wrote a first sketch *Calculi differentialis* for the purpose of instruction, which is still unpublished. The opening line exactly repeats John Bernoulli's definition but with a different nature for the variables: "A quantity composed somehow from one or a greater number of quantities is called its, or their, function." Euler offers some examples to explain what is meant by composition. Compositions are made by the basic operations of arithmetic and in addition by extraction of roots and taking of logarithms. Later on, in the *Introductio*, Euler called the composed term "analytic expression" (*expressio analytica*). The analytic expression, that is a *calculating rule*, a formula, is Euler's fundamental idea, from which he developed his analysis. When he built up analysis, the analytic expression was permanently extended, step by step, as he extended the admissible operations. The kind of composition was adapted to meet the needs of given problems; and so permitted higher transcendental functions arrived at by integration and even expressions that appeared implicitly only when solving equations. It is openness that characterizes Euler's concept of function.

Euler did all things as easily as he could. Therefore he fitted his concepts to the problems (not the other way round), and he did this in the case of functions too. Let me quote Henri Poincaré (1854–1912): "Formerly, when a new function was invented, it was in view of some practical end. Today they are invented on purpose to show our ancestor's reasoning at fault, and we shall never get anything more than that out of them." [*Science et Méthode*] Euler allowed complex numbers to be variables and that convincingly shows he had com-

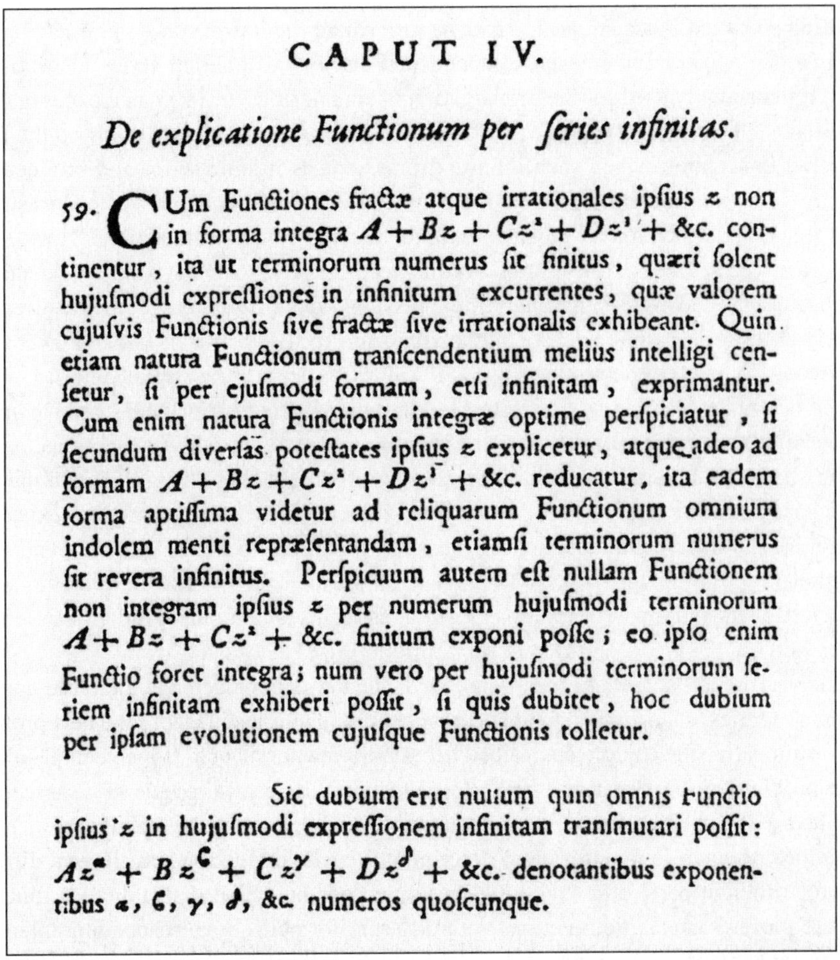

CAPUT IV.

De explicatione Functionum per series infinitas.

59. CUm Functiones fractæ atque irrationales ipsius *z* non in forma integra $A + Bz + Cz^2 + Dz^3 + \&c.$ continentur, ita ut terminorum numerus fit finitus, quæri folent hujufmodi expreffiones in infinitum excurrentes, quæ valorem cujufvis Functionis five fractæ five irrationalis exhibeant. Quin. etiam natura Functionum tranfcendentium melius intelligi cenfetur, fi per ejufmodi formam, etfi infinitam, exprimantur. Cum enim natura Functionis integræ optime perfpiciatur, fi fecundum diverfas poteftates ipfius *z* explicetur, atque adeo ad formam $A + Bz + Cz^2 + Dz^3 + \&c.$ reducatur, ita eadem forma aptiffima videtur ad reliquarum Functionum omnium indolem menti repræfentandam, etiamfi terminorum numerus fit revera infinitus. Perfpicuum autem eft nullam Functionem non integram ipfius *z* per numerum hujufmodi terminorum $A + Bz + Cz^2 + \&c.$ finitum exponi poffe; eo ipfo enim Functio foret integra; num vero per hujufmodi terminorum feriem infinitam exhiberi poffit, fi quis dubitet, hoc dubium per ipfam evolutionem cujufque Functionis tolletur.

Sic dubium erit nullum quin omnis Functio ipfius *z* in hujufmodi expreffionem infinitam tranfmutari poffit:

$$Az^\alpha + Bz^\varsigma + Cz^\gamma + Dz^\delta + \&c.$$ denotantibus exponentibus $\alpha, \varsigma, \gamma, \delta, \&c.$ numeros quofcunque.

Figure 6. Power series in Euler's *Introductio* (E101, 1748). Courtesy of Universitätsbibliothek Leipzig.

pletely left the geometrical viewpoint. Moreover, Euler even discussed the graph of such monsters as $y(x) = (-1)^x$ which he could easily write down but not visualize.

Furthermore, in the beginning Euler believed that any analytic expression could be expressed as a power series. This idea of extending finite algebraic (polynomial) expressions into infinite series vaguely anticipates the theorem of Karl Weierstrass (1815–1897): the polynomials are dense in the continuous functions on a closed and bounded interval. Roughly speaking, for Euler analysis was just infinite algebra and power series were its universal element. Euler's robust pragmatism may be illustrated by his remark:

> If anyone doubts that every function can be so expressed the doubt will be set aside by actually expanding functions.

Here Euler took his courage in both hands to lend countenance to his belief.

Obviously, Euler's concept describes analytic functions, called *functio continuae* by him. However, Euler extended the concept of the Taylor series and regarded general power series:

$$Az^\alpha + Bz^\beta + Cz^\gamma + Dz^\delta + \text{ etc., } (\alpha, \beta, \gamma, \delta, \dots \text{ arbitrary}),$$

including so-called Puiseux and Laurent series (where the powers α, β, γ, δ, etc. are rational [n/k, k fixed] and integer numbers for Puiseux and Laurent series respectively), which Euler actually used for the investigation of singularities. In 1905, in a paper on functions that can be represented analytically, Henri Lebesgue (1875–1941) showed the range of Euler's conception: when such infinite expressions as infinite series and products and continued fractions are allowed, then the class of functions is equal to that of measurable Borel functions, which for $\mathbb{R}^n$ coincide with the first class of Baire functions.

In later years, Euler put less stress on the need for any particular kind of the analytic form because he had noticed that analytic expressions were insufficient for the requirements of analysis, especially in the debate on the vibrating string (starting in 1747). Power series are already completely determined by their values on an arbitrary small interval, which obviously is not at all the case for arbitrary functions. Moreover, even well-posed boundary conditions in the problem of the vibrating string can lead to nonanalytic functions. A most natural shape is one with a non-differentiable point: the plucked string. If the initial state of the string is represented as an arbitrary hand-drawn curve, then we cannot expect the solution of the differential equation of the vibrating string to be an analytic expression; nevertheless the string will vibrate. The debate on the new class of functions continued for another 20 years and involved prominent mathematicians, among them Euler, Jean le Rond d'Alembert (1717–1783), and Daniel Bernoulli (1700–1782).

It is very remarkable that Euler, who loved calculating so much and therefore appreciated power series, changed his mind and adapted the function concept to the new problem.

To summarize the complicated debate from our viewpoint, what is the general solution of the problem of the vibrating string? I will mention the central points of disagreement. Euler and d'Alembert differed as to what kind of functions was to be admitted. Euler gave up the idea of *one* rule (one formula) describing the whole function and allowed different rules for different parts of a function. Such functions he called discontinuous functions (that are piecewise analytic functions with different formulas in corresponding intervals). Until Euler, a function was understood to be something expressed by one formula and this had been thought to grant continuity and differentiability in the modern sense. Today we know that series representation does not grant these properties; think of Weierstrass' 1855 counterexample of a continuous but nowhere differentiable function, among others.

For the mathematicians of the 18th century, in what way do functions given by one formula or several formulas differ essentially? A comparison may be helpful: You don't regard your Ego only as the sum of a daily experienced being.

The standpoint of a mathematical physicist—a new profession—was represented in the work of Euler: the solution of the wave equation can be deduced solely from initial conditions and velocities, i.e. a plucked string is possible. If there were no arithmetical expressions for calculation Euler felt forced to do it geometrically. To solve the wave equation the physicist Daniel Bernoulli, on the other hand, suggested trigonometric series. Euler rejected this possibility because the character of special, i.e., trigonometric, functions imposes certain restrictions on the form of a solution, which therefore cannot be fully general. This is an important question playing a crucial role in the further development: Can an expansion of an arbitrary function into a series be made by particular types of series? Euler gave cursory attention to trigonometric series and curiously, on this occasion, he unconsciously did reasonable work in determining the coefficients in a trigonometric expansion in a paper

"Disquisitio ulterior super seriebus" (E 704), read in 1777 but published posthumously in 1798. In 1829 it was Peter Gustav Lejeune Dirichlet (1805–1859), who showed that special trigonometric series—Fourier series—can represent a broad class of "arbitrary"functions, among them all the functions of classical physics. In a lecture attended by John Charles Fields (1863–1932) in Berlin in 1899, Herman Amandus Schwarz (1843–1921) rightly spoke of "empirical functions," which with the help of Fourier series can be made computable.

In Euler's *Institutiones calculi differentialis*, one important result of the vibrating string controversy appeared. In the preface, Euler gave a general definition of a function as a quantity whose values somehow change with the changes of the independent variables:

> If, therefore, x denotes a variable quantity, all quantities which depend in some way on x or are determined by it, are called functions of this variable.

Indeed, we have a new aspect: Euler speaks of the dependence of variables instead of the composition of an analytic expression. The crucial words for a mathematical interpretation, however, are "depend in some way" and "are determined." In the actual forming of such functions Euler cannot help using the known kinds of determining; e.g., he must use the standard algebraic and transcendental operations (as indicated in the old definitions). In other words, his definition given in 1748 in his *Introductio* and the 1755 one just quoted are more or less equivalent. For the pragmatic Euler, functionality was a matter of representation by calculable expressions and not so much a conceptual description of relations; furthermore he regarded number quantities only, admittedly he also accepted complex numbers as number quantities (but without any idea of a distance between them or real numbers). Neither in his analysis books nor in the discussion of the function $y = (-1)^x$ do we find such a general concept in use. Moreover, in his paper "*De usu functionum discontinuarum*" (E332), written in 1765, Euler remarked that the known calculus "can only be applied to curves whose nature can be contained in one analytic equation." Therefore any attempt to interpret the 1755 definition in modern terms does not at all meet Euler's aim.

However, I repeat, in the end Euler stated that there was no need for the relations between the quantities to be given by the same law throughout an interval (the functions that he called discontinuous), nor was it necessary that the relation be given by mathematical formulas. Like John Bernoulli in a similar situation earlier—he accepted curves freely drawn by hand (*cum libero manus ductu*) as functions.

Incidentally, it was Euler who created the functional symbol $f(x)$; John Bernoulli still used fx, as we like to write in the case of operators.

> §. 7. Fit autem $dx - \frac{x\,da}{a}$ integrabile fi multiplicatur per $\frac{1}{a}$, integrale enim erit $\frac{x}{a} + c$, defignante c quantitatem conftantem quamcunque ab a non pendentem. Quocirca, fi $f(\frac{x}{a} + c)$ denotet functionem quamcunque

Figure 7. First use of the symbol $f(x)$ for a function f of x, from Euler's paper "De infinitis curvis," (E44, 1740). Courtesy of Leopoldina, Halle.

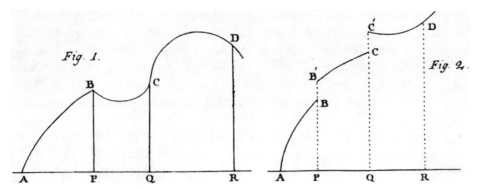

Figure 8. Figures from Antoine Arbogast's Prize paper "Sur la nature des fonctions arbitraire" (1791) showing discontinuous functions (irregular functions) in the 18th century sense. Courtesy of Leopoldina, Halle.

"Considering such [discontinuous] functions," Euler wrote to d'Alembert in 1763 "as are subject to no law of continuity [in the sense of the 18th century, i.e., expressed by one equation] opens to us a wholly new range of analysis." This understanding seems to contradict the 1765 quotation just mentioned. However, in it Euler describes the limitations of the known analysis, which had to use the repertoire of functions with which mathematicians were familiar. Consequently, for the vibrating string Euler gave non-analytic solutions in the form of geometrical (!) constructions.

In 1787, four years after Euler's death, the Petersburg Academy proposed for its prize competition a question on the nature of arbitrary functions. The paper *Sur la nature des fonctions arbitraire*, by Antoine Arbogast (1759–1803) was awarded the prize in 1790. In this paper, Arbogast summarized Euler's view of an extended concept of functions in this way:

> Euler had the daring idea not to subject these curves to any laws [i.e., to regard arbitrary curves], and it was he who said for the first time that curves may be any line, that is, irregular and discontinuous, or composed of different parts of curves [*functiones mixtas*] and drawn by hand in a free movement, which goes with no spatial restrictions.

Incidentally, Euler's denotation of "irregular" functions indicates the continued pain of his labor. How arbitrary is an arbitrary function? Is it as an arbitrary shaped string, i.e., arbitrariness within the scope of continuity (in the modern sense)?

Besides the vibrating string, there was another problem, the study of which gave a further impetus to the evolution of the function concept: the problem of heat conduction. In nature, the physical constraints of both problems differ essentially. The shape of the string is visible, is a geometric curve, while the temperature distribution is not; it is an algebraic expression. Therefore the concept of a function is freed from geometric perception by the latter problem and there emerges a general notion of analytic function.

Continuity (in the sense of the 18th century) was now called into question. The ordinates of a function were not supposed to be subject to *one* common law (i.e., a single analytic expression throughout, on intervals $A, B, C, \ldots$), let alone a law of continuity; functions represent a succession of values or ordinates each of which is arbitrary (i.e., the

FOURIER

Figure 9. Jean Baptiste Joseph Fourier (1768–1830) Courtesy of Sudhoff-Institut, Leipzig.

intervals $A, B, C, \ldots$ shrink to points). To sum it up, like Jean Baptiste Fourier (1768–1830) in his *Théorie Analytique de la Chaleur* (Analytic theory of heat, 1822): "They [the ordinates] succeed each other in any manner whatever, and each of them is given as it were a single quantity." This sounds like a description of an arbitrary correspondence no longer obliged by continuity, but actually Fourier apparently considered piecewise discontinuous functions. We will not discuss in detail how discontinuous a function Fourier might have considered, but obviously the time was again ripe for an extended function concept.

Besides the transition of the function concept from geometry to arithmetic, a further thing is remarkable: John Bernoulli, and even more so Euler, distinguished functions by their properties. For example, Euler divided functions into algebraic and transcendental, the former algebraic functions into rational and irrational, and the latter he classified into trigonometric, logarithmic, exponential, etc. Furthermore he distinguished between explicit and implicit, even and odd functions. This classification shows a transition: a function is not only a tool in analysis but has become an object itself in mathematics. Here we have one root of function spaces.

Modern mathematicians have also often given false interpretations of the definitions of functions by Nikolai I. Lobachevsky (1793–1856) and Dirichlet, given in 1834 and 1837 respectively. Like Euler in his analytic expression, both regarded continuous changes of functions only and therefore dealt not with modern functionality of mapping, but were still guided by "mechanical" motions. Lobachevsky speaks of "*postepenno ismenjajetsja*" (gradually change) as does Dirichlet who speaks of "*allmählich*" (gradual) and demands that the graph is "*gesetzlos gezeichnet gedacht*" (imagined lawlessly drawn). Dirichlet re-

§. 1.

Contemplabor hic denuo eiusmodi functiones cuiuspiam anguli φ, quas in series, quarum termini cosinus angulorum multiplorum ipsius φ continent, evolvere liceat. Scilicet si φ denotet talem functionem anguli φ, quae per evolutionem huiusmodi seriei oriatur:

$$\phi = A + B\cos\phi + C\cos 2\phi + D\cos 3\phi + E\cos 4\phi + \text{etc.}$$

manifestum est talem resolutionem semper succedere, quando eadem functio φ per solutionem communem in talem seriem converti potest:

$$\phi = \alpha + \beta\cos\phi + \gamma\cos\phi^2 + \delta\cos\phi^3 + \epsilon\cos\phi^4 + \text{etc.}$$

propterea quod omnes potestates cosinuum in cosinus multiplorum eiusdem anguli resolvi possunt, id quod in potestatibus sinuum non succedit, quoniam tantum potestates pares in cosinus multiplorum resolvuntur, potestates vero impares ad sinus multiplorum perducuntur. Quia vero omnes sinus

═══ 116 ═══

$$\phi = A + B\cos\phi + C\cos 2\phi + D\cos 3\phi + E\cos 4\phi + \text{etc.}$$

tum singulae quantitates A, B, C, D, E, etc. per sequentes formulas integrales determinantur, siquidem in singulis integratio a termino φ = 0, usque ad terminum φ = π extendatur, denotante π semiperipheriam circuli cuius radius = 1.

1. $A = \frac{1}{\pi}\int\phi\,\partial\phi.$

2. $B = \frac{2}{\pi}\int\phi\,\partial\phi\cos\phi.$

3. $C = \frac{2}{\pi}\int\phi\,\partial\phi\cos 2\phi.$

4. $D = \frac{2}{\pi}\int\phi\,\partial\phi\cos 3\phi.$

5. $E = \frac{2}{\pi}\int\phi\,\partial\phi\cos 4\phi.$

etc.   etc.

ubi notetur primum coefficientem esse $\frac{1}{\pi}$ dum sequentes omnes sunt $\frac{2}{\pi}$.

Figure 10. Fourier coefficients determined by Euler in his paper "Disquisitio ulterior super seriebus" (E704, 1798). Courtesy of Leopoldina, Halle.

garded functions not only as solutions of differential equations (defined by such equations) but as mathematical objects which are subject of mathematical operations such as integration. The question is now posed as: Can one integrate an arbitrary function? Dirichlet's famous everywhere discontinuous function served more as a counterexample, not so much as an extension of function concept. Incidentally, this function was initially given verbally only, later an analytic expression was discovered.

A one-to-one correspondence between arbitrary sets appears in 1888 in the famous paper *"Was sind und was sollen die Zahlen?"* (What are numbers and what are they for?) by Richard Dedekind (1831–1916), who spoke of systems instead of sets. In order to define continuous functions on arbitrary sets, some topology is needed first, whereas for sets of numbers a topology is automatically given by intuition. To paraphrase Neil Armstrong's famous quotation of about a quarter of a century ago: That's one small step for a modern mathematician, but one giant leap for the 19th century mathematician.

The tendency to render mathematics in arithmetical terms has continued since the days of Euler. I need only remind you of Joseph Louis Lagrange's (1736–1813) book *Théorie des fonctions analytiques* (Theory of analytic functions, 1797). Felix Klein (1844–1925) spoke of arithmetization. However, with his brilliant geometric intuition, he was not pleased by these abstract arithmetizing tendencies.

It was in the isoperimetric problems of the calculus of variations, posed in 1697, and their solutions in which analytic expressions arose and shifted the setting of analysis from geometry to arithmetic. This tendency, however, was not straightforward. In 1878 Karl Weierstrass delivered the course "*Einleitung in die Theorie der analytischen Functionen*" (Introduction to the theory of analytic functions). In lecture notes which were taken by Adolf Hurwitz we read:

> John Bernoulli first gave another and seemingly very general definition of function: if among two variable quantities there is a relation which determines along with the values of one quantity a certain number of definite values of the other one, then these quantities are called functions of each other.

And some lines later:

> First of all, this definition is only valid for real numbers. But it is completely untenable and completely infertile (*unhaltbar und unfruchtbar*).

Why did Weierstrass come to this strange point of view? For him power series were the heart of analysis. Weierstrass' ultimate aim was the numerical representation of a function. Above all, he objected to Bernoulli's definition because one cannot use it to deduce general properties such as differentiability. To quote Poincaré, "Weierstrass's method was above all a method of proof, (*la méthode de Weierstrass est avant tout une méthode de démonstration*)." Here Bernoulli and Weierstrass agree completely: the general notion that $f(x)$ is only an empty symbol. However, when Weierstrass proved his approximation theorem in 1885 (polynomials are uniformly dense in the continuous functions on a closed bounded interval) he changed his mind and accepted such functions as meaningful mathematical objects.

Incidentally, the quoted definition was not Bernoulli's. He neither spoke of "values of quantities" nor of "multivalued functions." The latter functions we find in Euler's 1728-manuscript, but we do *not* find such a concept in the famous controversy on the logarithms of negative numbers between John Bernoulli and Leibniz in 1712, not at all. Using a one-to-infinite relation, in 1749 Euler clarified the meaning of such functions in his paper "*De la controverse entre Messieurs Leibnitz et Bernoulli sur les logarithmes des nombres négatifs et imaginaires*" (Controversy between Mr. Leibniz and Mr. Bernoulli on the logarithms of negative and imaginary numbers) (E168). Moreover, a numerical interpretation ("value of quantity") is probably firstly stated by Augustin Louis Cauchy (1789–1857) in 1821 (*Cours d'Analyse*). Although both Weierstrass and Euler insisted on computability, a comparison with Weierstrass shows the advantage of Euler's pragmatic attitude.

More or less at the end of the 19th century, functions were regarded as fundamental for analysis and mathematical physics and therefore in about 1900 Hilbert also declared such functions as normal. "Non-analytic functions exist, and that is the only reason we consider them," Hilbert still declared in 1904! Having this in mind I will quote a remark on solutions of differential equations from a letter which Constantin Carathéodory (1873–1950), who had just got his PhD, wrote to Adolf Kneser (1862–1930) in 1905:

> I do not like this American fashion of avoiding analytic functions [in mathematics], because only such functions actually occur *in praxis* and if there are discontinuities then they are found in the topics described by functions, as happens in optics.

Only a dozen years later Carathéodory introduced his most influential book *Vorlesungen über reelle Funktionen* (Lectures on real functions, 1918) with the statement that he intended to give a systematic presentation of Lebesgue's revolutionary results.

History frequently repeats itself, but obviously mathematicians do not profit very much from the lessons of history. In 1883 when Vito Volterra (1860–1940) extended the function concept into a functional (*funzione delle linee*) he declared that not every functional can be expressed analytically. Then in about 1903, in a manner similar to the 18th century mathematicians who initially did not call continuity in question, Jacques Hadamard (1865–1963) still supposed all functionals to be continuous. Finally, the controversies between Hadamard's *calcul fonctione* and Maurice Fréchet's (1878–1973) *analyse général* mirror the old differences between the constructive and general function concept.

Is there anything we have learned in this lesson? The generation of disciples, which is not so firmly rooted in tradition as its teachers, reads and uses the old concepts and drafts more freely, as it starts from a different and more advanced viewpoint. The road to change is best taken without the heavy baggage of tradition, but with historical sense.

Conclusion

Of course, the story is much more complicated than as I have told it. Other mathematicians should have been mentioned; for example James Gregory (1638–1675), who was the first to define an analytic expression admitting the passage to the limit. However, he went more or less unnoticed.

In conclusion I should mention a few sources, for example the excellent papers of Henk Bos on curves in the 16th century, collected in the AMS volume *Lectures in the History of Mathematics* (1993) and Otto Toeplitz's (1881–1940) wonderful book *Die Entwicklung der Infinitesimalrechnung* (The development of the infinitesimal calculus) on the history of analysis.

This account is too brief to represent the whole truth, i.e., to describe the evolution of our intuitive idea of a functional dependence to a unifying idea permeating all mathematics and dealing with its geometric, algebraic, and logic aspects.

The last word belongs to Richard Courant (1888–1972). With respect to the unifying idea and the historical character of the function concept I quote from his *Differential and integral calculus*, vol. 1: "The presentation of analysis as a closed system of truth without reference to its origin and purpose has, it is true, an aesthetic charm and satisfies a deep philosophical need. But the attitude of those who consider analysis solely as an abstractly logical, introverted science is not only highly unsuitable for beginners but endangers the future of the subject."

I have stressed much technical stuff so let me conclude with a pleasant remark. I know highly gifted twins who recently passed their school exams and started to study philosophy and on this occasion they made—as they frequently do—poems, among them also mathematical ones. All of this is not unusual, however, the twins don't speak, they don't write, they are autistic and communicate only by computer. In one of the poems I found a summary of my talk put in verses. Let me quote these verses (in my translation):

> powers and roots celebrated a party,
> the variables were not invited,
> but they stayed through the end.

References

[1] Arbogast, Antoine, "Mémoire sur la nature des fonctions arbitraire," Prize paper of the St. Petersburg Academy, St. Pétersbourg, 1791.

[2] Bernoulli, Daniel, "Réflexions et écleircissemens sur les nouvelles vibrations des cordes," *Mémoires de l'Académie Royale des Sciences et Belles Lettres*, 9 (1753) 147–172.

[3] Bos, Henk, *Lectures in the History of Mathematics*, History of Mathematics, vol. 7. AMS/LMS 1991.

[4] ——, "Tractional Motion and the Legitimation of Transcendental Curves," *Centaurus* 31 no. 1 (1988) pp. 9–62.

[5] Boyer, Carl, "Proportion, equation, function: three steps in the development of a concept," *Scripta mathematica*, 12 (1946) 5–13.

[6] Burkhardt, Heinrich, "Entwicklung nach oscillierenden Functionen und und Integration der Differentialgleichungen der mathematischen Physik," *Jahresbericht der Deutschen Mathematiker-Vereinigung*, vol. 10/2. Leipzig: Teubner, 1901–1908.

[7] d'Alembert, Jean le Rond, "Recherches sur la courbe que forme une corde tendue mise en vibration," *Mém. Acad. Sci. Berlin* 3 (1747) 214–219; see also Additions, *Mém. Acad. Sci. Berlin* 6 (1750) 355–366.

[8] Descartes, René, *La Géométrie*, Leiden, 1737, published in facsimile with an English translation by D. E. Smith and M. Latham, Dover.

[9] Dirichlet, Peter Lejeune, "Die Darstellung ganz willkürlicher Functionen durch Sinus- und Cosinusreihen," H. Liebmann, ed. *Ostwald's Klassiker* no. 116. Leipzig: Engelmann, 1900.

[10] Euler, Leonhard, "De usu functionum discontinuarum in analysi," (E322) *Novi Commentarii Academiae Petropolitanea*, St. Petersburg 11 (1763) 1767, 67–102 = *Opera omnia* I/23, pp. 74–91.

[11] ——, "Eclaircissemens sur le mouvement des cordes vibrantes," (E317). *Melanges de philosophie et de la mathematique de la societe royale de Turin* 3, 1766, pp. 1–26 = *Opera omnia* II/10, pp. 377–396.

[12] ——, *Introductio in analysin infinitorum* (E101/102), Lausanne: Bousquet, 1748 = *Opera omnia* I/8-9.

[13] ——, Remarques sur les mémoires précédens de M. Bernoulli (E213). *Mémoires de l'Académie Royale des Sciences et Belles Lettres de Berlin*, 9 (1753) 1755, 196–222 = *Opera omnia* II/10, pp. 233–254.

[14] ——, "Sur la vibration des cordes," (E140) *Mémoires de l'Académie Royale des Sciences et Belles Lettres de Berlin*, 4 (1748) 1750, 69–85 = *Opera omnia* II/10, pp. 63–67.

[15] ——, *Institutiones calculi differentialis* (E212). St. Petersburg: Academy, 1755 = *Opera omnia* I/10.

[16] ——, *Institutionum calculi integralis* (E342, 366 and 385) St. Petersburg, 1768, 1769 and 1770. Reprinted in *Opera omnia* I/11–13.

[17] Fourier, Joseph, *Théorie Analytique de la Chaleur*, Paris: Didot, 1822 = *Oeuvres* 1, Paris: Gauthier-Villars, 1888.

[18] Felgner, Ulrich, "Der Begriff der Funktion," *Hausdorff, Gesammelte Werke*, vol. 2. Brieskorn et al. Berlin: Springer, 2002, pp. 621–633.

[19] Frege, Gottlieb, "Was ist eine Funktion?" Leipzig, 1904 = *Kleinere Schriften, I.* Angelelli, ed. Hildesheim: Olms, 1967, pp. 273–280.

[20] Grattan-Guinness, Ivor, *From the Calculus to Set Theory, 1630–1910*, Princeton: University Press 1980.

[21] Grattan-Guinness, Ivor, *The development of the foundations of mathematical analysis from Euler to Riemann*, Cambrdidge and London, 1970.

[22] Hadamard, Jacques, "Le calcul fonctionnel," *L'Enseignement mathématiques* 14 (1912) 5–18.

[23] Hilbert, David, *Einleitung in die Functionentheorie*, Handschriftenabteilung (Special Collections), University Library Göttingen, Cod. Ms. D. Hilbert 540.

[24] ——, "Mathematical Problems," *Bull. Amer. Math. Soc.* 8 (July 1902), 437–479. Originally published as "Mathematische Probleme. Vortrag, gehalten auf dem internationalen Mathematike-Congress zu Paris 1900," *Gött. Nachr.* 1900, 253–297, Vandenhoeck & Ruprecht, Göttingen. Translated by Dr. Mary Winston Newson, 1902.

[25] Juškevič (Juschkewitsch, Youshkevitch), Adolf, "The Concept of Function up to the Middle of the 19th century," *Archive for History of Exact Sciences*, 16 (1976–77) 37–85.

[26] ——, "Euler's unpublished manuscript Calculus Differentialis," *Leonhard Euler, Gedenkband des Kantons Basel-Stadt*. J.J. Burkhardt et. al. eds. Basel: Birkhäuser 1983, pp. 161–170.

[27] Kleiner, Israel, "Evolution of the Function Concept," *College Mathematics Journal*, 20 (1989) 282–300.

[28] l'Hospital, Guillaume Marquis de, *Analyse des Infiniments Petits*. Paris, 1696.

[29] Lagrange, Joseph-Louis, *Théorie des Fonctions Analytiques*, Paris, 1797, 2nd ed. 1813 = *Oeuvres* 9.

[30] Man-Keung Siu, "Concept of Functions," *Learn from the Masters!* F. Swetz et al., eds. MAA, 1991, pp. 105–121.

[31] Medvedev, Fyodor, *Scenes from the History of Real Functions*. Transl. by. R. Cook. Basel: Birkhäuser, 1991.

[32] Monna, A.F., "The concept of function," *Archive for History of Exact Sciences*, 9 (1972) 52–84.

[33] Panza, Mario, "Concept of Function, between Quantity and Form, in the 18th Century," *History of Mathematics and Education: Ideas and Experiences*, N.H. Jahnke et al., eds. Göttingen: Vandenhoeck, 1996, pp. 241–274.

[34] Poincaré, Henri, *Science et méthode*, Flammarion, Paris, 1908.

[35] Ravetz, Jerome, "Vibrating String and Arbitrary Functions," *The Logic of Personal Knowledge*. London: Routledge & Kegan Paul, 1961, pp. 71–89.

[36] Riemann, Bernhard, "Über die Darstellbarkeit einer Function durch eine trigonometrische Reihe," *Gesammelte Abhandlungen*, New York Dover 1953, pp. 227–271; also reprinted in *Gesammelte Werke*, new edited by R. Narasimhan. Leipzig/Heidelberg: Teubner/Springer 1990, pp. 227–265.

[37] Schramm, Matthias, "Steps Towards the Idea of Function," *History of Science* 4 (1965) 70–103.

[38] Spalt, Detlef, "... und doch gibt es ihn nicht: Der Begriff der reellen Funktion im 19. Jahrhundert," *Mathesis: Festschrift zum siebzigsten Geburtstag von Matthias Schramm*, R, Thiele, ed. Berlin: GNT-Verlag 2000, pp. 182–215.

[39] Suppes, Patrick, *Axiomatic set theory*, Van Nostrand, Princeton, 1960; Dover, 1972.

[40] Thiele, Rüdiger, "Frühe Variationsrechnung und Funktionskonzept," *Mathesis: Festschrift zum siebzigsten Geburtstag von Matthias Schramm*. Berlin: GNT-Verlag, 2000, pp. 128–182.

[41] ——, "The rise of the function concept," Euler volume ed. by Roger Baker, Kendrick Press, in press.

[42] Toeplitz, Otto, *Die Entwicklung der Infinitesimalrechnung: eine Einleitung in die Infinitesimalrechnung nach der genetischen Methode*, Springer, Berlin, 1949.

[43] Truesdell, Clifford, "The Rational Mechanics of Flexible or Elastic bodies," 1638–1788. *Euleri opera omnia*, ser. II, vol. 11,2. Zürich, 1960.

[44] Volkert, Klaus, *Die Krise der Anschauung*, Göttingen: Vandenhoeck & Ruprecht, 1987.

Enter, Stage Center:
The Early Drama of the
Hyperbolic Functions

Janet Heine Barnett

In addition to the standard definitions of the hyperbolic functions — for instance, $\cosh x = (e^x + e^{-x})/2$ — current calculus textbooks typically share two common features. One is a comment on the applicability of these functions to certain physical problems, such as the shape of a hanging cable known as the catenary. The second is a remark on the analogies that exist between properties of the hyperbolic functions and those of the trigonometric functions, such as the identities $\cosh^2 x - \sinh^2 x = 1$ and $\cos^2 x + \sin^2 x = 1$. Texts that offer historical sidebars are likely to credit development of the hyperbolic functions to the 18th century mathematician Johann Lambert. Implicit in this treatment is the suggestion that Lambert and others were interested in the hyperbolic functions in order to solve problems such as predicting the shape of the catenary. Left unanswered is the question of whether hyperbolic functions were developed in a deliberate effort to find functions with trig-like properties that were required by the physical problems, or whether these trig-like properties were unintended and unforeseen by-products of the solutions to the physical problems. The drama of the early years of the hyperbolic functions is far richer than either plot line would suggest.

Prologue: The Catenary Curve

What shape is assumed by a flexible inextensible cord hung freely from two fixed points? Those with an interest in the history of mathematics would guess (correctly) that this problem was first resolved in the late 17th century and involved the Bernoulli family in some way. The curve itself was first referred to as the "catenary" by Huygens in a 1690 letter to Leibniz but was studied as early as the 15th century by Leonardo da Vinci. Galileo mistakenly believed the curve would be a parabola [9]. A refutation of Galileo's claim appeared in the 1673 work *La Statique, ou la Science des Forces Mouvantes* of the French mathe-

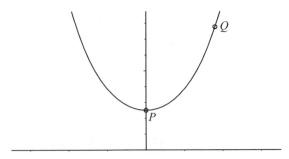

Figure 1. The Catenary Curve.

matician Ignace Gaston Pardies (1636–1673) [24]. According to Leibniz [18], the German mathematician Joachim Jungius (1587–1657) also demonstrated the discrepencies between the two curves using computational and experimental evidence; although Leibniz did not specify a date for Jungius' disproof, the year 1669 is generally cited as a (posthumous) publication date that would slightly pre-date that of Pardies. (Kowalski, for example, gave this date in his 1914 translation of the lectures that Johann Bernoulli wrote for the use of Guillaume Marquis de L'Hôpital in 1691–1692 [14]. For an English translation of those portions of Bernoulli's lectures that pertain to the catenary, see [2]). In fact, Huygens is credited with an even earlier refutation in 1646 at the age of seventeen [24]. None of these refutations, however, identified the "true" shape of the catenary.

Seventeenth-century mathematicians focused their attention on this problem when Jakob Bernoulli posed it as a challenge in 1690; this challenge appeared in the *Acta Eruditorum* paper in which Bernoulli solved the isochrone problem of constructing the curve along which a body will fall in the same time from any starting position. Issued at a time when the rivalry between Jakob and Johann Bernoulli was still friendly, this was one of the great challenge problems of the period. In June 1691, three independent solutions appeared in *Acta Eruditorum* ([1], [12], [18]). The proof given by Christian Huygens employed geo-metrical arguments, whereas those offered by Gottfried Leibniz and Johann Bernoulli used the new differential calculus. In modern terminology, the crux of Bernoulli's proof was to show that the curve in question satisfies the differential equation $dy/dx = s/k$, where s represents the arc length from the vertex P to an arbitrary point Q on the curve and k is a constant depending on the weight per unit length of cord as in Figure 1.

Showing that $y = k \cosh\left(\frac{x}{k}\right)$ is a solution of this differential equation is an accessible problem for today's second-semester calculus student. Seventeenth-century solutions of the problem differed from those of today's calculus students in a particularly notable way: *there was absolutely no mention of hyperbolic functions, or any other explicit function, in the solutions of 1691!* In these early days of calculus, curve constructions, and not explicit functions, were cast in the leading roles.

A suggestion of this earlier perspective can be found in a letter dated September 19, 1718 sent by Johann Bernoulli to Pierre Réymond de Montmort (1678–1719):

> The efforts of my brother were without success; for my part, I was more fortunate, for I found the skill (I say it without boasting, why should I conceal the truth?) to solve it in full and to reduce it to the rectification of the parabola. It is true that it cost me study that robbed me of rest for an entire night. It was much for those

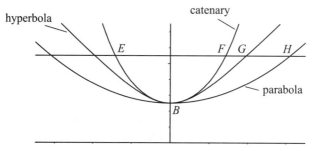

Figure 2. Bernoulli's Construction of the Catenary Curve.

days and for the slight age and practice I then had, but the next morning, filled with joy, I ran to my brother, who was still struggling miserably with this Gordian knot without getting anywhere, always thinking like Galileo that the catenary was a parabola. Stop! Stop! I say to him, don't torture yourself any more to try to prove the identity of the catenary with the parabola, since it is entirely false. The parabola indeed serves in the construction of the catenary, but the two curves are so different that one is algebraic, the other is transcendental ... (as quoted in [15, p. 473]).

The term *rectification* in this passage refers to the problem of determining the arc length of a curve. The particular parabola used in Bernoulli's construction (given by $y = x^2/8 + 1$ in modern notation) was defined geometrically by Bernoulli as having "latus rectum quadruple the latus rectum of an equilateral hyperbola that shares the same vertex and axis" [Bernoulli 1771, pp. 274–275]. Bernoulli used the arc length of the segment of this parabola between the vertex $B = (0, 1)$ and the point $H = (\sqrt{8(y-1)}, y)$ to construct a segment GE such that the point E would lie on the catenary. The length of segment GE was equal to the parabolic arc length BH, which in modern notation is given by

$$\text{Arclength} = \sqrt{y^2 - 1} + \ln\left(y + \sqrt{y^2 - 1}\right),$$

so that the catenary point E has coordinates

$$E = \left(-\ln\left(y + \sqrt{y^2 - 1}\right), y\right) = \left(x, \frac{e^x + e^{-x}}{2}\right).$$

The expression $\sqrt{y^2 - 1}$ in the arclength formula is the abscissa of the point $G\left(\sqrt{y^2 - 1}, y\right)$ on the equilateral hyperbola $(y^2 - x^2 = 1)$ that played both the central role described above in defining the parabola necessary for the construction, and a supporting role in constructing the point E. Because a procedure for rectifying a parabola was known by this time, the reduction of the catenary problem to the rectification of a parabola provided a complete 17th-century solution to the catenary problem.

Interestingly, another of the "first solvers" of the catenary problem, Christian Huygens, solved the rectification problem for the parabola as early as 1659. In fact, although this problem had been declared by Descartes as beyond the capacity of the human mind [5, page 90–91], the problem of rectifying a curve C was known to be equivalent to the problem of finding the area under an associated curve C' by the time Huygens took up the parabola question.

A general procedure for determining the curve C' was provided by Hendrick van Heuraet (1634–1660) in a paper that appeared in van Schooten's 1659 Latin edition of Descartes' *La Géométrie*. (In modern notation, C' is defined by

$$L(t) = \int_a^t \sqrt{1 + (dy/dx)^2}\, dx,$$

where $y = f(x)$ defines the original curve C.) Huygens used this procedure to show that rectification of a parabola is equivalent to finding the area under a hyperbola. A solution of this latter problem in the study of curves — determining the area under a hyperbola — was first published by Gregory of St. Vincent in 1647 [15, p. 354]. Anton de Sarasa later recognized (in 1649) that St. Vincent's solution to this problem provided a method for computation of logarithmic values.

As impressive as these early "pre-calculus" calculus results were, by the time the catenary challenge was posed by Jakob Bernoulli in 1690, the rate at which the study of curves was advancing was truly astounding, thanks to the groundbreaking techniques that had since been developed by Isaac Newton (1642–1727) and Gottfried Leibniz (1646–1716). Relations between the Bernoulli brothers fared less well over the ensuing decades, as indicated by a later passage from Johann Bernoulli's 1718 letter to Montmort:

> But then you astonish me by concluding that my brother found a method of solving this problem. ... I ask you, do you really think, if my brother had solved the problem in question, he would have been so obliging to me as not to appear among the solvers, just so as to cede me the glory of appearing alone on the stage in the quality of the first solver, along with Messrs. Huygens and Leibniz? (as quoted in [15, p. 473])

Historical evidence supports Johann's claim that Jakob was not a "first solver" of the catenary problem. But in the year immediately following that first solution, Jakob Bernoulli and others solved several variations of this problem. Huygens, for example, used physical arguments to show that the curve is a parabola if the total load of cord and suspended weights is uniform per horizontal foot, while for the true catenary, the weight per foot along the cable is uniform. Both Bernoulli brothers worked on determining the shape assumed by a hanging cord of variable density, a hanging cord of constant thickness, and a hanging cord acted upon at each point by a force directed to a fixed center. Johann Bernoulli also solved the converse problem: given the shape assumed by a flexible inelastic hanging cord, find the law of variation of density of the cord. Another nice result due to Jakob Bernoulli stated that, of all shapes that may be assumed by a flexible inelastic hanging cord, the catenary has the lowest center of gravity.

A later appearance of the catenary curve can be found in Leonhard Euler's work on the calculus of variations. In his 1744 *Methodus inveniendi lineas curvas maximi minimive proprietate gaudentes* (E65) [6], Euler showed that a catenary revolved about its axis (the catenoid) generates the only minimal surface of revolution. Calculating the surface area of this minimal surface is another straightforward exercise that can provide a nice historical introduction to the calculus of variations for second semester calculus students. Kline [15, p. 579] comments that Euler himself did not make effective use of the full power of the calculus in the *Methodus*; derivatives were replaced by difference quotients and integrals

Johann Bernoulli

by finite sums. Further, extensive use was made of geometric arguments. In tracing the story of the hyperbolic functions, this last point cannot be emphasized enough. From its earliest introduction in the 15th century through Euler's 1744 result on the catenoid, there was no connection between analytic expressions involving the exponential function and the catenary curve. Indeed, prior to the development of 18th-century analytic techniques, no such connection could have been made. Calculus in the age of the Bernoullis was "the Calculus of Curves," and the catenary curve is just that ... a *curve*. The hyperbolic functions did not, and could not, come into being until the full power of formal analysis had taken hold in the age of Euler.

Act I: The hyperbolic functions in Euler?

In seeking the first appearance of hyperbolic functions as *functions*, one naturally looks to the works of Euler. In fact, the expressions $(e^x + e^{-x})/2$ and $(e^x - e^{-x})/2$ did make an appearance in Volume I of Euler's *Introductio in analysin infinitorum* (E101) (1748) [7]. Euler's interest in these expressions seems natural in view of the equations $\cos x =$

$(e^{\sqrt{-1}x} + e^{-\sqrt{-1}x})/2$ and $\sqrt{-1}\sin x = (e^{\sqrt{-1}x} - e^{-\sqrt{-1}x})/2$ that he derived in this text. However, Euler's interest in what we would call hyperbolic functions appears to have been limited to their role in deriving infinite product representations for the sine and cosine functions. Euler did not use the word *hyperbolic* in reference to the expressions $(e^x + e^{-x})/2$, $(e^x - e^{-x})/2$, nor did he provide any special notation or name for them. Nevertheless, his use of these expressions is a classic example of Eulerian analysis, included here as an illustration of 18th-century mathematics. An analysis of this derivation, either in its historical form or in modern translation, would be suitable for student projects in pre-calculus and calculus, or as part of a mathematics history course.

To illustrate the style of Euler's analysis and the role played within it by the hyperbolic expressions, we employ his notation from the *Introductio* throughout this section. Although sufficiently like our own to make the work accessible to modern readers, there are interesting differences. For instance, Euler's use of periods in "sin . x" and "cos . x" suggests the notation still served as abbreviations for *sinus* and *cosinus*, rather than as symbolic function names. Like us, Euler and his contemporaries were intimately familiar with the infinite series representations for sin . x and cos . x but generally employed infinite series with less than modern regard for rigor. Thus, as established in Section 123 of the *Introductio*, Euler could (and did) rewrite the expression $(e^x + e^{-x})$ as:

$$(e^x + e^{-x}) = \left(1 + \frac{x}{i}\right)^i - \left(1 - \frac{x}{i}\right)^i = 2\left(\frac{x}{1} + \frac{x^3}{1 \cdot 2 \cdot 3} + \frac{x^5}{1 \cdot 2 \cdot 3 \cdot 4 \cdot 5} + \text{etc.}\right),$$

where i represented an infinitely large quantity (and *not* the square root of -1, denoted throughout the *Introductio* as $\sqrt{-1}$). Other results used by Euler are also familiarly unfamiliar to us, most notably the fact that $a^n - z^n$ has factors of the form

$$aa - 2az\cos . \frac{2k}{n}\pi + zz,$$

as established in Section 151 of the *Introductio*.

Euler's development of infinite product representations for sin . x and cos . x in the *Introductio* began in Section 156 by setting $n = i$, $a = 1 + \frac{x}{i}$, and $z = 1 - \frac{x}{i}$ in the expression $a^n - z^n$ (where, again, i is infinite, so, for example, $a^n = (1 + \frac{x}{i})^i = e^x$). After some algebra, the result of Section 151 cited above allowed Euler to conclude that $e^x + e^{-x}$ has factors of the form

$$2 - \frac{2xx}{ii} - 2\left(1 - \frac{xx}{ii}\right)\cos . \frac{2k}{n}\pi.$$

Substituting

$$\cos . \frac{2k}{n}\pi = 1 - \frac{2kk}{ii}\pi\pi$$

(the first two terms of the infinite series representation for cosine) into this latter expression and doing a bit more algebra, Euler obtained the equation

$$2 - \frac{2xx}{ii} - 2\left(1 - \frac{xx}{ii}\right)\cos . \frac{2k}{n}\pi = \frac{4xx}{ii} + \frac{4kk}{ii}\pi\pi - \frac{4kk\pi\pi xx}{i^4}.$$

Ergo (to quote Euler), $e^x + e^{-x}$ has factors of the form $1 + \frac{xx}{kk\pi\pi} - \frac{xx}{ii}$. Since i is an infinitely large quantity, Euler's arithmetic of infinite and infinitesimal numbers allowed the last term to drop out. (Tuckey and McKinzie give a thorough discussion of these ideas in [19].) The end result of these calculations, as presented in Section 156, was:

$$\frac{e^x - e^{-x}}{2} = x \left(1 + \frac{xx}{\pi\pi}\right)\left(1 + \frac{xx}{4\pi\pi}\right)\left(1 + \frac{xx}{9\pi\pi}\right)\left(1 + \frac{xx}{16\pi\pi}\right) \text{ etc.} \qquad (1)$$

A similar derivation (Section 157) derived the analogous product representation for $(e^x + e^{-x})/2$.

In Section 158, Euler employed these latter two results in the following manner. Recalling the well-known fact (which he derived in Section 134) that

$$\frac{e^{z\sqrt{-1}} - e^{-z\sqrt{-1}}}{2\sqrt{-1}} = \sin . z$$

$$= z - \frac{z^3}{1 \cdot 2 \cdot 3} + \frac{z^5}{1 \cdot 2 \cdot 3 \cdot 4 \cdot 5} - \frac{z^7}{1 \cdot 2 \cdot 3 \cdot 4 \cdot 5 \cdot 6 \cdot 7} + \text{etc.},$$

Euler let $x = z\sqrt{-1}$ in equation (1) above to get

$$\sin . z = z \left(1 - \frac{zz}{\pi\pi}\right)\left(1 - \frac{zz}{4\pi\pi}\right)\left(1 - \frac{zz}{9\pi\pi}\right)\left(1 - \frac{zz}{16\pi\pi}\right) \text{ etc.}$$

$$= z \left(1 - \frac{z}{\pi}\right)\left(1 + \frac{z}{\pi}\right)\left(1 - \frac{z}{2\pi}\right)\left(1 + \frac{z}{2\pi}\right)\left(1 - \frac{z}{3\pi}\right) \text{ etc.}$$

The same substitution applied to the series with even terms yielded the now-familiar product representation for cos . z.

Here we arrive at Euler's apparent goal: the derivation of these lovely infinite product representations for the sine and cosine. Although the expressions $(e^x + e^{-x})/2$ and $(e^x - e^{-x})/2$ played a role in obtaining these results, it was a supporting role, with the arrival of the hyperbolic functions on center stage yet to come.

Act II, Scene I: Lambert's introduction of the hyperbolic functions

Considered a forerunner in the development of noneuclidean geometries but best remembered today for his proof of the irrationality of π, Johann Heinrich Lambert was born in Mülhasen, Alsace on August 26, 1728. The Lambert family had moved to Mülhasen from Lorraine as Calvinist refugees in 1635. His father and grandfather were both tailors. Because of the family's impoverished circumstances (he was one of seven children), Lambert left school at age 12 to assist the family financially. Working first in his father's tailor shop and later as a clerk and private secretary, Lambert accepted a post as a private tutor in 1748 in the home of Reichsgraf Peter von Salis. As such, he gained access to a good library that he used for self-improvement until he resigned his post in 1759. Lambert led a largely peripatetic life over the next five years. He was first proposed as a member of the Academy of Sciences in Berlin in 1761. In January 1764, he was welcomed by the Swiss community of scholars, including Euler, then in residence in Berlin. According to Scriba [25], Lambert's appointment to the Academy was delayed due to "his strange appearance and behavior." Eventually, he received the patronage of Frederick the Great (who at first described him as "the greatest blockhead") and obtained a salaried position as a member of the physical class of the Academy on January 10, 1765. He remained in this position, regularly presenting papers to each of its classes, until his death in 1777 at the age of 49.

Lambert was a prolific writer, presenting over 150 papers to the Berlin Academy, in addition to other published and unpublished books and papers written in German, French and Latin. These included works on philosophy, logic, semantics, instrument design, land surveying and cartography, as well as mathematics, physics and astronomy. His interests appeared at times to shift almost randomly from one topic to another and often fell outside the mainstream of 18th-century science and mathematics. We leave it to the reader to decide whether his development of the hyperbolic functions is a case in point or an exception to this tendency.

Lambert first treated hyperbolic trigonometric functions in a paper presented to the Berlin Academy of Sciences in 1761 that quickly became famous: *Mémoire sur quelques propriétés remarquables des quantités transcendantes circulaires et logarithmiques* [16]. Rather than its consideration of hyperbolic functions, this paper was (and is) celebrated for giving the first proof of the irrationality of π. Lambert established this long-awaited result using continued fraction representations to show that z and $\tan z$ cannot both be rational; thus, because $\tan(\pi/4)$ is rational, π can not be.

Instead of concluding the paper at this climactic point, Lambert turned his attention in the last third of the paper to a comparison of the *"transcendantes circulaire"* [$\sin v, \cos v$] with their analogues, the *"quantités transcendantes logarithmiques"*

$$\left[\frac{e^v + e^{-v}}{2}, \frac{e^v - e^{-v}}{2} \right].$$

Beginning in Section 73, he first noted that the transcendental logarithmic quantities can be obtained from the transcendental circular quantities by taking all the signs in

$$\sin v = v - \frac{1}{2 \cdot 3} v^3 + \frac{1}{2 \cdot 3 \cdot 4 \cdot 5} v^5 - \frac{1}{2 \cdot 3 \cdot 4 \cdot 5 \cdot 6 \cdot 7} v^7 + \text{etc.}$$

to be positive, thereby obtaining:

$$\frac{e^v - e^{-v}}{2} = v + \frac{1}{2 \cdot 3} v^3 + \frac{1}{2 \cdot 3 \cdot 4 \cdot 5} v^5 + \frac{1}{2 \cdot 3 \cdot 4 \cdot 5 \cdot 6 \cdot 7} v^7 + \text{etc.},$$

and similarly for the cosine series. He then derived continued fraction representations (in Section 74) for the expressions $(e^v - e^{-v})/2$, $(e^v + e^{-v})/2$, and $(e^v - e^{-v})/(e^v + e^{-v})$, and noted that these continued fraction representations can be used to show that v and e^v cannot both be rational. The fact that none of its powers or roots are rational prompted Lambert to speculate that e satisfied *no* algebraic equation with rational coefficients, and hence is *transcendental*. Charles Hermite (1822–1901) finally proved this fact in 1873. (Ferdinand Lindemann (1852–1939) established the transcendence of π in 1882.)

Although Lambert did not introduce special notation for his *"quantités transcendantes logarithmiques"* in this paper, he did go on to develop the analogy between these functions and the circular trigonometric functions that he said "should exist" because:

... the expressions $e^u + e^{-u}$, $e^u - e^{-u}$, by substituting $u = v\sqrt{-1}$, give the circular quantities $e^{v\sqrt{-1}} + e^{-v\sqrt{-1}} = 2\cos v$, $e^{v\sqrt{-1}} - e^{-v\sqrt{-1}} = 2\sin v \cdot \sqrt{-1}$.

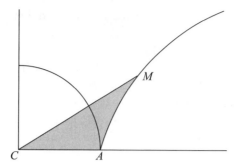

Figure 3. The parameter u represents twice the area of the shaded sector MCA.

Lambert was especially interested in developing this "affinity" as far as possible without introducing imaginary quantities. To do this, he introduced (in Section 75) a parameterization of an "equilateral hyperbola" ($x^2 - y^2 = 1$) to define the hyperbolic functions in a manner directly analogous to the definition of trigonometric functions by means of a unit circle ($x^2 + y^2 = 1$). Lambert's parameter was twice the area of the hyperbolic sector shown in Figure 3. Lambert used the letter M to denote a typical point on the hyperbola, with coordinates (ξ, η).

In Lambert's own diagram (Figure 4), the circle and the hyperbola are drawn together. The letter C marks the common center of the circle and the hyperbola, CA is the radius of the circle, CF the asymptote of the hyperbola, and AB the tangent line common to the circle and the hyperbola. The typical point on the hyperbola corresponds to a point N on

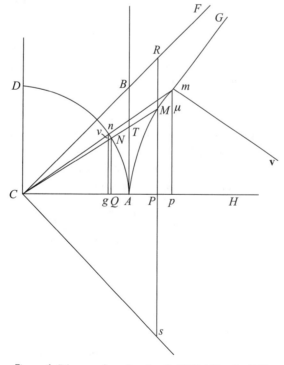

Figure 4. Diagram from Lambert's 1761 *Mémoire* [16].

the circle, with coordinates (x, y). Lowercase letters m and n mark nearby points on the hyperbola and the circle for use in differential computations.

Denoting the angle MCA by ϕ, Lambert listed several differential properties for quantities defined within this diagram, using a two-columned table intended to display the similarities between the "*logarithmiques*" and "*circulaires*" functions. The first seven lines of this table, reproduced below, defined the necessary variables and stated basic algebraic and trigonometric relations among them. Note especially the third line of this table, where $u/2$ (which Lambert denoted as $u : 2$) is defined to be the area of the hyperbolic "segment" $AMCA$.

		pour l'hyperbole		*pour le cercle*
l'abscisse		$CP = \xi \ldots$	$\ldots CQ = x$	
l'ordonné		$PM = \eta \ldots$	$\ldots QN = y$	
le segment		$AMCA = u : 2 \ldots$	$\ldots ANCA = v : 2$	

et il sera

$$\tan g\, \phi = \frac{\eta}{\xi} \ldots \qquad\qquad \ldots \tan g\, \phi = \frac{y}{x}$$

$$1 + \eta\eta = \xi\xi = \eta\eta \cot \phi^2 \ldots \qquad \ldots 1 - yy = xx = yy \cot \phi^2$$

$$\xi\xi - 1 = \eta\eta = \xi\xi \tan g\, \phi^2 \ldots \qquad \ldots 1 - xx = yy = xx \tan g\, \phi^2$$

$$CM^2 = \xi^2 + \eta^2 = \xi^2(1 + \tan g\, \phi^2) \qquad CN^2 = x^2 + y^2 = x^2(1 + \tan g\, \phi^2)$$

$$= \frac{1 + \tan g\, \phi^2}{1 - \tan g\, \phi^2} \qquad\qquad = \frac{1 + \tan g\, \phi^2}{1 + \tan g\, \phi^2} = 1$$

With these relations, it is a straightforward exercise to derive expressions for the differentials $d\xi$, $d\eta$, dx and dy (as a step toward finding infinite series for ξ and η). For example, given $\xi\xi - 1 = \eta\eta = \xi\xi \tan g\, \phi^2$ (tang would be tan in modern notation), it follows that $\xi = 1/\sqrt{1 - \tan g\, \phi^2}$. Lambert noted this fact, along with the resulting differential $d\xi = \tan g\, \phi \, d \tan g\phi / \left(1 - \tan g\, \phi^2\right)^{3:2}$, later in the table.

To see how expressions for du and dv might be obtained, note that u is defined to be twice the area of the hyperbolic sector $AMCA$. The differential du thus represents twice the area of the hyperbolic sector MCm. This differential sector can be approximated by the area of a circular sector of radius CM and angle $d\phi$; that is, $du = 2\left[CM^2 d\phi/2\right]$. Substituting $CM^2 = \left(1 + \tan g\, \phi^2\right) / \left(1 - \tan g\, \phi^2\right)$ from the table above yields

$$du = d\phi \cdot CM^2 = d\phi \cdot \frac{1 + \tan g\, \phi^2}{1 - \tan g\, \phi^2},$$

where $d\phi \cdot \left(1 + \tan g\, \phi^2\right) = d\left(\tan g\, \phi\right)$. Thus,

$$du = d \tan g \frac{\phi}{1 - \tan g\, \phi^2}.$$

Although Lambert omitted the details of these derivations, his table summarized them as shown below.

pour l'hyperbole	*pour le cercle*

$$+\,du = d\phi \cdot \left(\frac{1 + \tan g\,\phi^2}{1 - \tan g\phi^2} \right) \qquad\qquad dv = d\phi = \frac{d\tan g\,\phi}{1 + \tan g\,\phi^2}$$

$$= \frac{d\tan g\,\phi}{1 - \tan g\,\phi^2}$$

$$+\,d\xi = \frac{\tan g\,\phi\, d\tan g\,\phi}{\left(1 - \tan g\,\phi^2\right)^{3:2}} \qquad\qquad -\,dx = \frac{\tan g\,\phi\, d\tan g\,\phi}{\left(1 + \tan g\,\phi^2\right)^{3:2}}$$

$$+\,d\eta = \frac{d\tan g\,\phi}{\left(1 - \tan g\phi^2\right)^{3:2}} \qquad\qquad +\,dy = \frac{d\tan g\,\phi}{\left(1 + \tan g\,\phi^2\right)^{3:2}}$$

$$\vdots \qquad\qquad\qquad\qquad\qquad \vdots$$

$$+\,d\xi : du = \eta \ldots \qquad\qquad \ldots -\,dx : dv = y$$

$$+\,d\eta : du = \xi \ldots \qquad\qquad \ldots +\,dy : dv = x$$

$$+\,d\xi = d\eta \cdot \tan g\,\phi \ldots \qquad\qquad \ldots -\,dx : dy = \tan g\,\phi$$

From the relations $+\,d\xi : du = \eta$, $+\,d\eta : du = \xi$, along with standard techniques of the era for determining the coefficients of infinite series, Lambert then proved (Section 77):

$$\eta = u + \frac{1}{2\cdot 3}u^3 + \frac{1}{2\cdot 3\cdot 4\cdot 5}u^5 + \frac{1}{2\cdot 3\cdot 4\cdot 5\cdot 6\cdot 7}u^7 + \text{etc.}$$

$$\xi = u + \frac{1}{2}u^2 + \frac{1}{2\cdot 3\cdot 4}u^4 + \frac{1}{2\cdot 3\cdot 4\cdot 5\cdot 6}u^6 + \text{etc.,}$$

where we recall that ξ is the abscissa of a point on the hyperbola and η is the ordinate of that same point. But these are exactly the infinite series with which Lambert began his discussion of the "*quantités transcendantes logarithmiques.*"

Lambert was thus able to conclude (Section 78) that $\xi = \left(e^u + e^{-u}\right)/2$ and $\eta = \left(e^u - e^{-u}\right)/2$ are, respectively, the abscissa and ordinate of a point on the hyperbola for which u represents twice the area of the hyperbolic segment determined by that point.

A derivation of this result employing integration, as outlined in some modern calculus texts, is another nice problem for students. Contrary to the suggestion of some texts, it is this parameterization of the hyperbola by the hyperbolic sine and cosine, and the analogous parameterization of the circle by the circular sine and cosine, that seem to have motivated Lambert and others to provide the hyperbolic functions with trig-like names — not the similarity of their analytic identities. This is not to say that the similarities between the circular identities and the hyperbolic identities were without merit in Lambert's eyes — we shall see below that Lambert and others exploited these similarities for various purposes. But Lambert's immediate interest in his 1761 paper lay elsewhere, as we shall examine more closely in the following section.

Interlude: Giving credit where credit is due

As Lambert himself remarked at several points in his 1761 *Mémoire*, he was especially interested in developing the analogy between the two classes of functions (circular versus hyperbolic) as far as possible without the use of imaginary quantities, and it is the geometric representation (i.e., the parameterization) that provided him a means to this end. Lambert ascribed his own interest in this theme to the work of another 18th century mathematician, Monsieur le Chevalier François Daviet de Foncenex (1734–1798).

As a student at the Royal Artillery School of Turin, de Foncenex studied mathematics under a young Lagrange. As recounted by Delambre, the friendships Lagrange formed with de Foncenex and other students led to the formation of the Royal Academy of Science of Turin [8]. A major goal of the society was the publication of mathematical and scientific papers in their *Miscellanea Taurinensia*, or *Mélanges de Turin*. Both Lagrange and de Foncenex published several papers in early volumes of the *Miscellanea*, with de Foncenex crediting Lagrange for much of the inspiration behind his own work. Delambre argued that Lagrange provided de Foncenex with far more than inspiration, and it is true that de Foncenex's analytic style is strongly reminiscent of Lagrange. It is also true that de Foncenex did not live up to the mathematical promise demonstrated in his early work, although he was perhaps sidetracked from a mathematical career after being named head of the navy by the King of Sardinia as a result of his early successes in the *Miscellanea*.

In his earliest paper, *Réflexions sur les Quantités Imaginaire* [8], de Foncenex focused his attention on "the nature of imaginary roots," part of the debate concerning logarithms of negative quantities. In particular, de Foncenex wished to reconcile Euler's "incontestable calculations" proving that negative numbers have imaginary logarithms with an argument from Bernoulli that opposed this conclusion on grounds involving the continuity of the hyperbola (whose quadrature defines logarithms) at infinity. The analysis that de Foncenex developed of this problem led him to consider the relation between the circle and the equilateral hyperbola — exactly the same analogy pursued by Lambert.

In his 1761 *Mémoire*, Lambert fully credited de Foncenex with having shown how the affinity between the circular trigonometric functions and the hyperbolic trigonometric functions can be "seen in a very simple and direct fashion by comparing the circle and the equilateral hyperbola with the same center and same diameter." De Foncenex himself went no further in exploring "this affinity" than to conclude that, because $\sqrt{x^2 - r^2} = \sqrt{-1}\sqrt{r^2 - x^2}$, "the circular sectors and hyperbolic [sectors] that correspond to the same abscissa are always in the ratio of 1 to $\sqrt{-1}$." It is this use of an imaginary ratio to pass from the circle to the hyperbola Lambert seemed intent on avoiding.

Lambert returned to this theme one final time in Section 88 of the *Mémoire*. In another classic example of 18th-century analysis, Lambert first remarked that "one can easily find by using the differential formulas of Section 75" that:

$$v = \text{tang}\,\phi - \frac{1}{3}\,\text{tang}\,\phi^3 + \frac{1}{5}\text{tang}\,\phi^5 - \frac{1}{7}\text{tang}\,\phi^7 + \text{etc.}$$

$$\text{tang}\,\phi = u - \frac{1}{3}u^3 + \frac{2}{15}u^5 - \frac{17}{315}u^7 + \text{etc.}$$

"By substituting the value of the second of these series into the first ... and reciprocally" (but again with details omitted), Lambert obtained the following two series:

$$v = u - \frac{2}{3}u^3 + \frac{2}{3}u^5 - \frac{244}{315}u^7 + \text{etc.} \tag{2}$$

$$u = v + \frac{2}{3}v^3 + \frac{2}{3}v^5 + \frac{244}{315}v^7 + \text{etc.}$$

where (switching from previous usage) u equals twice the area of the circular sector and v equals twice the area of the hyperbolic sector. Finally, Lambert obtained the sought-after relation by noting that substitution of $u = v\sqrt{-1}$ into series (2) will yield $v = u\sqrt{-1}$.

In (semi)-modern notation, we can represent Lambert's results as $\tanh(v\sqrt{-1}) = \tan(u\sqrt{-1})$ and $\tanh(u) = \tan(v)$. Having thus established that imaginary hyperbolic sectors correspond to imaginary circular sectors, and similarly for real sectors, Lambert closed his 1761 *Mémoire*. The next scene examines how he pursued a new plot line suggested by this analogy: the use of hyperbolic functions to replace circular functions in the solution of certain problems.

Act II, Scene II: The reappearance of hyperbolic functions in Lambert

Lambert returned to the development of "transcendental logarithmic functions" and their similarities to circular trigonometric functions in his 1768 paper *Observations trigonométriques* [17]. In this treatment, a typical point on the hyperbola is called q. Letting ϕ denote the angle qCQ in Figure 5, Lambert first remarked that $\tang\,\phi = MN/MC = qp/pC$. Because

$$\frac{MN}{MC} = \frac{\sin\phi}{\cos\phi} \quad \text{and} \quad \frac{qp}{pC} = \frac{\sin\,\text{hyp}\,\phi}{\cos\,\text{hyp}\,\phi},$$

one has the option of using either the circular tangent function or the hyperbolic tangent function for the purpose of solving triangle qCP. *Note that the notation and terminology used here are Lambert's own!* Lambert himself commented that, in view of the analogous parameterizations that are possible for the circle and the hyperbola, there is "nothing repugnant to the original meaning" of the terms "sine" and "cosine" in the use of the terms "hyperbolic sine" and "hyperbolic cosine" to denote the abscissa and ordinate of the hyper-

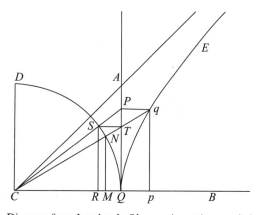

Figure 5. Diagram from Lambert's *Observations trigonométriques* [17].

bola. Although Lambert's notation for these functions differed from our current convention, the hyperbolic functions had now become fully-fledged players in their own right, complete with names and notation suggestive of their relation to the circular trigonometric functions.

The development of the hyperbolic functions in this paper included an extensive list of sum, difference and multi-angle identities that are, as Lambert remarked, easily derived from the formulas $\sin \text{hyp}\, v = (e^v - e^{-v})/2$, $\cos \text{hyp}\, v = (e^v + e^{-v})/2$. Of greater importance to Lambert's immediate purpose was the table of values he constructed for certain functions of "the transcendental angle ω." In particular, the transcendental angle ω, defined as angle PCQ in Figure 5 and related to the common angle ϕ via the relation $\sin \omega = \text{tang}\, \phi = \text{tang hyp}\, \phi$, served Lambert as a means to pass from circular functions to hyperbolic functions. (The transcendental angle associated with ϕ is also known as the *hyperbolic amplitude of* ϕ after Hoüel and the *longitude* after Gudermann.) For values of ω ranging from 1° to 90° in increments of 1 degree, Lambert's table included values of the hyperbolic sector, the hyperbolic sine and its logarithm, the hyperbolic cosine and its logarithm, as well as the tangent of the corresponding common angle and its logarithm. By replacing circular functions with hyperbolic functions, Lambert was able to simplify the computations required to determine the angle measures and the side lengths of certain triangles.

The triangles that interested Lambert arose from problems in astronomy in which one of the celestial bodies is below the horizon. It has since been noted that such problems can be solved using formulae from spherical trigonometry with arcs that are pure imaginaries. This is an intriguing observation, given that Lambert speculated elsewhere (in his work on noneuclidean geometry) on the idea that a sphere of imaginary radius might reflect the geometry of "the acute angle hypothesis." The acute angle hypothesis is one of three possibilities for the two (remaining) similar angles α, β of a quadrilateral assumed to have two right angles and two congruent sides: (1) angles α, β are right; (2) angles α, β are obtuse; and (3) angles α, β are acute. Girolamo Saccheri (1667–1733) introduced this quadrilateral in his *Euclides ab omi naevo vindicatus* of 1733 as an element of his efforts to prove Euclid's Fifth Postulate by contradiction. Both Saccheri and Lambert believed they could dispense with the obtuse angle hypothesis. Lambert's speculation about the acute angle hypothesis was the result of his inability to reject it.

It is worth emphasizing, however, that Lambert himself never put an imaginary radius into the formulae of spherical trigonometry in any of his published works. The triangles he treated are real triangles with real-valued arcs and real-valued sides. As noted by historian Jeremy Gray [10, pp. 156–158], the ability to articulate the notion of "geometry on a sphere of imaginary radius" was not yet within the grasp of mathematicians in the age of Euler. Gray argues convincingly that the 18th-century development of analysis was, nevertheless, critical for 19th-century breakthroughs in the study of noneuclidean geometry. As developed by Euler, Lambert and others, the language of analytic formulae proved flexible enough to discuss geometry in terms other than those set forth by Euclid, thereby allowing a reformulation of the problem and recognition that a new geometry for space was possible. Although rarely mentioned in today's calculus texts, the explicit connection eventually made by Beltrami in his 1868 paper, linking the hyperbolic functions to the noneuclidean geometry of an imaginary sphere, is an application of hyperbolic functions that is surely as tantalizing as the oft-cited catenary curve.

Flashback: Hyperbolic functions in Riccati

Although Lambert's primary reason for considering hyperbolic functions in 1768 was to simplify calculations involved in solving triangles, he clearly realized that there was no need to define new functions for this purpose; tables of logarithms of appropriate trigonometric values could be used to serve the same end. But, he argued, this is only one possible use for the hyperbolic trigonometric functions. The only example he provided was the simplification of solution methods for equations. Lambert did not elaborate on this idea beyond noting that the equation $0 = x^2 - 2a\cos\omega \cdot x + a^2$ is equivalent to the equation $0 = x^2 - 2a\cos\text{hyp }\psi \cdot x + a^2$ for an appropriately defined angle ψ. He did, however, cite an investigation of this idea that had appeared in the work of another 18th-century mathematician: Vincenzo de Riccati.

Vincenzo de Riccati was born on January 11, 1707, the second son of Jacopo Riccati for whom the Riccati equation in differential equations is named. Riccati (the son) received his early education at home and from the Jesuits. He entered the Jesuit order in 1726 and taught or studied in various locations, including Piacenza, Padua, Parma, and Rome. In 1739, Riccati moved to Bologna, where he taught mathematics in the College of San Francesco Saverio until Pope Clement XIV suppressed the Society of Jesus in 1773. Riccati then returned to his family home in Treviso, where he died on January 17, 1775.

Riccati first treated hyperbolic functions in his two volume *Opuscula ad res physicas et mathematicas pertinentium* (1757–1762) [21]. In this work, Riccati employed a hyperbola to define functions that he referred to as "sinus hyperbolico" and "cosinus hyperbolico," doing so in a manner analogous to the use of a circle to define the functions "sinus circulare" and "cosinus circulare." Taking u to be the quantity given by twice the area of the sector ACF divided by the length of the segment CA (whether in the circle or the hyperbola of Figure 6), Ricati defined the sine and cosine of the quantity u to be the segments GF and CG respectively of the appropriate diagram. Although Riccati did not explicitly assume either a unit circle or an equilaterial hyperbola, his definitions are equivalent to those of Lambert (and our own) in that case. In *Opusculum IV* of Volume I, Riccati derived several identities for the hyperbolic sine and cosine, applying these to the problem of determining roots of certain equations, especially cubics. He also determined their series representations. These latter results, which appeared in *Opusculum VI* in volume I, were earlier communicated by Riccati to Josepho Suzzio in a letter dated 1752.

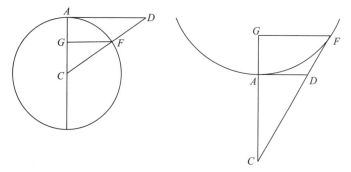

Figure 6. Diagrams rendered from Riccati's *Opuscula* [21].

In Riccati's *Institutiones analytica* (1765–1767) [22], written collaboratively with Giro-lamo Saldini, he further developed the theory, including the standard addition formulae and other identities for hyperbolic functions, their derivatives and their relation to the exponential function (already implicit in his *Opuscula*).

Reprise: Giving credit where credit is due

Although some of the ideas in Riccati's *Institutiones* of 1765–1767 also appeared in Lambert's 1761 *Mémoire*, this author knows of no evidence to suggest that Riccati was building on Lambert's work. The publication dates suggest that Riccati was familiar with the analogy between the circular and the hyperbolic functions some time earlier than Lambert came across the idea, and certainly no later. Conversely, even though Riccati's earliest publication appeared several years before Lambert's 1761 *Mémoire*, it appears that Lambert was unfamiliar with Riccati's work at that time. Certainly, the motivations of the two scholars for introducing the hyperbolic functions seem to have been quite different. Furthermore, Lambert was scrupulous in giving credit to colleagues when drawing on their work, as in the case of de Foncenex. In fact, Lambert credited Riccati with developing the terminology "hyperbolic sine" and "hyperbolic cosine" when he used these names for the first time in his 1768 *Observations trigonométriques*. It thus appears that it was only these new names — and perhaps the idea of using these functions to solve equations — that Lambert took from Riccati, finding them to be suitable nomenclature for mathematical characters whom he had already developed within a story line of his own creation.

Despite the apparent independence of their work, the fact remains that Riccati did have priority in publication. Why then is Lambert's name almost universally mentioned in this context, with Riccati receiving little or no credit? Histories of mathematics written in the 19th and early 20th centuries suggest this tendency to overlook Riccati's work is a relatively recent phenomenon. Von Braunmühl [26, pp. 133–134], for example, has the following to say in his 1903 history of trigonometry:

> In fact, Gregory St. Vincent, David Gregory and Craig through the quadrature of the equilateral hyperbola, erected the foundations [for the hyperbolic functions], even if unaware of the fact, Newton touched on the parallels between the circle and the equilateral hyperbola, and de Moivre seemed to have some understanding that, by substituting the real for the imaginary, the role of the circle is replaced by the equilateral hyperbola. Using geometric considerations, Vincenzo Riccati (1707–1775) was the first to found the theory of hyperbolic functions, as was recognized by Lambert himself. *(Author's translation.)*

Although the amount of recognition that Lambert afforded Riccati may be overestimated here, it is interesting that von Braunmühl then proceeded to discuss only Lambert's work on hyperbolic functions in detail, remarking that:

> This [hyperbolic function] theory is only of interest to us insofar as it came into use in the treatment of trigonometric problems, as was first opened up by Lambert. *(Author's translation.)*

In short, despite the fact that his interests often fell outside the mainstream of his own century, the motivation which Lambert provided for the hyperbolic functions was more central to mathematical interests as they later evolved than that provided by Riccati. The fact that Lambert's mathematical works, especially those on noneuclidean geometry, were studied by his immediate mathematical successors offers support for this idea, as does the wider availability of Lambert's works today. Lambert's work is also written in notation — and languages! — that are more familiar to today's scholars than that of Riccati. This alone makes it easier to tell Lambert's story in detail, just as we have done here.

Epilogue

And what of the physical applications for which the hyperbolic functions are so useful? Although neither Lambert nor Riccati mentioned these connections, they were known by the late 19th century, as evidenced by the publication of hyperbolic function tables and manuals for engineers in that period. Yet even as late as 1849, we hear Augustus de Morgan [4, p. 66] declare:

> The system of trigonometry, from the moment that $\sqrt{-1}$ is introduced, always presents an incomplete and one-sided appearance, unless the student have in his mind for comparison *(though it is rarely or never wanted for what is called use)*, another system [hyperbolic trigonometry] in which the there-called sines and cosines are real algebraic quantities. (Emphasis added.)

Although de Morgan's perspective offers yet another reason to study hyperbolic trigonometry, usefulness in solving problems (mathematical or physical) did not appear to concern him. This delay between the development of the mathematical machinery and its application to physical problems serves as a gentle reminder that the physical applications we sometimes cite as the *raison d'être* for a mathematical idea may only become visible with hindsight. Yet even Riccati's and Lambert's own uses for hyperbolic trigonometry went unacknowledged by de Morgan — an even stronger reminder of how quickly mathematics changed in the 19th-century and how greatly today's mathematics classroom might be enriched by remembering the mathematics of the age of Euler.

Acknowledgements

Many thanks to my Calculus II students from Spring 2000 for asking questions about the history of the hyperbolic functions and to the organizers of the 2001 New Orleans MAA Contributed Paper Session "Mathematics in the Age of Euler" for encouraging me to publish the answers. The editorial assistance of William Dunham, Frank Farris, and George W. Heine were invaluable in framing these answers for publication, as were the suggestions of the anonymous referees of *Mathematics Magazine* where this paper first appeared in February 2004 (volume 77, number 1, pages 15–30) and those of the reviewers of the current publication. Special thanks also to Larry D'Antonio and Ed Sandifer for raising new questions concerning the pre-1690 history of the catenary, and for suggesting where the answers might be found. In response to these questions, the first paragraph of the *Prologue* has been revised and four new references ([2], [14], [23], [24]) added; no other substantive changes have been made since the paper first appeared.

References

[1] Johannis Bernoulli, Solutio problematis funicularii, *Acta Eruditorum* (June 1691), pp. 274–276.

[2] Johann Bernoulli, Lectures on The Integral Calculus, translated by William A. Ferguson, Jr., *21st Century Science and Technology*, Spring 2004, pp. 34 – 42.

[3] J. B. J. Delambre, Notice sur la vie et les ouvrages de M. le Comte J. L. Lagrange, 1812. Reprinted in *Oeuvre de Lagrange* **I** , Gauthier-Villars, Paris, 1816, pp. ix–li.

[4] Augustus De Morgan, *Trigonometry and Double Algebra*, Metcalf and Palmer, Cambridge, 1849.

[5] René Descartes, *Geometry*, translated by David Eugene Smith and Marcia L. Latham, Dover, New York, 1954.

[6] Leonhardi Euleri, *Methodus inveniendi lineas curvas maximi minimive proprietate gaudentes* (E65), 1744. Reprinted in *Leonhardi Euleri Opera Omnia, Series Prima* **24**, B. G. Teubner, Leipzig and Berlin, 1952.

[7] ——, *Introductio in analysin infinitorum, Tomus Primus* (E101), 1748. Reprinted in *Leonhardi Euleri Opera Omnia, Series Prima* **8**, B. G. Teubner, Leipzig and Berlin, 1922.

[8] Daviet de Foncenex, Réflexions sur les quantités imaginaires, *Miscellanea philosophica-mathematica Societatis Privatae Taurinensis*, **I** (1759), pp. 113–146.

[9] Galileo, *Two New Sciences*, tr. Stillman Drake, U. of Wisconsin Press, Madison, 1974, p. 143.

[10] J.J. Gray, *Ideas of Space: Euclidean, Non-Euclidean and Relativistic*, Clarendon Press, Oxford, 1989.

[11] J.J. Gray and L. Tilling, Johann Heinrich Lambert, Mathematician and Scientist, 1728–1777, *Historia Mathematica* **5** (1978), pp. 13–41.

[12] Christiani Huygens, Dynaste Zulichemii, solutio problematis funicularii, *Acta Eruditorum* (June 1691), pp. 281–282.

[13] Victor Katz, *A History of Mathematics: An Introduction*, Harper Collins, New York, 1993.

[14] Gerhard Kowalewski, *Die erste Integralrechnung, Eine Auswahl aus Johann Bernoullis mathematischen Vorlesungen über die Methode der Integrale*, Wilhelm Engelmann, Leipzig and Berlin, 1914.

[15] Morris Kline, *Mathematical Thought from Ancient to Modern Times*, Oxford Univ. Pr., New York, 1978.

[16] Johann Lambert, Mémoire sur quelques propriétés remarquable des quantités transcendantes circulaires et logarithmiques, *Mémoires de l'Académie des Sciences de Berlin* **17**, (1761, 1768), 265–322. Reprinted in *Iohannis Henrici Lamberti Opera mathematica*, **2**, Orell Füssli, Turici, 1948, pp. 112–159.

[17] ——, Observations trigonométriques, *Mémoires de l'Académie des Sciences de Berlin* **24** (1768), 1770, 327–354. Reprinted in *Iohannis Henrici Lamberti Opera mathematica*, **2**, Orell Füssli, Turici, 1948, pp. 245–269.

[18] Gottfried Leibniz, Solutio problematis catenarii, *Acta Eruditorum* (June 1691), pp. 277–281.

[19] Mark McKinzie and Curtis Tuckey, Higher Trigonometry, Hyperreal Numbers, and Euler's Analysis of Infinites, *Mathematics Magazine* **74**:5 (2001), pp. 339–367.

[20] A. Natucci, Vincenzo Riccati, *Biographical Dictionary of Mathematicians*, Macmillan, New York, 1991, pp. 2126–2127.

[21] Vincenzo Riccati, *Opuscula ad res physicas et mathematicas pertinentium*, **I**, Apud Laelium a Vulpe Instituti Scientiarum Typographum, Bononiae, 1757–1762.

[22] Vincenzo Riccati (with G. Saladini), *Institutiones analyticae*, Apud Laelium a Vulpe Instituti Scientiarum Typographum, Bononiae, 1765–1767.

[23] Frederick V. Rickey, My favorite ways of using history in teaching calculus, *Learn From the Masters*, eds. F. Swetz et al. Mathematical Association of America, Washington DC, 1995, pp. 123–234.

[24] ——, The Bridge and the Catenary, 6 June 2002, retrieved 7 August 2006 from `www.dean.usma.edu/departments/math/people/rickey/hm/CalcNotes/bridge-catenary.pdf`.

[25] C. Scriba, Johann Heinrich Lambert, *Biographical Dictionary of Mathematicians*, Macmillan, New York, 1991, pp. 1323–1328.

[26] A. Von Braunmühl, *Vorlesungen über Geschichten der Trigonometrie*, Druck und Verlag von B. G. Teubner, Leipzig, 1903.

Euler's Solution of the Basel Problem—The Longer Story

C. Edward Sandifer[1]

Abstract. Most accounts of Euler's brilliant summing of the reciprocals of the squares of positive integers describe only one of his four solutions to the problem. The usual solution is only the third of three solutions given in that 1736 paper, and he gave a fourth solution five years later. We describe some of Euler's earlier results that led up to the 1736 paper, give all three of the solutions given there, as well as other interesting results in the same paper, and give an account of his 1741 solution as well.

Introduction

Mathematicians in the 17th century posed their own distinctive kinds of problems. Descartes' new geometry and Viète's new algebra gave them the tools of analytic geometry. Mathematicians, or "Geometers," as they called themselves, used these new tools to solve the old problems in conics from Apollonius and to inspire new problems of their own. Most of the new problems of the era submitted easily to the new methods. A few of the more difficult ones were based on the ideas of arc length, tangent lines and areas. Most of these precursors to calculus either were solved using clever and difficult applications of the early and undeveloped ideas of calculus, or they waited for the discovery of calculus itself for their solutions.

Let us pause to look at how some of these early problems were posed. In the figure below, BCD is a curve and AE is an axis. The segment CT is tangent to BCD at the point C and the segment CN is normal to the curve at C.

In the vocabulary of the 17th century, these segments have names, and often no distinction was made between the name of the segment and its length. We still call CM an *ordinate*. The segment CT was called the *tangent*. Note that the tangent was only the segment from the curve to the axis. MT was called the *subtangent*. CN was the *normal*

---

[1]Based on a presentation at the AMS Special Session on the History of Mathematics, New York University, on April 13, 2003.

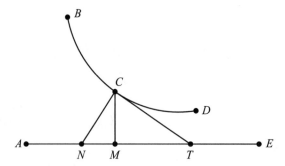

and NM was the *subnormal*. There were a variety of problems posed about these various segments.

The problem of the subtangent asked what curve had the property that, for any point C on the curve, the subtangent MT was a given constant length. In his great 1686 paper, the "Nova methodus," Leibniz showed that the curve with a constant subtangent was what he called a "logarithmic" curve, but we would call an exponential curve. The related problem of the tractrix was posed by Claude Perrault, brother of Charles Perrault, author of such children's classics as "Cinderella" and "Puss in Boots." A tractrix is a curve with a constant tangent, and Leibniz was also the first to give an explicit solution to that problem.

There were a number of other problems about curves. One was the brachistochrone problem, to find the curve between two given points down which a particle will slide in the shortest time. Another was the isoperimetric problem, to find the curve of a given length that encloses the largest possible area. Both problems yielded to the tools of calculus.

Some problems involved series. Huygens and Leibniz independently solved the problem of summing the reciprocals of the triangular numbers. Triangular numbers are numbers of the form $\frac{n(n+1)}{2}$, and are so named because they give the number of objects arranged in a triangle with 1 in the first row, 2 in the second row, 3 in the third row, and so on down to n in the last row. The first several triangular numbers, starting with $n = 1$, are 1, 3, 6, 10, 15 and 21. We give Leibniz's solution in modern notation rather than his 17th century notation.

Let

$$S = \sum_{n=1}^{\infty} \frac{2}{n(n+1)} = \frac{2}{1(1+1)} + \frac{2}{2(2+1)} + \frac{2}{3(3+1)} + \cdots.$$

By partial fractions,

$$\frac{2}{n(n+1)} = \frac{2}{n} - \frac{2}{n+1},$$

so the series telescopes. That is,

$$S = \left(\frac{2}{1} - \frac{2}{1+1}\right) + \left(\frac{2}{2} - \frac{2}{2+1}\right) + \left(\frac{2}{3} + \frac{2}{3+1}\right) + \cdots.$$

The second term in each group cancels the first term in the next group. Leibniz did not know to worry about issues of convergence, so he blithely regrouped, leaving the sum $S = \frac{2}{1} = 2$.

A few problems became important when they resisted solution with the tools of calculus. We should note that other problems, for example Fermat's problems in number theory, were mostly ignored for several decades or forgotten altogether. Not all unsolved problems become *important* unsolved problems.

One important unsolved problem of the time was the so-called Basel problem, posed by Pietro Mengoli (1625–1686) in 1644. Mengoli asked for the sum of the reciprocals of the perfect squares, that is

$$1 + \frac{1}{4} + \frac{1}{9} + \frac{1}{16} + \cdots = \sum_{n=1}^{\infty} \frac{1}{n^2}.$$

The problem became well known when Jakob Bernoulli wrote about it in 1689. Jakob was the brother of Euler's teacher and mentor Johann Bernoulli, who probably showed the problem to Euler. By the 1730's, the problem had thwarted many of the day's best mathematicians, and it had achieved the same kind of mystique that Fermat's Last Theorem had before 1993.

It seems, though, that Euler did not come to the Basel problem directly. Indeed, his attack on the problem began with one of those forgotten problems of the early 18th century, the interpolation of series.

When Euler arrived in St. Petersburg in 1727, Christian Goldbach was the Secretary of the Imperial Academy of Sciences. Goldbach became a kind of mentor for the young Euler who initiated this relationship with a letter of 13 October 1729.[2] The letter got right down to business:

> Most Celebrated Sir: I have been thinking about the laws by which a series may be interpolated.... The most Celebrated Bernoulli suggested that I write to you.

Euler continued the letter by proclaiming, with only this little preamble, that the general term of the "series" that we now call the factorial numbers, 1, 2, 6, 24, 120, etc. is given by

$$\frac{1 \cdot 2^m}{1+m} \cdot \frac{2^{1-m} \cdot 3^m}{2+m} \cdot \frac{3^{1-m} \cdot 4^m}{3+m} \cdot \frac{4^{1-m} \cdot 5^m}{4+m} \text{ etc.}$$

This is a remarkable infinite product. The modern eye immediately wants to do some cancellation among factors in the numerator to "reduce" this to

$$\frac{1}{1+m} \cdot \frac{2}{2+m} \cdot \frac{3}{3+m} \cdot \frac{4}{4+m} \text{ etc.}$$

We can see how this works by rewriting $m!$ as a quotient of infinite products,

$$m! = \frac{1 \cdot 2 \cdot 3 \cdot 4 \cdots m \cdot (m+1) \cdot (m+2) \cdots}{(m+1) \cdot (m+2) \cdots}$$

Then, we see that the value of m "shifts" the denominator, and when m is a positive integer, each of the factors in the denominator exactly cancels with a factor in the numerator, leaving exactly $m!$.

---

[2] At the time, indeed until the Revolution of 1914, Russia used the old Julian calendar. The rest of Europe had converted to the Gregorian calendar still in use today. Hence, dates in Russia were eleven days behind the dates in the rest of Europe. October 13 in St. Petersburg was October 24 elsewhere. Following usual practice, we will give Julian dates when events occur in Russia, Gregorian dates elsewhere, and both if there may be confusion.

So, why didn't Euler use the simpler form? It turns out that Euler's form converges, albeit slowly, to $m!$ without any rearrangement of factors. The modern-looking form converges to zero. Even at this early date, when Euler was only 22, he was aware of issues of convergence, even though he never completely understood them.

Euler then substituted $m = \frac{1}{2}$ and wrote

The term with exponent $\frac{1}{2}$ is equal to $\frac{1}{2}\sqrt{\sqrt{-1} \cdot l - 1}$, which is equal to the side of the square equal to the circle with diameter $= 1$.

Here Euler used l to denote the natural logarithm and he did not use yet the symbol π. The mathematical community had not yet adopted a standard symbol for the value we now call π. In part this was because they still regarded π as a ratio, and they still sometimes maintained a distinction between ratios and numbers.

That Euler's radical equals $\frac{\sqrt{\pi}}{2}$ follows easily[3] from knowing $e^{\pi i} = -1$ by taking logs of both sides, but the fact was not widely known at the time, and the notation would have been quite foreign. As we will see later, the expression $e^{\pi i} = -1$, often known as "the Euler identity" is due to Euler, but the idea itself predates Euler. Some people credit Roger Cotes (1682–1716) in 1714. [N, p. 162]

In the paper, E19, though not in the letter, Euler went into more detail, substituting $\frac{1}{2}$ into the form above and getting

$$\frac{2 \cdot 4 \cdot 6 \cdot 8}{3 \cdot 5 \cdot 7 \cdot 9} \text{ etc.}$$

which he compared to Wallis's formula

$$\frac{4}{\pi} = \frac{3 \cdot 3 \cdot 5 \cdot 5 \cdot 7 \cdot 7 \cdots}{2 \cdot 4 \cdot 4 \cdot 6 \cdot 6 \cdot 8 \cdots}$$

to get the result he claimed.

Euler spent most of the remainder of the paper E19 developing integral formulas that interpolate products of arithmetic sequences. Since the sequence 1, 2, 3, 4,... is a special arithmetic sequence, these formulas were generalizing the factorial function, and their interpolations generalized the gamma function.

In the very last sections of the paper, Euler made some speculative remarks. He was motivated by the idea that the nth derivative of a polynomial x^k could be written as

$$k(k-1)\cdots(k-n+1)x^{k-n} = \frac{k!}{(k-n)!}x^{k-n}.$$

Since Euler had generalized the factorial function, he could give a definition to the nth derivative, even if n were a fraction. In his words:

> To round off this discussion, let me add something which certainly is more curious than useful. It is known that dx^n denotes the differential of x of order n and if p denotes any function of x and dx is taken to be constant then ...the ratio of dx^p to dx^n can be expressed algebraically.... We now ask, if n is a fractional number, what the value of that ratio should be.

---

[3] There is a little trick involved. It may help to note that $e^{-\pi i} = -1$, too.

Before returning to Euler's letter to Goldbach, let us remind the reader that the harmonic progression is the sequence of reciprocals of the positive integers. It begins $1, \frac{1}{2}, \frac{1}{3}, \frac{1}{4}, \frac{1}{5}, \ldots$. Its progression of partial sums would begin $1, \frac{3}{2}, \frac{11}{6}, \frac{25}{12}, \frac{137}{60}, \ldots$.

Euler wanted to do something with this sequence of partial sums that resembled what he did with the sequence of factorial numbers. He wanted to interpolate the sequence, that is, to give meaning to the sequence for values that fall between the whole numbers for which it is naturally defined. He told Goldbach, without any substantiation, "I have found that the general term, whose index is $-\frac{1}{2}$ is $-2l2$. The term whose exponent is $\frac{1}{2}$ is $2 - 2l2$" where "$l2$ signifies the hyperbolic logarithm of two, which is $= 0,69314738056$." In Euler's day, as in much of the world today, they used commas as decimal points. Euler said nothing more of this in the letter, but he treated the subject thoroughly, as we will see below, in the paper E20.

Six weeks later, Goldbach replied from Moscow with a letter dated December 1/12, 1729, in which he repeated Euler's form for the gamma function and asks the sum of the "hypergeometric series" $1 + 1 \cdot 2 + 1 \cdot 2 \cdot 3 + 1 \cdot 2 \cdot 3 \cdot 4 + \cdots$. As a final note, he wrote,

> P.S. A note to you is that Fermat has observed that all numbers with the formula $2^{2^x} + 1$, that is 3, 5, 17, etc. are primes, but he himself was not able to prove this, and, as far as I know, nobody since him has proved it, either.

This casual remark helped to spark Euler's lifelong interest in number theory, and he soon did much more with this in E26, "Observations on some theorems of Fermat." That is a story for another time, though.

Euler replied to Goldbach from St. Petersburg on January 8/19, 1730 with an outline of some of the integral methods he was using to analyze the form for the gamma function, steps he would detail in his paper E19. He closed with a note "I have been able to discover nothing about the observation noticed by Fermat."

Goldbach's reply from Moscow was written more than four months later on May 22/June 2, 1730. Goldbach echoed back one of Euler's integral forms for the gamma function, and forwarded a couple of other of Fermat's observations on number theory.

After this fourth letter, Euler and Goldbach exchanged letters at a more rapid pace, but they did not return to these topics. It is clear from these letters that the mathematical insights and initiative were Euler's, but that Goldbach was a willing, if inept, partner in the correspondence.

Let us examine how Euler expanded his remarks on the interpolation of the partial sums of the harmonic series in E20. He asked us to look at the integral $\int_0^1 \frac{1-x^n}{1-x} dx$, or, as Euler said, "$\int \frac{1-x^n}{1-x} dx$, and take it $= 0$ if $x = 0$, and then set $x = 1$." This peculiar wording is how Euler said to take the integral from 0 to 1. It amounts to taking a particular antiderivative, chosen so that the constant of integration makes the value of the antiderivative equal to zero at the left hand endpoint. For integer values of n, the integrand expands to give $1 + x + x^2 + \cdots + x^{n-1}$. This finite series integrates to give

$$x + \frac{x^2}{2} + \frac{x^3}{3} + \cdots + \frac{x^n}{n},$$

which, integrated from 0 to 1, gives the nth partial sum of the harmonic series.

The integral, though, is defined even if n is not an integer, and Euler took this integral to be the interpolation of the series. In particular, if $n = \frac{1}{2}$, the integrand is $(1 - \sqrt{x})/(1 - x)$

or, equivalently, $1/(1 + \sqrt{x})$. Integrating this from 0 to 1 gives $2 - 2\ln 2$. This explains his unsubstantiated remark in his first letter to Goldbach.

Euler generalized this idea to the case of series of fractions where the numerator is any geometric series and the denominator is any arithmetic series. He went on to use partial fractions to extend it to the case where the denominator is any polynomial with distinct real roots. Partial fractions did not enable him to deal with complex or multiple roots. We note that the Basel problem is a case with multiple roots.

To deal with multiple roots, Euler needed to invent another trick. Note that when Euler integrated $1 + x + x^2 + \cdots + x^{n-1}$ he got

$$x + \frac{x^2}{2} + \frac{x^3}{3} + \cdots + \frac{x^n}{n}.$$

Integrating again gives

$$\frac{x^2}{1 \cdot 2} + \frac{x^3}{2 \cdot 3} + \frac{x^4}{3 \cdot 4} + \cdots + \frac{x^{n+1}}{n \cdot (n+1)},$$

closely related to the series studied by Huygens and Leibniz. However, if he divided by x before integrating again, or, as Euler wrote it, if he took

$$\int \frac{dx}{x} \int \frac{1 - x^n}{1 - x} dx$$

he got

$$x + \frac{x}{4} + \frac{x^2}{9} + \frac{x^3}{16} + \cdots + \frac{x^n}{n^2}.$$

This series, if $x = 1$ and n goes to infinity, would be a solution to the Basel problem. The integral, however, is intractable and appears to the modern reader to be nonsense, as well. To make the integral make sense in modern notation, we would write

$$\int_0^1 \frac{dx}{x} \left(\int_0^x \frac{1 - t^{n-1}}{1 - t} dt \right).$$

As we have seen, Euler did not yet have the notation to write it this way, but the technique of Euler's time, to choose the appropriate antiderivative at each step, then evaluate the antiderivative at the end of the calculation, made his double integral a perfectly clear and unambiguous meaning to his contemporaries.

The integral was still intractable, but Euler devised some clever approximations to get the integral to six decimal places, 1.644924. Euler noted that to achieve such accuracy using direct calculation requires more than 1000 terms, so his estimate of the solution to the Basel problem was far more accurate than any available to his competitors. He later improved his estimate to 17 decimal places. Moreover, Euler was a genius at arithmetic, so he probably recognized this value as what would turn out to be the exact solution to the Basel problem, $\pi^2/6$. Euler didn't share this with the world, so he had a valuable advantage as he raced to solve the problem; he knew the answer.

Euler later assembled all his results on these topics into Chapter XVII "De interpolatione serierum" (On the interpolation of series) of Part II of his 1755 *Institutiones calculi differentialis*. [E212]

Let us move forward in time from 1729, when Euler wrote E19, and 1730, when he wrote E20, to 1735, when he wrote E41, his solution to the Basel problem and his first really important mathematical accomplishment. Euler gave four distinct solutions to the Basel problem, three in E41 and a fourth in E63, written in 1741. The "usual" solution is the third one, recounted excellently in [D]. Briefly, Euler noted that the function $\frac{\sin x}{x}$ has roots at $\pm\pi, \pm 2\pi, \pm 3\pi, \pm 4\pi$, etc. and made the bold assumption that it is the same function as the infinite product, which has the same roots,

$$\left(1 - \frac{x}{\pi}\right)\left(1 + \frac{x}{\pi}\right)\left(1 - \frac{x}{2\pi}\right)\left(1 + \frac{x}{2\pi}\right)\left(1 - \frac{x}{3\pi}\right)\left(1 + \frac{x}{3\pi}\right)\cdots.$$

This last, he rewrote as

$$\left(1 - \frac{x^2}{\pi^2}\right)\left(1 - \frac{x^2}{4\pi^2}\right)\left(1 - \frac{x^2}{9\pi^2}\right)\cdots$$

then noted that the coefficient on x^2 in the expansion will be

$$-\frac{1}{\pi^2} - \frac{1}{4\pi^2} - \frac{1}{9\pi^2} - \cdots.$$

Meanwhile, he noted that the Taylor series expansion of $\frac{\sin x}{x}$ at $x = 0$ is

$$1 - \frac{x^2}{3!} + \frac{x^4}{5!} - \frac{x^6}{7!} + \cdots.$$

Matching coefficients, he found that

$$-\frac{1}{\pi^2} - \frac{1}{4\pi^2} - \frac{1}{9\pi^2} - \cdots = \frac{-1}{3!}$$

so that

$$1 + \frac{1}{4} + \frac{1}{9} + \frac{1}{16} + \cdots = \frac{\pi^2}{6}.$$

Euler gave considerably more detail, he used p where we use π, and he did not use the factorial notation, so his exposition took a good deal longer. He is often criticized for failing to justify his conclusion that $\frac{\sin x}{x}$ equals the infinite product just because they have the same roots. Modern critics note, for example, that $e^x \frac{\sin x}{x}$ also has the same roots, yet it is not equal to the given infinite product. Euler did revisit the question of infinite products and their roots in E63, written in 1741, where he did a little bit to strengthen his case, but it still did not approach modern standards of analytical rigor.

Let us look at Euler's first and less elegant solution to the Basel problem, as it is so seldom described elsewhere, and it gives us insight into how Euler came upon the more elegant solution we describe above.

Euler took s to be the length of an arc on a circle of radius 1, and took $y = \sin s$. He writes the Taylor series

$$y = s - \frac{s^3}{1 \cdot 2 \cdot 3} + \frac{s^5}{1 \cdot 2 \cdot 3 \cdot 4 \cdot 5} - \frac{s^7}{1 \cdot 2 \cdot 3 \cdot 4 \cdot 5 \cdot 6 \cdot 7} + \text{etc.}$$

Dividing by y and subtracting the result from 1 transforms this into

$$0 = 1 - \frac{s}{y} + \frac{s^3}{1 \cdot 2 \cdot 3y} - \frac{s^5}{1 \cdot 2 \cdot 3 \cdot 4 \cdot 5y} + \text{etc.}$$

Euler factored this as if it were a polynomial to write

$$1 - \frac{s}{y} + \frac{s^3}{1 \cdot 2 \cdot 3y} - \frac{s^5}{1 \cdot 2 \cdot 3 \cdot 4 \cdot 5y} + \text{etc.} = \left(1 - \frac{s}{A}\right)\left(1 - \frac{s}{B}\right)\left(1 - \frac{s}{C}\right)\left(1 - \frac{s}{D}\right) \text{etc.}$$

Matching the terms containing s to the first power gives

$$\frac{1}{y} = \frac{1}{A} + \frac{1}{B} + \frac{1}{C} + \frac{1}{D} + \text{etc.}$$

Euler noted that if he matched terms containing s^2, he would get zero on the left and "the sum of factors taken two at a time" (without repetition) from the terms of the series on the right. He described terms containing s^3 up to s^5 similarly.

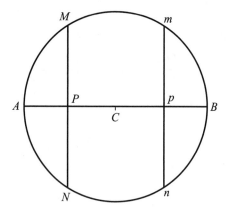

Now, in the figure above, Euler took the arc length AM to be s and also took $AM = A$, where A is the smallest positive arc with the same sine as s.[4] That sine is $y = PM$. He also took p to be the "semiperiphery of a circle of radius 1," that is to say π. Now, by the periodicity of the sine functions, the other arcs with the same sine as s are

$$A, \ \pi - A, \ 2\pi + A, \ 3\pi - A, \ 4\pi + A, \ 5\pi - A, \ 6\pi + A, \ \text{etc.}$$

and

$$-\pi - A, \ -2\pi + A, \ -3\pi - A, \ -4\pi + A, \ -5\pi - A, \ \text{etc.}$$

This gave Euler values for A, B, C, etc. in his series and his infinite product above, so he could say that

$$\frac{1}{y} = \frac{1}{A} + \frac{1}{\pi - A} + \frac{1}{-\pi - A} + \frac{1}{2\pi + A} + \frac{1}{-2\pi + A} + \frac{1}{3\pi - A} + \frac{1}{-3\pi + A}$$

Matching coefficients again, he noted that the sum of the products taken two at a time would be zero, taken three at a time would be $\frac{-1}{1 \cdot 2 \cdot 3y}$, and so forth.

Euler recalled some facts about series that he used quite often, but that are today seldom seen. If $\alpha = a + b + c + d + e + f + $ etc. is a series, and if β is "the sum of these terms

---

[4]Note how Euler used the symbol A to mean several things here. It is a term in the sequence A, B, C, etc., a point in the diagram, and also an arc. This was common practice in Euler's time, and it was up to the reader to keep it straight. The meaning is usually clear from the context.

taken two at a time" without repetition, that is $\beta = ab + ac + bc + ad + bc + ae + bd + af + be + cd +$ etc. then

$$a^2 + b^2 + c^2 + d^2 + \text{ etc.} = \alpha^2 - 2\beta.$$

Euler went into a good deal of detail here, denoting by $\alpha, \beta, \gamma, \delta$, etc. the sums of the terms taken one, two, three and four at a time, respectively, and denoting by P, Q, R, S, etc. the sums of the terms taken to the first, second, third and fourth powers respectively. Then he got

$$P = \alpha$$
$$Q = P\alpha - 2\beta$$
$$R = Q\alpha - P\beta + 3\gamma$$
$$S = R\alpha - Q\beta + P\gamma - 4\delta, \text{ etc.}$$

In Euler's series,

$$\alpha = \frac{1}{y}$$
$$\beta = 0$$
$$\gamma = \frac{-1}{1 \cdot 2 \cdot 3y}$$
$$\delta = 0$$
$$\varepsilon = \frac{+1}{1 \cdot 2 \cdot 3 \cdot 4 \cdot 5y}$$
$$\zeta = 0 \quad \text{etc.}$$

and so

$$P = \frac{1}{y}$$
$$Q = \frac{P}{y} = \frac{1}{y^2}$$
$$R = \frac{Q}{y} - \frac{1}{1 \cdot 2y}$$
$$S = \frac{R}{y} - \frac{P}{1 \cdot 2 \cdot 3y}$$

Up to this point, Euler did his development in some generality, without taking any particular value for the arc s. He next took $q = \frac{\pi}{2}$, and set $s = q$, so that $y = 1$. This made $P = 1$, so the sum of the first powers of the terms of his series became

$$1 = \frac{1}{q} + \frac{1}{q} + \frac{-1}{3q} + \frac{-1}{3q} + \frac{1}{5q} + \frac{1}{5q} + \frac{-1}{7q} + \frac{-1}{7q} + \text{ etc.}$$
$$= \frac{2}{q}\left(1 - \frac{1}{3} + \frac{1}{5} - \frac{1}{7} + \text{ etc.}\right)$$

This says that

$$1 - \frac{1}{3} + \frac{1}{5} - \frac{1}{7} + \frac{1}{9} - \frac{1}{11} + \text{ etc. } = \frac{\pi}{4}$$

a fact that was well known to Euler and that he attributed to Leibniz. Euler included this particular calculation to check that his methods had not led him astray.

Now, Euler turned to the sum of the squares of his sequence, or

$$\frac{1}{q^2} + \frac{1}{q^2} + \frac{1}{9q^2} + \frac{1}{9q^2} + \frac{1}{25q^2} + \frac{1}{25q^2} + \text{ etc. } = \frac{2}{q^2}\left(\frac{1}{1} + \frac{1}{9} + \frac{1}{25} + \frac{1}{49} + \text{ etc.}\right).$$

This sum equals Q, by definition. But $Q = 1/y^2$ and $y = 1$, so $Q = 1$. Substitution gives

$$1 + \frac{1}{9} + \frac{1}{25} + \frac{1}{49} + \text{ etc. } = \frac{q^2}{2} = \frac{\pi^2}{8}.$$

That is, the sum of the reciprocals of the odd squares is $\frac{\pi^2}{8}$. Since every even square is a power of 4 times an odd square, Euler knew that

$$1 + \frac{1}{4} + \frac{1}{9} + \frac{1}{16} + \frac{1}{25} + \frac{1}{36} + \text{ etc. } = \left(1 + \frac{1}{9} + \frac{1}{25} + \frac{1}{49} + \text{ etc.}\right)$$

$$\times \left(1 + \frac{1}{4} + \frac{1}{16} + \frac{1}{64} + \frac{1}{256} + \text{ etc.}\right)$$

$$= \frac{\pi^2}{8} \cdot \frac{1}{1 - \frac{1}{4}}$$

$$= \frac{\pi^2}{6}$$

and the Basel problem was solved. In typical Eulerian style, Euler continued matching higher order coefficients and evaluating sums of reciprocals of higher even powers, as well as alternating reciprocals of higher odd powers of odd numbers.

Euler's second solution to the Basel problem was based on taking $y = \frac{\sqrt{3}}{2}$ in place of $y = 1$ and doing a calculation similar to the one above.

Euler seemed to believe that there was something more to be done with this technique of infinite products. It is not quite clear whether he had doubts about the reliability of the technique, or he hoped that it could yield new results on a par with his solution to the Basel problem. In 1743, in one of his first mathematical papers written after he moved to Berlin, he wrote a twenty page paper, E61 with a twenty word title, "De summis serierum recip-rocarum ex potestatibus numerorum naturalium ortarum dissertatio altera, in qua eaedem summationes ex fonte maxime diverso derivantur" (On the sums of reciprocals of powers of natural numbers arising from the previous dissertation in which those summations are derived in a different way). This was based in part on E130, written in 1739 but, because of the immense publication delays in the St, Petersburg journals at the time, not published un-til 1750, "De seriebus quibusdam considerationes" (On considerations about certain series). In both papers, he made his calculations more clearly and in more generality. He succeeded in re-deriving known results, providing evidence that the techniques were reliable, but he found no important new results, nor does he provide more rigor.

It is worth noting in passing that in E61, Euler did some of his series calculations using complex numbers. He had recently adopted the symbols e and π to denote their now familiar constants. In the course of his calculations in E61, he remarked that the series for

$$\sin s = s - \frac{s^3}{1 \cdot 2 \cdot 3} + \frac{s^5}{1 \cdot 2 \cdot 3 \cdot 4 \cdot 5} - \frac{s^7}{1 \cdot 2 \cdot 3 \cdots 7} + \text{etc.} = \frac{e^{s\sqrt{-1}} - e^{-s\sqrt{-1}}}{2\sqrt{-1}}.$$

This was Euler's first use of this fact, and it is one of several mathematical facts now known as an "Euler formula."

Later in the same paragraph, he wrote, "denoting by e that number whose logarithm is $= 1$," that

$$e^z = \left(1 + \frac{z}{n}\right)^n$$

"where n is an infinite number." Euler did not have the tools of limits, so he often calculated with infinite and infinitesimal numbers.

Perhaps Euler sensed that his method of infinite products would continue to provoke criticism. In 1741 he wrote in French a fourth solution to the Basel problem. This paper, E63, "Démonstration de la somme de cette suite $1 + \frac{1}{4} + \frac{1}{9} + \frac{1}{16} + \frac{1}{25} + \frac{1}{36} +$ etc." (Proof of the sum of this series $1 + \frac{1}{4} + \frac{1}{9} + \frac{1}{16} + \frac{1}{25} + \frac{1}{36} +$ etc.) used only elementary calculus tools, Taylor series and integration by parts, to obtain the result.

Euler took $x = \sin s$, so $s = \arcsin x$ and $ds = dx/\sqrt{1-xx}$. Euler chose to write s as an integral, so $s = \int dx/\sqrt{1-xx}$. Euler followed the practice of his time and was not very explicit about what the bounds of integration ought to be. Here he gave a hint that, in the case $x = 1$, the integral would give $\frac{\pi}{2}$ where "It is clear that I employ here the letter π to indicate the number of Ludolf of Kuelen, 3.14159265, etc." By this time, Euler had been using π to denote that constant for several years, but the convention would take many years more before it was universally adopted.

Next, Euler considered

$$s \, ds = \frac{dx}{\sqrt{1-xx}} \int \frac{dx}{\sqrt{1-xx}}.$$

Integrating from 0 to 1 gave $\frac{\pi\pi}{8}$ on the left. This done, he turned his attention to the integral on the right.

Euler expanded this integral for s, first using the generalized binomial theorem with $m = \frac{-1}{2}$, then integrating, to get

$$\int \frac{dx}{\sqrt{1-xx}} = x + \frac{1}{2 \cdot 3}x^3 + \frac{1 \cdot 3}{2 \cdot 4 \cdot 5}x^5 + \frac{1 \cdot 3 \cdot 5}{2 \cdot 4 \cdot 6 \cdot 7}x^7 + \frac{1 \cdot 3 \cdot 5 \cdot 7}{2 \cdot 4 \cdot 6 \cdot 8 \cdot 9}x^9 + \text{etc.}$$

Now, multiplying by $ds = dx/\sqrt{1-xx}$ gives

$$s \, ds = \frac{x \, dx}{\sqrt{1-xx}} + \frac{1}{2 \cdot 3}\frac{x^3 \, dx}{\sqrt{1-xx}} + \frac{1 \cdot 3}{2 \cdot 4 \cdot 5}\frac{x^5 \, dx}{\sqrt{1-xx}}$$
$$+ \frac{1 \cdot 3 \cdot 5}{2 \cdot 4 \cdot 6 \cdot 7}\frac{x^7 \, dx}{\sqrt{1-xx}} + \frac{1 \cdot 3 \cdot 5 \cdot 7}{2 \cdot 4 \cdot 6 \cdot 8 \cdot 9}\frac{x^9 \, dx}{\sqrt{1-xx}} + \text{etc.}$$

Here, he said, "One will see clearly, if he gives it proper reflection that in general,"

$$\int \frac{x^{n+2} \, dx}{\sqrt{1-xx}} = \frac{n+1}{n+2} \int \frac{x^n \, dx}{\sqrt{1-xx}} - \frac{x^{n+1}}{n+2}\sqrt{1-xx}$$

By "proper reflection" Euler meant "integration by parts." Here, the integral is to be taken from 0 to 1, and so the second term on the right drops out, leaving us with only

$$\int \frac{x^{n+2}\,dx}{\sqrt{1-xx}} = \frac{n+1}{n+2} \int \frac{x^n\,dx}{\sqrt{1-xx}}.$$

With this, Euler could evaluate the integrals in each term of the integral of $s\,ds$:

$$\int \frac{x\,dx}{\sqrt{1-xx}} = 1 - \sqrt{1-xx} = 1$$

$$\int \frac{x^3\,dx}{\sqrt{1-xx}} = \frac{2}{3} \int \frac{x\,dx}{\sqrt{1-xx}} = \frac{2}{3}$$

$$\int \frac{x^5\,dx}{\sqrt{1-xx}} = \frac{4}{5} \int \frac{x^3\,dx}{\sqrt{1-xx}} = \frac{2\cdot 4}{3\cdot 5}$$

$$\int \frac{x^7\,dx}{\sqrt{1-xx}} = \frac{6}{7} \int \frac{x^5\,dx}{\sqrt{1-xx}} = \frac{2\cdot 4\cdot 6}{3\cdot 5\cdot 7}.$$

Now Euler could integrate $s\,ds$ to get

$$\frac{\pi\pi}{8} = \frac{ss}{2} = \int s\,ds$$

$$= \int \frac{x\,dx}{\sqrt{1-xx}} + \frac{1}{2\cdot 3} \int \frac{x^3\,dx}{\sqrt{1-xx}} + \frac{1\cdot 3}{2\cdot 4\cdot 5} \int \frac{x^5\,dx}{\sqrt{1-xx}}$$

$$+ \frac{1\cdot 3\cdot 5}{2\cdot 4\cdot 6\cdot 7} \int \frac{x^7\,dx}{\sqrt{1-xx}} + \text{etc.}$$

Substituting the values for the integrals that he found above gave

$$\frac{\pi\pi}{8} = 1 + \frac{1}{3\cdot 3} + \frac{1}{5\cdot 5} + \frac{1}{7\cdot 7} + \text{etc.}$$

Here, as in his first proof, this sum of the reciprocals of the odd squares gave the sum of the reciprocals of all squares to be

$$\frac{\pi\pi}{6} = 1 + \frac{1}{4} + \frac{1}{9} + \frac{1}{16} + \frac{1}{25} + \text{etc.}$$

Acknowledgement

Thanks are due to Craig Waff for the use of his copy of the Eneström index, and for his other advice and encouragement.

References

Electronic copies of all of the original sources cited here are available on line at EulerArchive.org.

[D]   Dunham, William, *Euler The Master of Us All*, Mathematical Association of America, Washington, DC, 1999.

[E19]   Euler, Leonhard, "De progressionibus transcendentibus seu quarum termini generales algebraice dari nequeunt" (On transcendental progressions, that is, those whose general terms cannot be given algebraically), *Comm. Acad. sci. Petrop.* 5 (1730/31), 1738, p 36–57. Reprinted in *Opera Omnia*, Ser. I v. 14, p. 1–24. English translation by Stacy Langton available at `EulerArchive.org`.

[E20]   ——, "De summatione innumerabilium progressionum" (On the summation of innumerable progressions), *Comm. Acad. sci. Petrop.* 5 (1730/31) 1738, p. 91–105, Reprinted in *Opera Omnia*, Ser. I v. 14, p. 25–41.

[E41]   ——, "De summis serierum reciprocarum" (On the sums of series of reciprocals), *Comm. Acad. sci. Petrop.* 7 (1734/35) 1740, p. 123–134, Reprinted in *Opera Omnia*, Ser. I v. 14, p. 73–86.

[E61]   ——, "De summis serierum reciprocarum ex potestatibus numerorum naturalium ortarum dissertatio altera, in qua eadem summationes ex fonte maxime diverso derivantur" (On the sum of series of reciprocals of powers of natural numbers that arise in an earlier dissertation, in which the same summations are derived in a different manner), *Miscellanea Berolinensia*, 1743, p. 172–192, Reprinted in *Opera Omnia*, Ser. I v. 14, p. 138–155.

[E63]   ——, "Démonstration de la somme de cette suite $1 + \frac{1}{4} + \frac{1}{9} + \frac{1}{16} + \frac{1}{25} + \frac{1}{36} +$ etc." (Proof of the sum of this series $1 + \frac{1}{4} + \frac{1}{9} + \frac{1}{16} + \frac{1}{25} + \frac{1}{36} +$ etc.), *Journ. lit. d'Allemagne, de Suisse et du Nord*, 2:1, 1743, p. 115–127, Reprinted in *Opera Omnia*, Ser. I v. 14, p. 177186.

[E130] ——, "De seriebus quibusdam considerationes" (Considerations about certain series), *Comm. Acad. sci. Petrop.* 12 (1740) 1750, Reprinted in *Opera Omnia*, Ser. I v. 14, p. 407–462.

[E212] ——, *Institutiones calculi differentialis*, (*Instructions in the calculus of differentials*), St. Petersburg, 1755. Reprinted in *Opera Omnia*, Ser. I, v. 10.

[En]   Eneström, Gustaf, *Verzeichnis der schriften Leonhard Eulers*, Jahresbericht der Deutschen Mathematiker-Vereinigung, Teubner, Leipzig, 1913.

[J]   Juškevič, A. P., and E. Winter, eds., *Leonhard Euler und Christian Goldbach Briefwechsel 17291764*, Akademie-Verlag, Berlin, 1965.

[N]   Nahin, Paul, *An Imaginary Tale: The Story of $\sqrt{-1}$*, Princeton Univ. Press, Princeton, NJ, 1998.

Euler and Elliptic Integrals[1]

Lawrence D'Antonio

Introduction

Elliptic integrals appear in many places in the work of Leonhard Euler. The theory and application of elliptic integrals were a significant interest of Euler's for decades. Although Euler was not the first mathematician to consider these integrals—for they can be found in earlier work of Johann and Jakob Bernoulli and that of the Italian mathematician Count Fagnano—there is no doubt that Euler's contributions form the foundation of the subject on which all later work rests.

The work of 19th century mathematicians such as Legendre, Abel, Jacobi, Weierstrass, Clebsch, Cayley and many others initiated the study of elliptic functions. They were one of the major themes of 19th century mathematics. In the 20th century, one finds the research of Poincaré, Hurwitz, Beppo Levi, Mordell, Weil, Tate, Mazur and others focused on the topic of elliptic curves. This culminates in the proof of Fermat's Last Theorem, a subject to which Euler had made some of the first contributions.

An elliptic integral has the form

$$\int \frac{R(x)}{\sqrt{f(x)}} \, dx,$$

where $R(x)$ is a rational function and $f(x)$ is a polynomial of degree 3 or 4 without multiple roots. Euler did not use the phrase "elliptic integrals" and does not give a specific definition of them. In spite of this Euler does give a unified theory of such integrals, especially in his masterpieces E251 and E252.

A reasonable question to ask is, where are the ellipses? The name "elliptic integrals" refers to the fact that the arclength of an ellipse can be expressed as an elliptic integral, a fact that was known to Euler. Consider the usual parametrization of the ellipse, with $a > b > 0$:

$$x = a \cos t, \quad y = b \sin t$$

[1]Based on a talk given at the Euler 2k+2 meeting of The Euler Society, Rumford, Maine, August 2002.

and let $c^2 = a^2 - b^2$, $k = \frac{c}{a}$. This gives for the differential of arclength,

$$ds^2 = dx^2 + dy^2 = (a^2 \cos^2 t + b^2 \sin^2 t) \, dt^2$$
$$= (a^2 - c^2 \sin^2 t) \, dt^2 = a^2(1 - k^2 \sin^2 t) \, dt^2.$$

Therefore, the arclength of an ellipse is

$$s = a \int \sqrt{1 - k^2 \sin^2 t} \, dt.$$

In Legendre's classification [26], this is called an elliptic integral of the second kind. Although Euler considered different types of elliptic integrals, he never classified them. We can put this integral into the standard form by the substitution $u = \sin t$, which leads to

$$s = a \int \sqrt{\frac{1 - k^2 u^2}{1 - u^2}} du = a \int \frac{1 - k^2 u^2}{\sqrt{(1 - u^2)(1 - k^2 u^2)}} \, du.$$

The Early History of Elliptic Integrals

There are three occurrences of elliptic integrals in the mathematical literature before Euler. Jakob Bernoulli was the first to use elliptic integrals in his study of elastic curves in June 1694. Later that year they appeared in the papers of Jakob and Johann Bernoulli on the paracentric isochrone curve. In a series of papers in 1716–1721, Count Fagnano further developed the theory of elliptic integrals in his research on the lemniscate, this curve having first appeared in Jakob Bernoulli's work on the paracentric isochrone.

Elastica

Problems in elasticity had been studied since the time of Galileo. Both Jakob and Johann Bernoulli had made significant contributions to these problems. In particular, the problem of the elastica or elastic band had first been proposed by Jakob Bernoulli in 1691. Bernoulli stated that the problem of the elastica consists in finding

> "the bendings or curvatures of beams, drawn bows, or of springs of any kind, caused by their own weight or by an attached weight or by any other compressing forces."
> [2, §3]

In his paper of 1694 [4], Jakob Bernoulli studies the curvature of the elastica. Consider an elastic rod, that is initially vertical. Place a weight on the upper end of the rod. The rod will bend until an equilibrium configuration, called the elastica or elastic curve, is obtained. Let the upper end be the origin of the coordinate system. Bernoulli finds the fundamental equation describing the elastica to be

$$dy = \int \frac{x^2 dx}{\sqrt{a^4 - x^4}}.$$

This is the first appearance of an elliptic integral in the mathematical literature. Bernoulli then comments on the integrability of this equation:

> "I have serious cause to believe that the construction of our curve depends neither on the quadrature nor on the rectification of any conic section." [4, p. 592]

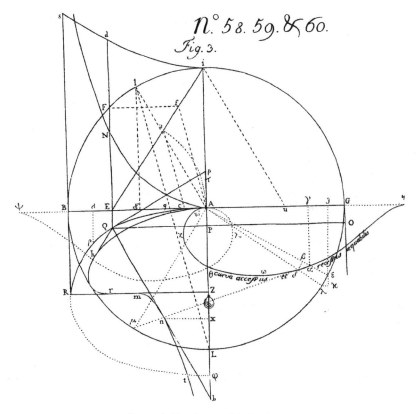

Figure 1. The Paracentric Isochrone

Paracentric Isochrone

The paracentric isochrone is a curve first described by Leibniz in 1689 [25]. To define the paracentric isochrone let a fixed point A be given and let a particle descend under gravity from that fixed point so that the particle moves in a vertical plane, with the point α being its current position, in such a way that the distance of α from A is proportional to the time taken to reach that point.

As was the case in the race to describe the catenary, the Bernoulli brothers, Jakob and Johann, wrote several articles to attempt to solve the problem of the isochrone [3, ?, ?, ?]. The most significant of these articles, "Constructio curvae accessus et recessus aequabilis, ope rectificationis curvae cujusdam algebraicae," by Jakob Bernoulli, was published in the September 1694 issue of *Acta Eruditorum* [5]. To find the equation of the paracentric isochrone, one must first find an appropriate differential equation. Referring to the rather bewildering Figure 1, the starting point is labeled A and the paracentric isochrone itself is the curve labeled *curva accessus et recessus aequalibis*. Define $t = A\alpha$, where the point α is on the curve just to the left of the word *recessus*, $z = \zeta\varepsilon$ where the point ε is on the circle just under the word *recessus*, ζ is on the diameter of the circle, and $a = Ai$ is the radius of the circle. Bernoulli finds the formula for the isochrone,

$$\frac{dt}{\sqrt{at}} = \frac{a\,dz}{\sqrt{az(a^2 - z^2)}}.$$

Substituting $az = u^2$ Bernoulli arrives at the integral later known as the "lemniscatic" integral, for it is related to the arclength of the lemniscate.

$$\frac{dt}{\sqrt{at}} = \frac{2a\,du}{\sqrt{a^4 - u^4}}. \tag{1}$$

The right-hand side is an elliptic integral.

Bernoulli knows that the right-hand side cannot be integrated in elementary terms, so he tries to reduce the problem to the rectification of some curve. That is, he wishes to find $x(z), y(z)$ so that the quantity

$$\sqrt{dx^2 + dy^2},$$

which will be the differential of arclength for some curve, equals the expressions in Equation (1).

Bernoulli wants to find an algebraic curve with the desired arclength function. He defines the variables

$$x = \sqrt{az + z^2}, \; y = \sqrt{az - z^2}. \tag{2}$$

This leads to the arclength differential

$$ds = \sqrt{dx^2 + dy^2} = \frac{a}{\sqrt{2}} \cdot \frac{a\,dz}{\sqrt{az(a^2 - z^2)}}.$$

The curve determined by x, y has the paracentric isochrone as its arclength. But what curve is determined by x, y? It easily follows from Equation (2) that

$$(x^2 + y^2)^2 = 2a^2(x^2 - y^2),$$

which is the standard equation of the lemniscate in Cartesian coordinates. So the paracentric isochrone is the arclength of the lemniscate. At this point, Bernoulli states that "notae octonari ∞ ... sive lemnisci, *d'un noeud de ruban* Gallis" ("note the figure eight ∞ ... or the lemniscate, a knotted French ribbon"), [5, p. 609]. The graph of the lemniscate does not appear in Figure 1, perhaps because Bernoulli felt that the figure was already too complicated.

Fagnano

Count Giulio Carlo de' Toschi di Fagnano (1682-1766) gave the first theoretical analysis of elliptic integrals. In particular, he realized their connection to the arclengths of the ellipse, hyperbola, lemniscate and cycloid. His most famous result is the Fagnano duplication formula for the lemniscate. Let C be the center of the lemniscate and S, I be two points on the lemniscate. Define the chords $z = \overline{CS}, \; u = \overline{CI}$. If z, u satisfy the algebraic relation

$$\frac{u\sqrt{2}}{\sqrt{1 - u^4}} = \frac{\sqrt{1 - \sqrt{1 - z^4}}}{z},$$

then the arclengths on the lemniscate satisfy $\overparen{CS} = 2\,\overparen{CI}$. This implies that if we are given the point I on the lemniscate then the point S may be found by a compass and straightedge construction. This major result can be found in the two-part article "Metodo per misurare la lemniscata" [20, 21], published in 1718 in the *Giornale de' Letterati d'Italia*.

Fagnano's works were collected together in the *Produzioni matematiche* of 1750. Then in 1751, Maupertuis submitted Fagnano's work to the Berlin Academy for consideration of Fagnano as a foreign member. On December 23, 1751, the work was assigned to Euler to evaluate. This can certainly be considered one of the most significant Christmas presents in the history of mathematics. Although Euler was already well aware of elliptic integrals, it is the work of Fagnano that motivated Euler to a deeper study of their properties.

Elliptic Integrals in Euler's Work

The first significant appearance of elliptic integrals in the work of Euler is in his letter to Johann Bernoulli of December 20, 1738. In this letter Euler states the remarkable identity

$$\int_0^a \frac{a^2 dx}{\sqrt{a^4 - x^4}} \cdot \int_0^a \frac{x^2 dx}{\sqrt{a^4 - x^4}} = \frac{\pi a^2}{4}.$$

The proof of this identity can be found in the late paper E605, "De miris proprietatibus curvae elasticae sub aequatione $y = \int xx\,dx/\sqrt{1 - x^4}$ contentae" (On the remarkable properties of the elastic curve contained in the equation $y = \int xx\,dx/\sqrt{1 - x^4}$) [17], written in 1782.

This letter leads to a rather interesting exchange between Euler and Bernoulli. After the letter of the 20th, Bernoulli writes back that he had long ago shown that the sum of these integrals equals the length of a quarter arc of an ellipse.

Euler responds that identities such as the above "seem to me more noteworthy in proportion to the indirectness of the route by which they are proved or discovered," while Bernoulli's property is of the kind that "comes of itself as soon as one looks for it." In this exchange with his famous mentor Euler appears to be very confident in his mathematical accomplishments.

Euler's work on elliptic integrals can be divided into the following categories:

- the appearance of elliptic integrals in his papers on elasticity,

- the extension of Fagnano's work on the lemniscate, leading up to the Euler Addition Theorem,

- Euler's research on the three body problem.

Elasticity

Euler wrote many important papers which initiate the theory of mathematical elasticity, although the Bernoullis certainly wrote extensively prior to Euler. We will focus on Euler's appendix to the treatise E65, *Methodus inveniendi lineas curvas maximi minimive proprietate gaudentes* (A method for finding curved lines enjoying properties of maximum or minimum) [10], published in 1744.

The problem stated in this appendix is to find the equation of the elastica. Euler presents this as a problem in the calculus of variations. He states in the introduction that,

"[T]he most illustrious and, in this sublime fashion of studying nature, most perspicacious man, Daniel Bernoulli, pointed out to me that the entire force stored in the curved elastic band may be expressed by a certain formula, which he calls the potential force, and that this expression must be a minimum." [27, p. 78]

This is one of a group of optimization problems studied in the 17th and 18th centuries, solved using the calculus of variations. For example, the problem of the catenary sought to find the curve hanging between two points with the lowest center of gravity, i.e., the shape of a flexible chain fixed at both ends, acted upon by gravity). The problem of finding this curve was originally posed by Jakob Bernoulli and then solved simultaneously in 1691 by Leibniz, Huygens, and Johann Bernoulli, who took great joy in solving the problem before his brother. For more on the problem of the catenary, see pp. 85–89 in this volume.

Euler derives the formulae for the elastica

$$dy = \frac{(a^2 - c^2 + x^2)dx}{\sqrt{(c^2 - x^2)(2a^2 - c^2 + x^2)}}$$

$$ds = \frac{a^2 dx}{\sqrt{(c^2 - x^2)(2a^2 - c^2 + x^2)}}.$$

These are elliptic integrals, which cannot be evaluated by elementary methods. Instead, Euler expands the integrands into series and integrates for x going from 0 to c to arrive at,

$$AC = f = \frac{\pi a}{2\sqrt{2}}\left(1 + \frac{1^2}{2^2} \cdot \frac{c^2}{2a^2} + \frac{1^2 3^2}{2^2 4^2} \cdot \frac{c^4}{4a^4} + \cdots\right)$$

$$AD = b = \frac{\pi a}{2\sqrt{2}}\left(1 - \frac{1^2}{2^2} \cdot \frac{3}{1} \cdot \frac{c^2}{2a^2} - \frac{1^2 3^2}{2^2 4^2} \cdot \frac{5}{3} \cdot \frac{c^4}{4a^4} - \cdots\right).$$

Euler then goes on to enumerate the different varieties of elastic curves, finding nine types of such curves. He also applies this analysis to solving the problem of how much weight a column may support before buckling.

Rectification of the Ellipse

Euler's work on the problem of determining the arclength of the ellipse appears in papers published over a period of forty years. The most developed thought of Euler appears in E448, "Nova series infinita maxime convergens perimetrum ellipsis exprimens" (A new infinite series that expresses the perimeter of an ellipse, and which converges very rapidly), published in the *Novi Commentarii* in 1774 [16].

Euler approximates the perimeter of the ellipse using the following technique. Consider the formula for the ellipse,

$$\frac{x^2}{a^2} + \frac{y^2}{b^2} = 1.$$

Euler uses the substitution,

$$x = a\sqrt{\frac{1+z}{2}}, \quad y = b\sqrt{\frac{1-z}{2}}.$$

This gives the integral for the arclength of a quarter of the ellipse,

$$s = \frac{1}{2\sqrt{2}} \int_{-1}^{1} dz \sqrt{\frac{a^2 + b^2 - (a^2 - b^2)z}{1 - z^2}}.$$

Letting

$$c^2 = a^2 + b^2, n = \frac{a^2 - b^2}{a^2 + b^2},$$

the quarter perimeter of the ellipse is written as an elliptic integral

$$s = \frac{c}{2\sqrt{2}} \int_{-1}^{1} dz \sqrt{\frac{1 - nz}{1 - z^2}}.$$

Expanding in series

$$\sqrt{1 - nz} = 1 - \frac{1}{2}nz - \frac{1 \cdot 1}{2 \cdot 4}n^2 z^2 - \frac{1 \cdot 1 \cdot 3}{2 \cdot 4 \cdot 6}n^3 z^3 - \cdots$$

and using the integral identities,

$$\int_{-1}^{1} \sqrt{\frac{dz}{1 - z^2}} = \pi, \qquad \int_{-1}^{1} \sqrt{\frac{z\, dz}{1 - z^2}} = 0,$$

$$\int_{-1}^{1} \frac{z^{\lambda+2}\, dz}{\sqrt{1 - z^2}} = \frac{\lambda + 1}{\lambda + 2} \int_{-1}^{1} \sqrt{\frac{z\, dz}{1 - z^2}},$$

the perimeter of the entire ellipse is given by the series formula

$$s = c\,\pi\,\sqrt{2}\left(1 - \frac{1 \cdot 1}{4 \cdot 4}n^2 - \frac{1 \cdot 1 \cdot 3 \cdot 5}{4 \cdot 4 \cdot 8 \cdot 8}n^4 - \frac{1 \cdot 1 \cdot 3 \cdot 5 \cdot 7 \cdot 9}{4 \cdot 4 \cdot 8 \cdot 8 \cdot 12 \cdot 12}n^6 - \cdots\right).$$

Using only the first term from this series Euler obtains the approximation for the perimeter of an ellipse,

$$\pi\,\sqrt{2(a^2 + b^2)}.$$

Euler's extension of Fagnano's work

Jacobi named December 23, 1751 the birthday of elliptic functions, for it was on this day that Euler received for review the collected papers of Count Giulio Fagnano. Euler's study of the work of Fagnano, together with Euler's earlier work on elliptic integrals, led to two extremely important papers, E251 [11] and E252 [12], which will be the focus of this discussion. It is here that Euler presents his addition theorem for elliptic integrals, which later serves as the foundation for Jacobi's theory of elliptic functions. The original version of E252 was written earlier than the work appearing as E251, but the order as published versions is reversed, presumably because Euler used the Euler Addition Theorem from E251 in the published version of E252.

Euler's Addition Theorem

The differential equation

$$\int \frac{dx}{\sqrt{1-x^4}} = \int \frac{dy}{\sqrt{1-y^4}}$$

has the complete integral

$$x^2 + y^2 + c^2 x^2 y^2 = c^2 + 2xy\sqrt{1-c^4}. \tag{3}$$

Proof: Taking the differential of (3) we obtain

$$dx\,(x + ccxy^2 - y\sqrt{1-c^4}) + dy\,(y + ccx^2y - x\sqrt{1-c^4}) = 0. \tag{4}$$

But solving (3) directly (using $x = 0 \Rightarrow y = c$) leads to the algebraic relations

$$y = \frac{x\sqrt{1-c^4} + c\sqrt{1-x^4}}{1+c^2x^2}, \quad x = \frac{y\sqrt{1-c^4} - c\sqrt{1-y^4}}{1+c^2y^2}.$$

This gives the pair of equations,

$$x + c^2xy^2 - y\sqrt{1-c^4} = -c\sqrt{1-y^4},$$
$$y + c^2x^2y - x\sqrt{1-c^4} = c\sqrt{1-x^4}.$$

Substituting the left-hand sides of these equations into (4) results in the differential equation

$$-c\,dx\sqrt{1-y^4} + c\,dy\sqrt{1-x^4} = 0.$$

Euler arrives at the lemniscatic integral

$$\int \frac{dx}{\sqrt{1-x^4}} = \int \frac{dy}{\sqrt{1-y^4}}.$$

A modern way of expressing this is the result

$$\int_0^u \frac{du}{\sqrt{1-u^4}} + \int_0^v \frac{dv}{\sqrt{1-v^4}} = \int_0^r \frac{dr}{\sqrt{1-r^4}} \Leftrightarrow$$
$$r = \frac{u\sqrt{1-v^4} + v\sqrt{1-u^4}}{1+u^2v^2}.$$

Three Body Problem

There were various attempts during the 18th century to find the motions of three bodies under gravitational attraction. Euler studied the problem under the assumption that two of the bodies were in fixed positions, which he calls two fixed centers. So the problem to be solved is that of finding the motion of a body attracted by two fixed centers according to the Newtonian inverse square law. In the 1760s, Euler wrote a series of three papers on this problem, E301, E328 and E337 [13, 14, 15].

Suppose that the two fixed centers are at points A, B and the body in motion is located at point M, as indicated in Figure 2. In this diagram, MP is perpendicular to AB. Also,

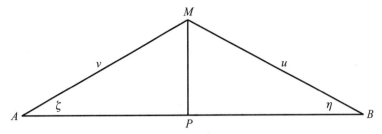

Figure 2. Three body problem

Euler defines the angles $\zeta = \angle BAM, \eta = \angle ABM$. Let $AB = a, AM = v, BM = u$ and define

$$x = AP = v \cos \zeta$$
$$y = PM = v \sin \zeta = u \sin \eta.$$

Euler obtains the desired equation of motion for the point M.

$$\frac{dr}{\sqrt{\alpha r + 2E\, rr + \beta r^3}} = \frac{ds}{\sqrt{\gamma s + 2E\, ss + \delta s^3}}.$$

Here,

$$\alpha = A + B + D, \ \beta = D - A - B,$$
$$\gamma = B - A - D, \ \delta = A - B - D,$$
$$p = \tan(\zeta/2), \ q = \tan(\eta/2),$$
$$r = pq, s = \frac{p}{q}.$$

In these equations A, B are constants defined by taking the gravitational attraction of M towards point A to be A/v^2 and that of M towards point B as B/u^2. Also, D, E are constants of integration.

This equation of motion involves elliptic integrals, so Euler takes the solution no farther, although he does consider a special case in [15] where this motion follows an algebraic curve.

After Euler

As we have seen, Euler used elliptic integrals to compute arclengths of the ellipse, hyperbola, and lemniscate. It is a natural extension to Euler's work to ask which curves have arclengths which are expressible as elliptic integrals? To make the question more concrete, recall that elliptic integrals of the first kind have the form

$$\int \frac{dt}{\sqrt{1 - k^2 \sin^2 t}}.$$

The question can then be put, which algebraic curves have arclengths which are elliptic integrals of the first kind? Serret [29, §§563-565] discovered that all such curves come from a one-parameter family of curves, known as Serret's curves. For a discussion of these curves see [28, §3.3].

Elliptic integrals play a significant role in many different applications, several of which have been discussed in this paper. Describing the motion of the simple pendulum requires the use of elliptic integrals [23]. The primary legacy of Euler's work in elliptic integrals is the development of the theory of elliptic functions and elliptic curves. Further discussion of these topics can be found in the histories of Brill and Noether [8], Enneper [9] and Houzel [24].

References

[1] Bernoulli, Jakob, *Opera*, Geneva, 1744, reprinted Bruxelles: Culture et Civilisation, 1967.

[2] ——, "Additamentum ad Problema Funicularium," appears at the end of "Specimen alterum Calculi differentialis in dimetienda Spirali Logarithmica, Loxodromiis Nautarum, & Areis Tri-angulorum Sphaericorum: una cum Additamento quodam ad Problema Funicularium, aliisque," *Acta Eruditorum*, June 1691, pp. 282–290, in *Opera* I, pp. 442–453.

[3] ——, "Solutio Problematis Leibnitiani: De Curva Accessus et Recessus aequalibis a puncto dato, mediante rectificatione Curvae Elasticae," *Acta Eruditorum*, June 1694, pp. 276–280, in *Opera* I, pp. 601–607.

[4] ——, "Curvatura Laminae Elasticae," *Acta Eruditorum*, June 1694, pp. 262–276, in *Opera* I, pp. 576–600.

[5] ——, "Constructio curvae accessus et recessus aequabilis, ope rectificationis curvae cujusdam algebraicae," *Acta Eruditorum*, September 1694, in *Opera*, pp. 608–612.

[6] Bernoulli, Johann, "Constructio facilis Curvae recessus aequabilis a puncto dato, per Rectifica-tionem Curvae Algebraicae," *Acta Eruditorum*, October 1694.

[7] ——, "Methodus commoda & naturalis reducendi Quadraturas transcendentes cujusvis gradus ad Longitudines Curvarum algebraicarum," *Acta Eruditorum*, August 1724, pp. 356–366.

[8] Brill, A., and M. Noether, "Die Entwicklung der Theorie der algebraischen Functionen in älterer und neurer Zeit," *Jahresber. der Deutschen Math. Verein*, 3(1892-1893), pp. 111-566.

[9] Enneper, A., *Elliptische functionen: Theorie und geschichte* 2nd ed., S.L. Nebert, Halle, 1890.

[10] Euler, L., *Methodus inveniendi lineas curvas maximi minimive proprietate gaudentes, sive solu-tio problematis isoperimetrici lattissimo sensu accepti* (E65), 1744, reprinted in *Opera Omnia*, Series 1, Volume 24.

[11] ——, "De integratione aequationis differentialis $\frac{mdx}{\sqrt{1-x^4}} = \frac{ndy}{\sqrt{1-y^4}}$" (E251), *Novi Comm. acad. sci. Petro.* 6 (1756/7), 1761, pp. 37–57, reprinted in *Opera Omnia*, Series 1, Volume 20, pp. 58–79.

[12] ——, "Observationes de comparatione arcuum curvarum irrectificabilium" (E252), *Novi Comm. acad. sci. Petro.*, 6 (1756/7), 1761, pp. 58–84, reprinted in *Opera Omnia*, Series 1, Volume 20, pp. 80–107.

[13] ——, "De motu corporis ad duo centra virium fixa attracti" (E301), *Novi Comm. acad. sci. Petro.*, 10 (1764), 1766, pp. 207–242, reprinted in *Opera Omnia*, Series 2, Volume 6, pp. 209–246.

[14] ——, "De motu corporis ad duo centra virium fixa attracti" (E328), *Novi Comm. acad. sci. Petro.*, 11 (1765), 1767, pp. 152–184, reprinted in *Opera Omnia*, Series 2, Volume 6, pp. 247–273.

[15] ——, "Problème: un corps étant attiré en raison réciproque quarrée des distances vers deux points fixes donnés trouver les cas ou la courbe décrite par ce corps sera algébrique résolu par M. Euler" (E337), *Mémoires de l'académie des sciences de Berlin*, 16 (1760), 1767, pp. 228–249, reprinted in *Opera Omnia*, Series 2, Volume 6, pp. 274–293.

[16] ——, "Nova series infinita maxime convergens perimetrum ellipsis exprimens" (E448), *Novi Comm. acad. sci. Petro.*, 18 (1773), 1774, pp. 71-84, reprinted in *Opera Omnia*, Series 1, Volume 20, pp. 357–370.

[17] ——, "De miris proprietatibus curvae elasticae sub aequatione $y = \int \frac{xx\,dx}{\sqrt{1-x^4}}$ contentae" (E605), *Acta acad. sci. Petro.* 1782, 1786, pp. 34-61, reprinted in *Opera Omnia*, Series 1, Volume 21, pp. 91–118.

[18] Fagnano, G., *Produzioni matematiche*, Pesaro, 1750.

[19] ——, *Opere matematiche*, ed. V. Volterra, G. Loria, D. Gambioli, Dante Alighieri, Milano, 1911–12.

[20] ——, "Metodo per misurare la lemniscata I," *Giornale di Litterati d'Italia*, vol. 29(1717), p. 258, in *Opere matematiche*, vol. 2, pp. 293–297.

[21] ——, "Metodo per misurare la lemniscata II," *Giornale di Litterati d'Italia*, vol. 30(1718), p. 87, in *Opere matematiche*, vol. 2, pp. 304–313.

[22] Fricke, R., "Elliptische Funktionen," *Enzyklo. Math. Wissenschaften*, vol. II B3, pp. 177–345, Teubner, Leipzig, 1901–1921.

[23] Greenhill, A.G., *The applications of elliptic functions*, Macmillan and Co., London, 1892.

[24] Houzel, C., "Fonctions elliptiques et intégral abéliennes," in *Abrégé d'histoire des mathématiques 1700–1900* vol. II, Chapter VII, ed. Jean Dieudonné, Hermann, Paris, 1978.

[25] Leibniz, G., "De Linea Isochrona, in qua grave sine acceleratione descendit, et de Controversia cum Dn. Abbate de Conti," *Acta Eruditorum*, 1689, pp. 195–198, also in *Mathematische Schriften*, ed. K. Gerhard, G. Olms, Hildesheim, Vol. V, pp. 234–237.

[26] Legendre, A. M., *Traité des fonctions elliptiques et des intégrales Eulériennes avec des tables pour en faciliter le calcul numérique*, Huzard-Courcier, Paris, 1825–1828.

[27] Oldfather, W.A., C.A. Ellis and D.M. Brown, "Leonard Euler's Elastic Curves," *Isis*, 20(1933), pp. 72–160.

[28] Prasolov, V. and Y. Solovyev, *Elliptic Functions and Elliptic Integrals*, American Mathematical Society, Providence, 1997.

[29] Serret, J.-A., *Cours de calcul différential et intégral*, t. 1-3, Gauthier-Villars, Paris, 1879.

Euler's Observations on Harmonic Progressions[1]

Mark McKinzie

Given widespread interest in the harmonic series as a mathematical object and Leonhard Euler's place in the history of mathematics as a supreme mathematician (*analysis incarnate*), it is natural to expect him to make interesting observations when he discusses the harmonic series in one of the earliest endeavors of his mathematical career. Indeed, his article "De progressionibus harmonicus observationes" (which we will refer to throughout as E43, being the 43rd entry in Eneström's index of Euler's work), has several quite notable results:

- Euler shows that the harmonic series has an infinite sum by analyzing whether the sum of the tail of the series is negligible—in effect, using a nascent Cauchy Condition. While this is certainly not the first discovery of the divergence of the harmonic series, it appears to be the first proof of the divergence of a series based on this style of argument.

- Euler studies the relationship between the harmonic series and the natural logarithm; his article is the first to identify and approximate the quantity $1 + \frac{1}{2} + \cdots + \frac{1}{i} - \log(i+1)$ (where i is infinite); Euler shows that this quantity is finite and constant (it doesn't depend on the choice of the infinite quantity i), and approximates its value as 0.577218. Throughout E43, Euler uses the symbol C for this constant [perhaps because it arises from an integration problem]; most modern texts use γ in reference to it.

- Incidental to the above, Euler produces a variety of interesting conditionally convergent, but not alternating, series, examples of which rarely appear in the traditional calculus curriculum.

In this article, we will follow Euler's text, interspersing some historical and mathematical commentary along the way.

---

[1] Based on a talk given at the Euler2k+2 meeting of the Euler Society, Rumford, ME, August 2002.

Euler and the infinite

One challenge facing the modern reader of Euler's early work in the calculus is his explicit use of an arithmetic which includes infinite and infinitesimal numbers, both as numerical quantities and as indices of various operations (the number of summands in a series, or the degree of a polynomial, for example). It is a common practice to translate such arguments into modern contexts (either transforming them to arguments using limits of finite quantities in the style of modern mainstream calculus, or directly using the hyperreal number systems of non-standard analysis). Such an exercise, while providing some insight into the modern analytic system, reveals somewhat less about the original text and its content. In this article, I have chosen to reproduce Euler's mathematical arguments essentially verbatim, without attempting to alter Euler's presentation to conform to modern notions of rigor.

What does Euler mean when he refers to i as an infinite number? Is Euler using this as an abbreviation for a limit process? Is Euler's notion of infinity consistent with Cantor's? Or does Euler have in mind some other notion, perhaps an extension of the real continuum to include such numbers? These questions have no simple answers (or rather, none that are not controversial), for Euler himself is not always clear on this issue, and his views on such foundational questions evolve over the course of his career.

What follows is a faithful presentation of his thoughts on the harmonic series from early in his development as a mathematician.

The harmonic series has an infinite sum

Euler opens E43 by defining a harmonic progression to be a series of the form

$$\frac{c}{a}, \quad \frac{c}{a+b}, \quad \frac{c}{a+2b}, \quad \frac{c}{a+3b}, \dots,$$

that is, a series in which each term is the harmonic mean of its neighbors. From the context of several passages in E43, it is clear that Euler is assuming that the parameters a, b, and c are finite and positive.

Section 2 of E43 presents a criterion for determining whether an infinite sum takes on a finite or infinite value:

> 2. Though in these series the terms perpetually decrease, nevertheless the sum of this kind of series, continued infinitely, is always infinite. This indicates one does not need a method of summing these series, yet the truth unquestionably is manifest from the following principle:
>
> A series which has a finite sum when continued infinitely, even if it is continued further [etiamsi ea duplo longius continuetur], it receives insignificant growth, but in fact that which is added after infinitely many terms will be infinitely small. Indeed unless it has this property, the sum of the series infinitely continued was not bounded and therefore not finite. Consequently, if continued beyond where infinitesimal terms appear, the additional sum is of finite magnitude, the sum of the series ought necessarily be infinite. Therefore from this initial investigation we obtain, whether a series and its sum is infinite or whether it is finite. [2][2]

---

[2]I have used my own translations for all quoted passages in this article.

What Euler here describes, then, is a scheme for determining whether a given infinite series has a finite sum. Given the sum of the first infinitely many terms $a_1 + a_2 + a_3 + \cdots + a_i$, Euler considers the additional growth gotten by extending the sum still farther $(a_1 + a_2 + a_3 + \cdots + a_i) + a_{i+1} + a_{i+2} + \cdots$. Euler considers it a necessary and sufficient condition for the series to have a finite sum, that the additional terms have a negligible (i.e., infinitely small) sum.

Two aspects of Euler's criterion have drawn comment. Firstly, Euler seems to have merely argued for the necessity of his condition: he argues for the statement 'if the series has a finite sum, then the tail sums must be negligible' and for its contrapositive 'if the tail sum isn't negligible the series can't have a finite sum'. That Euler regards the criterion as being both necessary *and* sufficient will become clear once we see his examples below. Secondly, there is a translation issue of some controversy. A literal translation would render the phrase "*etiamsi ea duplo longius continuetur*" as "*even if it is continued twice as far*"; in terms of modern notions, this is akin to demanding of a series $\sum a_i$ that for large enough i,

$$a_{i+1} + a_{i+2} + \cdots + a_{2i} < \varepsilon$$

A looser translation might merely demand that if the series is extended (an arbitrary amount) further, the augment is negligible; in effect, for i and $m > i$ chosen sufficiently large,

$$a_{i+1} + a_{i+2} + \cdots + a_m < \varepsilon$$

Fortunately, we do not have to choose arbitrarily between these mutually inconsistent readings of the condition, for we have several examples to hand in which Euler applies the condition to specific examples; in each case, he examines the sum

$$a_{i+1} + a_{i+2} + \cdots + a_{ni} < \varepsilon$$

that is, rather than extending the series *twice* as far, he is going to extend it *by some arbitrary multiple* of the initial index.

Euler applies this convergence criterion to two examples; his arguments illustrate his use of the condition as being both necessary and sufficient for the series to have a finite sum, and they show what Euler meant by the ambiguous phrasing "*etiamsi ea duplo longius continuetur*." Euler's method is as follows: he considers the sum from the ith term to the nith term, and finds both lower and upper bounds for that sum. If he can show that the lower bound is nonzero, he concludes that the original series has an infinite sum. Alternately, if he can show that the upper bound is negligible, he concludes that the original series has a finite sum.

3. And so the series

$$\frac{c}{a}, \quad \frac{c}{a+b}, \quad \frac{c}{a+2b}, \quad \text{etc.}$$

is continued infinitely to the infinitesimal term $\frac{c}{a+(i-1)b}$, where i denotes an infinite number, which is the index of this term. Now this series is continued further, from the term $\frac{c}{a+ib}$ to the term $\frac{c}{a+(ni-1)b}$, whose index is ni. These additional terms above are $(n-1)i$ in number. Their sum is certainly less than

$$\frac{(n-1)ic}{a+ib},$$

and greater than

$$\frac{(n-1)ic}{a+(ni-1)b}.$$

However, since i is infinitely large, a vanishes in both denominators. Wherefore the sum is greater than

$$\frac{(n-1)c}{nb},$$

but less than

$$\frac{(n-1)c}{b}.$$

From which we observe that this sum is bounded [away from zero] and so consequently the proposed series $\frac{c}{a}$, $\frac{c}{a+b}$ etc. when continued infinitely has an infinitely large sum.

Here Euler has started with the sum of the first i terms of the series, and extended it to the sum of the first ni terms. He is able to conclude that the series has an infinite sum by showing that this extension is bounded below by a positive number, as follows. Each of the $(n-1)i$ summands in the extension is bounded below by the last summand $\frac{c}{a+(ni-1)b}$, and hence the sum of all those terms is bounded by $\frac{(n-1)ic}{a+(ni-1)b}$. Finally, since

$$\frac{(n-1)ic}{a+(ni-1)b} = \frac{(n-1)c}{\frac{a}{i}+(n-\frac{1}{i})b}$$

and since i was chosen as infinite, both the a and the -1 in the denominator vanish, leaving a lower bound for the additional sum of $\frac{(n-1)c}{nb}$. Since b and c were the finite parameters for the original series in question, and n was the chosen multiple for our series extension, this sum is finite and nonzero; hence Euler concludes that harmonic series diverge. (In particular, for the 'standard' harmonic series, with $a = b = c = 1$, Euler has shown that $\frac{1}{i+1} + \frac{1}{i+2} + \cdots + \frac{1}{ni} > \frac{n-1}{n}$.)

A family of series, some convergent, some divergent

Euler next applies this method to series of the form

$$\frac{c}{a} + \frac{c}{a+b} + \frac{c}{a+2^\alpha b} + \cdots + \frac{c}{a+i^\alpha b}$$

Considering the sum past the first i summands to the nith summand, he notes that these $(n-1)i$ summands will be bounded *below* by the last summand of the tail $\frac{c}{a+(ni-1)^\alpha b}$ and bounded *above* by the first summand of the tail $\frac{c}{a+i^\alpha b}$, and hence (after some simplifications) their sum will be greater than $\frac{(n-1)c}{n^\alpha i^{\alpha-1}b}$ and less than $\frac{(n-1)c}{i^{\alpha-1}b}$. From this, Euler concludes that if $\alpha > 1$, the tail will be infinitely small (since the upper bound for the sum involves division by a positive power of an infinite number); if $\alpha < 1$, the tail will be infinite (since the lower bound for the sum involves division by a negative power of an infinite number); and finally, if $\alpha = 1$, we have the harmonic series previously addressed.[3]

---

[3]It is worth noting here that for Euler's inferences regarding α to be valid, he must assume that n itself is a *finite* number, which for Euler is a significant restriction. Indeed, in modern terms, the condition that for Σa_i and for a *fixed* finite value of n, given ε one can choose i sufficiently large so that $a_{i+1} + \cdots + a_{ni} < \varepsilon$, is *not* equivalent to the modern Cauchy Condition. A debate on this point occurred in print in the journal *Bibliotheca Mathematica* in 1905 between Eneström and Pringsheim, with Pringsheim's analysis [7] holding sway.

From this discussion, it is clear that Euler regards his criterion from section 2 to be both necessary and also sufficient for a series to have a finite sum.

The relation between the natural logarithm and the sum of a harmonic series

Under the guise of wanting to determine a precise value for the sum

$$\frac{c}{a + ib} + \frac{c}{a + (i + 1)b} + \cdots + \frac{c}{a + (ni - 1)b},$$

in section 6 of E43, Euler introduces a function

$$s(i) = \frac{c}{a} + \frac{c}{a + b} + \cdots + \frac{c}{a + (i - 1)b}.$$

He notes that if i is increased by 1, then s will be increased by $\frac{c}{a+ib}$, and from this Euler concludes that $di/ds = 1/\frac{c}{a+ib}$ or $ds = \frac{c\,di}{a+ib}$. Integrating the latter expression yields a closed-form equation for $s(i)$, namely $s(i) = C + \frac{c}{b}\ln(a + ib)$, where C is a constant. (Euler's next steps will lay the groundwork for showing that in fact this constant C is finite, and for finding numerical approximations of its value.)

Some interesting conditionally convergent series

Having argued that

$$\frac{c}{a} + \frac{c}{a + b} + \cdots + \frac{c}{a + (i - 1)b} = C + \frac{c}{b}\ln(a + ib),$$

Euler notes that the sum of the ith through the nith terms will be $\left(C + \frac{c}{b}\ln(a + nib)\right) - \left(C + \frac{c}{b}\ln(a + ib)\right)$. This expression simplifies to $\frac{c}{b}\ln\left(\frac{a+nib}{a+ib}\right)$, which (since i is infinite and a finite) is the same as $\frac{c}{b}\ln(n)$.

Euler applies this relation between the logarithm and a difference of two series to find a variety of interesting conditionally convergent series. For the (standard) harmonic series $1 + \frac{1}{2} + \frac{1}{3} + \frac{1}{4} +$ etc. the previous results with $c = a = b = 1$ yield

$$\ln(n) = \left(1 + \frac{1}{2} + \frac{1}{3} + \cdots + \frac{1}{ni}\right) - \left(1 + \frac{1}{2} + \frac{1}{3} + \cdots + \frac{1}{i}\right)$$

Euler notes that there are n times more summands in the first series than in the second, and so he will subtract each summand in the second series from the corresponding group of n summands in the first series as follows:

$$\ln n = 1 + \frac{1}{2} + \cdots + \frac{1}{n} + \frac{1}{n + 1} + \cdots + \frac{1}{2n} + \frac{1}{2n + 1} + \cdots + \frac{1}{3n} + \text{etc.}$$

$$- 1 \qquad\qquad -\frac{1}{2} \qquad\qquad -\frac{1}{3}$$

For various values of n, the following series arise:

$$\ln 2 = 1 - \frac{1}{2} + \frac{1}{3} - \frac{1}{4} + \frac{1}{5} - \frac{1}{6} + \frac{1}{7} - \frac{1}{8} + \frac{1}{9} - \frac{1}{10} + \frac{1}{11} - \frac{1}{12} + \text{etc.},$$

$$\ln 3 = 1 + \frac{1}{2} - \frac{2}{3} + \frac{1}{4} + \frac{1}{5} - \frac{2}{6} + \frac{1}{7} + \frac{1}{8} - \frac{2}{9} + \frac{1}{10} + \frac{1}{11} - \frac{2}{12} + \text{etc.},$$

$$\ln 4 = 1 + \frac{1}{2} + \frac{1}{3} - \frac{3}{4} + \frac{1}{5} + \frac{1}{6} + \frac{1}{7} - \frac{3}{8} + \frac{1}{9} + \frac{1}{10} + \frac{1}{11} - \frac{3}{12} + \text{etc.},$$

$$\ln 5 = 1 + \frac{1}{2} + \frac{1}{3} + \frac{1}{4} - \frac{4}{5} + \frac{1}{6} + \frac{1}{7} + \frac{1}{8} + \frac{1}{9} - \frac{4}{10} + \frac{1}{11} + \frac{1}{12} + \text{etc.},$$

$$\ln 6 = 1 + \frac{1}{2} + \frac{1}{3} + \frac{1}{4} + \frac{1}{5} - \frac{5}{6} + \frac{1}{7} + \frac{1}{8} + \frac{1}{9} + \frac{1}{10} + \frac{1}{11} - \frac{5}{12} + \text{etc.},$$

etc.

"In this way, series which converge to logarithmic numbers are easily found."[2, §8]

It isn't terribly difficult to show that indeed these series do converge, and as well to verify that their sums are the corresponding logarithms, although in fact the computer algebra system Maple only explicitly recognized the series for $\ln 2$, $\ln 3$, $\ln 4$, and $\ln 6$; for other examples (through $n = 40$), Maple produces far more complicated closed-form expressions for the numerical sums, ones whose numerical values indeed correspond to $\ln(n)$.

Euler gives an alternate derivation of these series results toward the end of E43. His argument (which applied to the general harmonic progression $\frac{c}{a} + \frac{c}{a+b} + \cdots$) can be greatly simplified if we focus only on the standard harmonic series: Since $\ln(1 + x) = x - \frac{1}{2}x^2 + \frac{1}{3}x^3 - \frac{1}{4}x^4 + \cdots$, it follows that

$$\ln(1 - x) = -\left(x + \frac{1}{2}x^2 + \frac{1}{3}x^3 + \frac{1}{4}x^4 + \cdots\right)$$

and

$$\ln(1 - x^n) = -\left(x^n + \frac{1}{2}x^{2n} + \frac{1}{3}x^{3n} + \frac{1}{4}x^{4n} + \cdots\right)$$

Thus

$$\ln\left(\frac{1 - x^n}{1 - x}\right) = \left(x + \frac{1}{2}x^2 + \frac{1}{3}x^3 + \frac{1}{4}x^4 + \cdots\right) - \left(x^n + \frac{1}{2}x^{2n} + \frac{1}{3}x^{3n} + \frac{1}{4}x^{4n} + \cdots\right)$$

On the left, we have $\ln(1 + x + x^2 + \cdots + x^{n-1})$. On the right, if we combine like terms we get a power series whose coefficients correspond to the summands for the numerical series that Euler has created:

$$1x + \frac{1}{2}x^2 + \cdots + \frac{1}{n}x^n + \frac{1}{n+1}x^{n+1} + \cdots + \frac{1}{2n}x^{2n} + \frac{1}{2n+1}x^{2n+1} + \cdots + \frac{1}{3n}x^{3n} + \text{etc.}$$

$$- 1x^n \qquad\qquad -\frac{1}{2}x^{2n} \qquad\qquad -\frac{1}{3}x^{3n} \cdots$$

Setting $x = 1$ yields the various series formulas for $\ln(n)$.

Series involving $\ln((i + 1)/i)$; computing C

Euler is interested in evaluating

$$C = 1 + \frac{1}{2} + \frac{1}{3} + \frac{1}{4} + \cdots + \frac{1}{i} - \ln(i + 1)$$

exactly, and turns his attention to finding ways of expressing each of the summands $\frac{1}{n}$ in terms of series. Section 9 of E43 applies relationships between various logarithms (e.g., that $\ln 6 = \ln 2 + \ln 3$) to generate relationships among sums of rationals; for example, since $0 = 2 \cdot \ln 2 - \ln 4$, we have

$$0 = 2 \cdot \left(1 - \frac{1}{2} + \frac{1}{3} - \frac{1}{4} + \frac{1}{5} - \cdots\right) - \left(1 + \frac{1}{2} + \frac{1}{3} - \frac{3}{4} + \frac{1}{5} + \frac{1}{6} + \frac{1}{7} - \frac{3}{8} + \cdots\right)$$

so that

$$0 = 1 - \frac{3}{2} + \frac{1}{3} + \frac{1}{4} + \frac{1}{5} - \frac{3}{6} + \cdots$$

or equivalently

$$\frac{1}{2} = \frac{1}{3} + \frac{1}{4} + \frac{1}{5} - \frac{3}{6} + \frac{1}{7} + \frac{1}{8} + \frac{1}{9} - \frac{3}{10} + \cdots$$

Likewise, by combining the series for $\ln 6$, $\ln 2$, and $\ln 3$, Euler finds that

$$0 = \ln 6 - \ln 2 - \ln 3 =$$

$$\left(1 + \frac{1}{2} + \frac{1}{3} + \frac{1}{4} + \frac{1}{5} - \frac{5}{6} + \cdots\right)$$

$$-\left(1 - \frac{1}{2} + \frac{1}{3} - \frac{1}{4} + \frac{1}{5} - \frac{1}{6} + \cdots\right)$$

$$-\left(1 + \frac{1}{2} - \frac{2}{3} + \frac{1}{4} + \frac{1}{5} - \frac{2}{6} + \cdots\right)$$

which becomes

$$0 = 1 - \frac{1}{2} - \frac{2}{3} - \frac{1}{4} + \frac{1}{5} + \frac{2}{6} + \frac{1}{7} - \frac{1}{8} - \frac{2}{9} - \frac{1}{10} + \cdots$$

or

$$1 = \frac{1}{2} + \frac{2}{3} + \frac{1}{4} - \frac{1}{5} - \frac{2}{6} - \frac{1}{7} + \frac{1}{8} + \frac{2}{9} + \frac{1}{10} - \text{etc.},$$

Euler's goal in this section would seem to be that of finding series of rationals which converge to 1, 1/2, 1/3, etc., in hopes that the sums of these series would yield patterns that would give insight into the harmonic series. However, after building just a few examples, Euler abandons that line of inquiry in favor of the following: he presents series involving logarithms of the form $\ln \frac{1+i}{i}$, each solved for $\frac{1}{i}$. For example, from the series for $\ln 2$, we have

$$1 = \ln 2 + \frac{1}{2} - \frac{1}{3} + \frac{1}{4} - \frac{1}{5} + \frac{1}{6} - \frac{1}{7} + \cdots$$

Euler next presents

$$\frac{1}{2} = \ln \frac{3}{2} + \frac{1}{2 \cdot 4} - \frac{1}{3 \cdot 8} + \frac{1}{4 \cdot 16} - \frac{1}{5 \cdot 32} + \cdots,$$

which appears to be an instance of the identities

$$\ln(1 + \frac{1}{i}) = \frac{1}{i} - \frac{1}{2 \cdot i^2} + \frac{1}{3 \cdot i^3} - \frac{1}{4 \cdot i^4} + \frac{1}{5 \cdot i^5} - \cdots,$$

and

$$\frac{1}{i} = \ln\frac{i+1}{i} + \frac{1}{2 \cdot i^2} - \frac{1}{3 \cdot i^3} + \frac{1}{4 \cdot i^4} - \frac{1}{5 \cdot i^5} + \cdots$$

(Euler doesn't make explicit how he had generated the series

$$\frac{1}{2} = \ln\frac{3}{2} + \frac{1}{2 \cdot 4} - \frac{1}{3 \cdot 8} + \frac{1}{4 \cdot 16} + \cdots;$$

attempts to generate it from the series he had obtained earlier for $\ln 3$ and $\ln 2$ proved fruitless.) Thus we have a parade of series expansions corresponding to the terms of the harmonic series:

$$1 = \ln 2 + \frac{1}{2} - \frac{1}{3} + \frac{1}{4} - \frac{1}{5} + \frac{1}{6} - \frac{1}{7} + \text{etc.}$$

$$\frac{1}{2} = \ln\frac{3}{2} + \frac{1}{2 \cdot 4} - \frac{1}{3 \cdot 8} + \frac{1}{4 \cdot 16} - \frac{1}{5 \cdot 32} + \text{etc.}$$

$$\frac{1}{3} = \ln\frac{4}{3} + \frac{1}{2 \cdot 9} - \frac{1}{3 \cdot 27} + \frac{1}{4 \cdot 81} - \frac{1}{5 \cdot 243} + \text{etc.}$$

$$\frac{1}{4} = \ln\frac{5}{4} + \frac{1}{2 \cdot 16} - \frac{1}{3 \cdot 64} + \frac{1}{4 \cdot 256} - \frac{1}{5 \cdot 1024} + \text{etc.}$$

$$\vdots$$

$$\frac{1}{i} = \ln\frac{i+1}{i} + \frac{1}{2 \cdot i^2} - \frac{1}{3 \cdot i^3} + \frac{1}{4 \cdot i^4} - \frac{1}{5 \cdot i^5} + \text{etc.}$$

Adding these equations together, combining terms on the right-hand side in the natural way, Euler concludes that

$$1 + \frac{1}{2} + \frac{1}{3} + \cdots + \frac{1}{i} = \ln(i+1) + \frac{1}{2}\left(1 + \frac{1}{4} + \frac{1}{9} + \frac{1}{16} + \cdots + \frac{1}{i^2}\right)$$

$$- \frac{1}{3}\left(1 + \frac{1}{8} + \frac{1}{27} + \frac{1}{64} + \cdots + \frac{1}{i^3}\right)$$

$$+ \frac{1}{4}\left(1 + \frac{1}{16} + \frac{1}{81} + \frac{1}{256} + \cdots + \frac{1}{i^4}\right)$$

$$\text{etc.}$$

Earlier, Euler had shown that that $1 + \frac{1}{2} + \frac{1}{3} + \cdots + \frac{1}{i} = \ln(1+i) + C$ when i is infinite by integrating $ds = \frac{c\,di}{a+ib}$. The preceding argument gives a means of computing the constant

C, namely

$$C = + \frac{1}{2}\left(1 + \frac{1}{4} + \frac{1}{9} + \frac{1}{16} + \cdots + \frac{1}{i^2}\right)$$

$$- \frac{1}{3}\left(1 + \frac{1}{8} + \frac{1}{27} + \frac{1}{64} + \cdots + \frac{1}{i^3}\right)$$

$$+ \frac{1}{4}\left(1 + \frac{1}{16} + \frac{1}{81} + \frac{1}{256} + \cdots + \frac{1}{i^4}\right)$$

etc.

Since each of the series $\sum 1/k^p$ converges, Euler concludes that the constant C is finite, since we have represented C as the sum of a convergent alternating series; from the above representation Euler finds that $C = 0.577218$.

Why isn't it called 'The Euler Criterion' for series convergence?

One is tempted to cite Stigler's Law of Eponymy[4] in this regard, but there are more compelling reasons. As stated and applied in E43, the criterion given is not completely correct, a point first made by Pringsheim [7] in 1905. Pringsheim noted that if we apply Euler's argument to the series $\sum \frac{1}{k \ln k}$, the sum from the ith term to the nith term would be

$$\frac{1}{(i+1)\ln(i+1)} + \cdots + \frac{1}{ni \ln(ni)}$$

with each of these $(n-1)i$ summands bounded above by $\frac{1}{(i+1)\ln(i+1)}$. Thus the entire sum is bounded above by $\frac{(n-1)i}{(i+1)\ln(i+1)}$, which is essentially $\frac{n-1}{\ln(i+1)}$. For i infinite (and here the finiteness of n is crucial), we would conclude that the sum of these terms is negligible. Thus Euler would be led to the erroneous conclusion that the series $\sum \frac{1}{k \ln k}$ has a finite sum.

It is easy enough, once one is aware of such examples, to find a reasonable modification of Euler's criterion and arrive at a complete and correct convergence criterion (Laugwitz has written extensively on this point; see for example [5]). However, there is no evidence that Euler, his contemporaries, or the generation of mathematicians immediately following were interested in Euler's analysis of tails of infinite series. Gustaf Eneström, in commenting on Euler's potential priority for the discovery of the Cauchy Condition, noted that

> I have looked in vain for a reference to the Eulerian convergence condition in the accessible mathematical writings of the 18th century. The discovery appears therefore to remain completely unheeded, and the mathematicians who attack the convergence question at the start of the 19th century were surely not influenced by Euler. [1]

This lack of interest speaks to several issues:

- **Why didn't Euler make more of the convergence condition?** For indeed, so far as I am aware, Euler never returned to this topic in any of his subsequent work. One likely

---

[4]Named for Stephen Stigler, the claim that no scientific result is actually named for its originator. Naturally, this claim did not originate with Stigler, who credited Thomas Merton with its discovery.[9]

reason is as follows: for most series that Euler worked with, he was perfectly able to determine whether their sums were finite or infinite by more direct means; in particular, during the period in which E43 was being written, Euler was exploring the relationship between infinite series and improper integrals, and would have had at hand very powerful methods (e.g., the 'Euler-Maclaurin series summation formula') for deciding such questions.

One further aspect of the above: the Cauchy condition plays its most significant role as a theoretical tool, allowing one to describe convergence of a series (or sequence) without making direct reference to the limit value itself. The traditional epsilon-delta definition of series convergence over the reals makes explicit reference to the limit value; one defines what it means *for a series (or sequence) to converge to the number L*, and then based on that definition proves as a consequence the Cauchy Condition which guarantees that a series (or sequence) of reals converges *to some limiting value*. The Cauchy Condition becomes a central tool to the foundations of 19th century mathematics in that it allows one to extend the rational numbers to a complete continuum, constructing the reals as equivalence classes of Cauchy sequences of rationals, avoiding the circularity intrinsic to the modern definition of a convergent series or sequence. Such foundational questions were not part of the mathematical culture of Euler's era, and hence the potential of Euler's nascent Cauchy Condition would not have been recognized.

- **Why weren't subsequent generations of mathematicians aware of Euler's work on the convergence condition?** This question is rather interesting, for Euler's article on harmonic progressions is notable for its introduction of the constant gamma.

One conjecture centers on the fact that many of Euler's discoveries were most widely studied from his textbooks rather than his research articles (a point argued in [6]). If the mathematicians who followed Euler used *other* sources for their exposure to gamma, then they would not have seen Euler's analysis of the harmonic series and its infinite sum. However, one must note that much of the historical literature on gamma *does* cite Euler's original article on the topic, without mentioning the initial work on series convergence (Glaisher's article [3] from 1872 is typical in this regard). The earliest commentary on Euler's potential priority for the Cauchy Condition is Richard Reiff, writing in 1889, in his *Geschichte der unendlichen Reihen*, a history of infinite numerical series. Even most modern commentaries on the number gamma (or on the history of series for that matter) neglect to comment on Euler's convergence criterion (c.f., Stammbach's history of the harmonic series [8], or Havil's extensive monograph on gamma [4]). One presumes that modern commentators neglect to mention Euler's convergence criterion because it appears to be incorrect as stated; in any event, this is a phenomenon of limited concern.

However, why Euler's presentation of a series convergence condition wasn't the subject of contemporary commentary remains an elusive yet important question. That several mathematicians (Bolzano, da Cunha, Fourier, and of course Cauchy) arrived at the 'Cauchy' Condition around the beginning of the 19th century is well known, and much has been written about the question of the independence of these discoveries. To my knowledge, the question of the influence of Euler's article E43 on these mathematicians has not been addressed, and (if such influence occurred) would provide a natural explanation for such apparently independent simultaneous discovery.

References

[1] Gustav Eneström, Über eine von Euler aufgestellte allgemeine Konvergenzbedingung, *Bibliotheca Mathematica* **6** (1905), 186–189.

[2] Leonhard Euler, De progressionibus harmonicus observationes, *Commentarii Academiæ Scientarium Petropolitanæ* **9** (1734) 1741, Reprinted in *Opera Omnia,* series 1, volume 14, 87–100.

[3] James W. L. Glaisher, On the history of Euler's constant, *Messenger of Mathematics* (n.s.) **1** (1872), 25–30.

[4] Julian Havil, *Gamma: Exploring Euler's Constant*, Princeton University Press, 2003.

[5] Detlef Laugwitz, Euler und das "Cauchysche" Konvergenzkriterium, *Abh. Math. Sem. Univ. Hamburg* **45** (1976) 91–95.

[6] ——, On the historical development of infinitesimal mathematics, *Amer. Math. Monthly* **104** (1997), 447-455.

[7] Alfred Pringsheim, Über ein Eulersches Konvergenzkriterium, *Bibliotheca Mathematica* **6** (1905), 252–256.

[8] Urs Stammbach, Die harmonische Reihe: Historisches und Mathematisches, *Elem. Math.* **54** (1999), 93–106.

[9] Stephen Stigler, *Statistics on the Table: The History of Statistical Concepts and Methods*, Harvard University Press, 1999.

Origins of a classic formalist argument: power series expansions of the logarithmic and exponential functions[1]

Mark McKinzie

One of the Euler's best known works is his *Introductio in analysin infinitorum* [8] of 1748, a textbook intended in part as a precalculus text, to prepare the reader to take on the subtleties of the calculus. Chapter VII of Euler's *Introductio* gives the construction of power series expansions for the exponential and logarithmic functions, using the binomial theorem and the arithmetic of infinite and infinitesimal numbers rather than the differential calculus. These arguments have been widely recounted (in source books and history texts) as paradigm examples of Euler's methodology for working with infinitary processes and, more generally, as defining examples of mathematical formalism, characteristic of 18th century tastes for mathematical argumentation and rigor. In this article, we trace these power series derivations to their original appearance in print (a 1695 article by Edmond Halley), and show Halley's inspiration for developing the method. Surprisingly, the formal derivation of the logarithmic power series is rooted in two traditional numerical techniques: Briggs' construction of tables of logarithms, and Halley's generalization of Newton's method for approximating roots of equations.

Euler on the power series for a^x

Euler's treatment of the exponential function is found in sections 114–116 of the *Introductio in analysin infinitorum* (1748).[2] Euler starts with a fixed base $a > 1$, and considers an infinitesimal power ω of a. We know that this power differs from 1 by an infinitesimal, but we don't know whether that infinitesimal will be greater than or less than ω. Euler introduces a parameter k (depending on a), and sets $a^\omega = 1 + k\omega$. [The reader who

---

[1] Based on a talk given at the 2001 Joint Mathematics Meetings in New Orleans.

[2] While in most matters I have followed John Blanton's translation of Euler's text, I have restored the notation to that of Euler's original. The one exception to this practice: I have used the modern notation "$\log_a(1 + x)$" (and similarly "$\log(1 + x)$" for the common logarithm) in lieu of Euler's "$l(1 + x)$".

knows calculus will recognize k as $\frac{f(0+\omega)-f(0)}{\omega}$, that is, essentially $f'(0)$, for the function $f(x) = a^x$.]

For any finite number z, set $i = \frac{z}{\omega}$, an infinite number. Now $a^z = (a^\omega)^i = \left(1 + \frac{kz}{i}\right)^i$; as i is infinite, when we expand this last expression using the binomial theorem we obtain an infinite series:

$$a^z = (1 + \frac{kz}{i})^i$$
$$= 1 + \frac{1}{1}kz + \frac{1(i-1)}{1 \cdot 2i}k^2z^2 + \frac{1(i-1)(i-2)}{1 \cdot 2i \cdot 3i}k^3z^3 + \frac{1(i-1)(i-2)(i-3)}{1 \cdot 2i \cdot 3i \cdot 4i}k^4z^4 + \cdots.$$

Further, i being infinite implies that $\frac{i-1}{2i} = \frac{1}{2}$, $\frac{i-2}{3i} = \frac{1}{3}$, $\frac{i-3}{4i} = \frac{1}{4}$, and so on, yielding the expansion

$$a^z = 1 + \frac{kz}{1} + \frac{k^2z^2}{1 \cdot 2} + \frac{k^3z^3}{1 \cdot 2 \cdot 3} + \frac{k^4z^4}{1 \cdot 2 \cdot 3 \cdot 4} + \cdots.$$

Finally, Euler notes that if we choose our base a so that the corresponding value of k is one, setting $z = 1$ reveals that the base a will be

$$a = (1 + \frac{1}{i})^i = 1 + \frac{1}{1} + \frac{1}{1 \cdot 2} + \frac{1}{1 \cdot 2 \cdot 3} + \cdots = 2.71828\ldots = e.$$

We now have

$$e^z = (1 + \frac{z}{i})^i = 1 + \frac{z}{1} + \frac{z^2}{1 \cdot 2} + \frac{z^3}{1 \cdot 2 \cdot 3} + \frac{z^4}{1 \cdot 2 \cdot 3 \cdot 4} + \cdots.$$

Euler on the power series for the logarithm

If one inverts the equation $a^z = (1 + kz/i)^i$, one finds an equation for the logarithm, which in its turn is susceptible to the binomial theorem. For x finite, choose i infinite such that $1 + x = a^{i\omega}$, that is, $a^{i\omega} = (1 + k\omega)^i = 1 + x$. Thus $\log_a(1 + x) = i\omega$. Further, solving $(1 + k\omega)^i = 1 + x$ for ω reveals that $\omega = \frac{1}{k}\left((1 + x)^{1/i} - 1\right)$, and thus $\log_a(1 + x) = \frac{i}{k}\left((1 + x)^{1/i} - 1\right)$.

Euler expands $(1 + x)^{1/i}$ using the binomial theorem:

$$(1+x)^{1/i} = 1 + \frac{1}{i}x - \frac{1(i-1)}{i \cdot 2i}x^2 + \frac{1(i-1)(2i-1)}{i \cdot 2i \cdot 3i}x^3 - \frac{1(i-1)(2i-1)(3i-1)}{i \cdot 2i \cdot 3i \cdot 4i}x^4 + \cdots$$

and concludes that

$$\log_a(1 + x) = \frac{1}{k}\left(\frac{x}{1} - \frac{x^2}{2} + \frac{x^3}{3} - \frac{x^4}{4} + \cdots\right)$$

using the fact that i is infinite to simplify the coefficients. (Again, if we choose our base to be $a = e$, so that $k = 1$, we find the power series for the natural logarithm.)

These types of arguments for the power series for the logarithm and exponential did not originate with Euler; in fact, they are found in a number of early 18th century texts. Somewhat surprisingly, these formalist arguments have their roots in the techniques used by (human) calculators in the construction of logarithmic tables.

Briggs' method for constructing common logarithms

Henry Briggs' *Arithmetica Logarithmica* [2] (published in 1624) contains introductory material outlining methods of constructing logarithmic tables, and is followed by a table of common logarithms for the integers from 1 to 20,000, and from 90,000 to 100,000. Briggs discusses several methods of constructing a table of logarithms; the one relevant to our discussion is outlined in Chapters 6 and 7 of the introduction to Briggs' text. Having set the logarithm of 1 to be 0 and the logarithm of 10 to be 1, Briggs fixes the number of significant digits he intends for his logarithm table. Briggs then presents a table [2, p. 10] (reproduced as Table 1 on page 146) of 2^nth roots of 10 and their common logarithms, indexed by the number of root extractions. The table was built, starting with 10 whose logarithm is 1, by extracting successive square roots (using the traditional paper and pencil algorithm), while dividing the successive logarithms by 2.

In the final two rows of the table, Briggs finds that extracting a square root of a number just larger than one has the same result as dividing the fractional part of that number by 2 (to within the degree of accuracy of the table); if we work with 33 digit expansions as Briggs does, we find that in the 53rd row, the 2^{53}rd root of 10 is

$$1.0000,00000,00000,02556,38298,64006,470,$$

while in the 54th row the 2^{54}th root of 10 is 1.0000,00000,00000,01278,19149,32003,235. It follows that for numbers of this magnitude, the extraction of square roots is a linear function (up to the degree of precision in the table). Since the entries in the column of logarithms have been in a linear relationship throughout the process, this linearity makes it possible to determine the common logarithm of any number of the form $1 + x10^{-15}$, for $x < 1$.

From the third column, Briggs knows the common logarithms of the 2^{53}rd and 2^{54}th roots of 10 to be

$$0.00000,00000,00000,11102,23024,62515,65404$$

and

$$0.00000,00000,00000,05551,11512,31257,82702,$$

respectively. By linearity, we can find the logarithm of $1 + x10^{-15}$, by multiplying x by the ratio of 5551115123125782702 to 12781914932003235, that is, by multiplying by 434294481903251804, and prepending 16 zeros.

For *any* number greater than 1, if one repeatedly extracts square roots of that number, one will eventually obtain a number on the order of $1 + x10^{-15}$, for $x < 1$; one finds the logarithm of this root by multiplying x by 434294481903251804, prepending a decimal point followed by 16 zeros, and repeatedly doubling the result the appropriate number of times.

In Chapter 7 of his work, Briggs notes that this process can be hastened if one first finds a power of one's number which begins with a 1 followed by one or more zeros, as then the number of necessary square root extractions will be reduced. For example, to construct the logarithm of 2, Briggs notes that $2^{10} = 1024$. Dividing this by 1000, Briggs sets out to find the logarithm of 1.024. This he does by repeated root extraction, until the 47th extraction yields the value 1.0000, 00000, 00000, 01685, 16057, 05394, 977.

	Numeri continue Medij inter Denariu & Unitate 10	Logarithmi rationales 1,000
1	31622,77660,16837,93319,98893,54	0,50
2	17782,79410,03892,28011,97304,13	0,25
3	13335,21432,16332,40256,65389,308	0,125
4	11547,81984,68945,81796,61918,213	0,0625
5	10746,07828,32131,74972,13817,6538	0,03125
6	10366,32928,43769,79972,90627,3131	0,01562,5
7	10181,51721,71818,18414,73723,8144	0,00781,25
8	10090,35044,84144,74377,59005,1391	0,00390,625
9	10045,07364,25446,25256,64670,6113	0,00195,3125
10	10022,51148,29291,29154,65611,7367	0,00097,65625
11	10011,24941,39987,98758,85395,51805	0,00048,82812,5
12	10005,62312,60220,86366,18495,91839	0,00024,41406,25
13	10002,81116,78778,01323,99249,64325	0,00012,20703,125
14	10001,40548,51694,72581,62767,32715	0,00006,10351,5625
15	10000,70271,78941,14355,38811,70845	0,00003,05175,78125
16	10000,35135,27746,18566,08581,37077	0,00001,52587,89062,5
17	10000,17567,48442,26738,33846,78274	0,00000,76293,94531,25
18	10000,08783,70363,46121,46574,07431	0,00000,38146,97265,625
19	10000,04391,84217,31672,36281,88083	0,00000,19073,48632,8125
20	10000,02195,91867,55542,03317,07719	0,00000,09536,74316,40625
21	10000,01097,95873,50204,09754,72940	0,00000,04768,37158,20312,5
22	10000,00548,97921,68211,14626,60250,4	0,00000,02384,18579,10156,25
23	10000,00274,48957,07382,95091,25449,9	0,00000,01192,09289,55078,125
24	10000,00137,24477,59510,83282,69572,5	0,00000,00596,04644,77549,0625
25	10000,00068,62238,56210,25737,18748,2	0,00000,00298,02322,38769,53125
26	10000,00034,31119,22218,83912,75020,8	0,00000,00149,01161,19384,76562,5
27	10000,00017,15559,59637,84719,93879,1	0,00000,00074,50580,59692,38281,25
28	10000,00008,57779,79451,03051,17588,8	0,00000,00037,25290,29846,19140,625
29	10000,00004,28889,89633,54198,42901,3	0,00000,00018,62645,14923,09570,3125
30	10000,00002,14444,94793,77767,42970,4	0,00000,00009,31322,57461,54785,15625
31	10000,00001,07222,47391,14050,76926,8	0,00000,00004,65661,28730,77392,57812,5
32	10000,00000,53611,23694,13317,14831,4	0,00000,00002,32830,64365,38696,28906,25
33	10000,00000,26805,61846,70731,51508,7	0,00000,00001,16415,32182,69348,14453,125
34	10000,00000,13402,80923,26383,99277,7	0,00000,00000,58207,66091,34674,07226,5625
35	10000,00000,06701,40461,60946,55519,6	0,00000,00000,29103,83045,67337,03613,28125
36	10000,00000,03350,70230,79911,91730,0	0,00000,00000,14551,91522,83668,51806,64062,5
37	10000,00000,01675,35115,39815,61857,6	0,00000,00000,07275,95761,41834,25903,32031,25
38	10000,00000,00837,67557,69872,72426,9	0,00000,00000,03637,97880,70917,12951,66015,625
39	10000,00000,00418,83778,84927,59087,9	0,00000,00000,01818,98940,35458,56475,83007,8125
40	10000,00000,00209,41889,42461,60262,5	0,00000,00000,00909,49470,17729,28237,91503,90625
41	10000,00000,00104,70944,71230,25311,0	0,00000,00000,00454,74735,08864,64118,95751,95312
42	10000,00000,00052,35472,35614,98950,4	0,00000,00000,00227,37367,54432,32059,47875,97656
43	10000,00000,00026,17736,17807,46048,9	0,00000,00000,00113,68683,77216,16029,73937,98828
44	10000,00000,00013,08868,08903,72167,8	0,00000,00000,00056,84341,88608,08014,86968,99414
45	10000,00000,00006,54434,04451,85869,75	0,00000,00000,00028,42170,94304,04007,43484,49707
46	10000,00000,00003,27217,02225,92881,337	0,00000,00000,00014,21085,47152,02003,71742,24853
47	10000,00000,00001,63608,51112,96427,283	0,00000,00000,00007,10542,73576,01001,85871,12426
48	10000,00000,00000,81804,25556,48210,295	0,00000,00000,00003,55271,36788,00500,92935,56213
49	10000,00000,00000,40902,12778,24104,311	0,00000,00000,00001,77635,68394,00250,46467,78106
50	10000,00000,00000,20451,06389,12051,946	0,00000,00000,00000,88817,84197,00125,23233,89053
51	10000,00000,00000,10225,53194,56025,921 L	0,00000,00000,00000,44408,92098,50062,61616,94526
52	10000,00000,00000,05112,76597,28012,947 M	0,00000,00000,00000,22204,46049,25031,30808,47263
53	10000,00000,00000,02556,38298,64006,470 N	0,00000,00000,00000,11102,23024,62515,65404,23631
54	10000,00000,00000,01278,19149,32003,235 P	0,00000,00000,00000,05551,11512,31257,82702,11815

Table 1. Briggs's computation of the logarithm of $10^{1/2^{54}}$ [2, p. 10]

Briggs multiplies the decimal part by 43429..., and concludes that the logarithm of the $1.024^{1/2^{47}}$ is $0.00000, 00000, 00000, 07318, 55936, 90623, 9368$. Doubling this result 47 times (or simply multiplying by $2^{47} = 140737488355328$), Briggs finds that the logarithm of 1.024 is $0.01029, 99566, 39811, 95265, 27744$, and knows this to be accurate to 17 or 18 decimals. Adding 3 to this, he finds the logarithm of 1024; dividing that result by 10 yields the logarithm of 2:

number	common logarithm
2^{47}th root of 1.024	$0.00000, 00000, 00000, 07318, 55936, 90623, 9368$
1.024	$0.01029, 99566, 39811, 95265, 27744$
1024	$3.01029, 99566, 39811, 95265, 27744$
2	$0.30102, 99956, 63981, 19526, 52774$

Briggs outlines a similar method for building the logarithm of 6, using the fact that $6^9 = 10077696$. He also discusses other methods of building the logarithms of prime numbers from known logarithms, e.g., $2401 = 49 \times 49 = 7^4$, while $2400 = 48 \times 50 = 6 \times 8 \times 5 \times 10$, thus upon building the logarithm of $2401/2400 = 1.00041\bar{6}$, the logarithm of 7 can be found from the constructed logs of 2, 3, 5, and 10. In similar fashion, Briggs constructs the logarithms of all the primes up to 97 [2].

In modern notation, Briggs' method amounts to the following: given a number $1 + x$ greater than 1, whose logarithm to a fixed base is to be found, extract its nth root for n sufficiently large (large enough to obtain a result so near to 1 that the logarithm of that nth root can be found by linear scaling). The logarithm of this root $(1 + x)^{1/n}$ is found by taking a constant multiple of its fractional part:

$$\log_a (1 + x)^{1/n} = C \left((1 + x)^{1/n} - 1 \right)$$

where the constant C depends on the degree of accuracy one demands, as well as the base of the logarithms in question. Finally, one obtains the logarithm of $1 + x$ itself by multiplying by n:

$$\log_a (1 + x) = C \cdot n \left((1 + x)^{1/n} - 1 \right)$$

This formula does not explicitly appear in Briggs' work. Rather, it first appears in the second of a series of articles from the 1690s by Edmond Halley. How Halley came upon this identity is our current focus.

Halley's 1694 article on finding roots of equations

In his article "Methodus Nova Accurata & facilis inveniendi Radices Æquationum quarumcumque generaliter, sine prævia Reductione" [9], from the *Philosophical Transactions* of 1694, Edmond Halley presents a method of approximating nth roots of numbers, using only the arithmetic operations and the extractions of square roots. In addition, Halley extends the method to approximating roots of arbitrary polynomials.

He opens the paper by mentioning similar prior work. He notes that Viète had presented an iterative method of approximating roots of equations, and that this method had been built upon by Harriot and Oughtred. The method of Newton is cited, as presented in

Chapter 94 of Wallis's *Algebra* [16]. Finally, Raphson's 1690 publication *Analysis Æqua-tionum Universalis*, in which appear numerous examples of what is now known as the "Newton-Raphson Algorithm," is mentioned. (Halley merely mentions these sources; he doesn't discuss their mathematics.) All of these methods involve (in effect) linearization of the terms of the equation, and an iterative approximation schema.

Of more direct interest to Halley is a paper by Thomas Fantet de Lagny [5] from the *Journal des Sçavans* in 1692. Lagny's article presents algebraic expressions for approximating cube roots. To approximate the cube root of a given number n, find the largest perfect cube a^3 less than n, and express n as $a^3 + b$. Lagny presents two approximations, namely

$$a + \frac{ab}{3a^3 + b} < \sqrt[3]{a^3 + b} < a + \frac{ab + a}{3a^3 + b + 1}$$

$$\frac{1}{2}a + \sqrt{\frac{1}{4}a^2 + \frac{b-1}{3a}} < \sqrt[3]{a^3 + b} < \frac{1}{2}a + \sqrt{\frac{1}{4}a^2 + \frac{b}{3a}}$$

(which he terms the "rational" and "irrational" approximations, respectively). Lagny's article merely presents these formulæ, without proof, and illustrates their use.

In Halley's 1694 article, he argues for the rational and irrational approximations

$$\sqrt[3]{a^3 + b} \approx a + \frac{ab}{3a^3 + b}$$

$$\sqrt[3]{a^3 + b} \approx \frac{1}{2}a + \sqrt{\frac{1}{4}a^2 + \frac{b}{3a}}$$

as follows: To approximate the cube root of a non-cube, we write the number as $a^3 + b$ (where as before a^3 is the largest integer cube less than the number), and set $\sqrt[3]{a^3 + b} = a + e$. By the choice of a, we know that $0 < e < 1$. Now

$$a^3 + b = (a + e)^3 = a^3 + 3a^2e + 3ae^2 + e^3$$

so that $b = 3a^2e + 3ae^2 + e^3$. Halley notes that as e is less than one, e^3 will be negligible, and so he is left to solve the quadratic

$$b = 3a^2e + 3ae^2$$

for e. The "rational" solution is obtained from this as follows: for a first approximation, he disregards the quadratic term, and solving $b = 3a^2e$ finds that $e = b/3a^2$. (This initial approximation is precisely that which results from applying the Newton-Raphson algorithm to the function $f(x) = x^3 - (a^3 + b)$, with initial estimate $x = a$.) Halley uses this result to get a better approximation: from $b = 3a^2e + 3ae^2$ he concludes that $e = b/(3a^2 + 3ae)$; substituting $b/3a^2$ for e on the right-hand side Halley concludes that

$$e = \frac{b}{3a^2 + 3a \cdot \frac{b}{3a^2}} = \frac{ab}{3a^3 + b},$$

so that $a + e = a + ab/(3a^3 + b)$.

Halley's "irrational" approximation stems from finding an exact solution to the quadratic $b = 3a^2e + 3ae^2$, by means of completing the square. Solving $e^2 + ae = b/3a$, we find that $(e + \frac{1}{2}a)^2 = \frac{b}{3a} + \frac{1}{4}a^2$; Halley takes the positive square root, and adds $\frac{1}{2}a$ to both sides, concluding that

$$a + e = \frac{1}{2}a + \sqrt{\frac{b}{3a} + \frac{1}{4}a^2}.$$

Halley goes on to consider the case where a is too large an approximate solution by looking at $a^3 - b$, but the rational and irrational solutions he derives in this case are equivalent to the formulas derived above if b is allowed to be negative.

Halley extends the method, giving similar approximations for nth roots, namely that

$$\sqrt[n]{a^n + b} \approx \begin{cases} a + \dfrac{ab}{na^n + \frac{n-1}{2} \cdot b} & \text{"rational" solution} \\[3ex] \dfrac{n-2}{n-1}a + \sqrt{\dfrac{2b}{n(n-1)a^{n-2}} + \dfrac{a^2}{(n-1)^2}} & \text{"irrational" solution} \end{cases}$$

(Halley doesn't state these results generally, but the pattern is made clear from the examples with $n = 2, 3, \ldots, 7$.)

Halley also suggests this process might be used more generally on any polynomial equation: given an approximation to a root a, if upon substituting $a + e$ into the equation and multiplying out, the resulting equation has the form

$$b = se + te^2 + ue^3 + ve^4,$$

then one will have the rational approximate solution

$$a + e = a + \frac{sb}{s^2 + tb}$$

and one will have the irrational approximation

$$a + e = a - \frac{\frac{1}{2}s - \sqrt{bt + \frac{1}{4}s^2}}{t}.$$

These formulas result from disregarding all terms of order greater than two (if we presume e to be small), and either approximating the solution of the quadratic (in the rational case as discussed above) or by finding an exact solution to the quadratic by completing the square.

Halley illustrates these methods first for approximating pure roots, and later for solving more general polynomials. One of his examples involves finding the length of the side of a cube whose measure is equal to an "English Gallon," a cube of volume 231 cubic inches.[3] Halley sets $a = 6$ and $b = 15$; a first application of the irrational approximation yields

$$\sqrt[3]{231} \approx \frac{1}{2}a + \sqrt{\frac{1}{4}a^2 + \frac{b}{3a}} = 3 + \sqrt{9 + \frac{15}{18}} \approx 6.1358.$$

[3] At the time, this was one of several standards for volume measure, all going by the name "gallon." In 1707, an Act of Parliament defined the standard wine gallon as follows: "That any round Vessel (commonly called a Cylinder) having an even bottom, and being seven inches diameter throughout, and six inches deep from the top of the inside to the bottom, or any Vessel containing two hundred thirty one cubical inches, and no more, shall be deemed and taken to be a lawful Wine-Gallon." [1] If one equates the volume of such a cylinder with 231 cubic inches, solving for π yields 22/7. Somehow this example of π-related legislation has thus far evaded the vast literature of π ephemera.

A second application of the method (with $a = 6.1358$, $a^3 = 231.000853895$, and $b = -.000853895$) yields

$$\sqrt[3]{231} \approx 3.0679 + \sqrt{9.41201041 - \frac{.000853895}{18.4074}} \approx 6.13579243966.$$

Being able to replace an extremely difficult cube root extraction with two far simpler square root extractions and some modest arithmetic is a significant savings.

In addition to applying these methods iteratively, Halley presents a second means of obtaining better approximate roots. Rather than discarding the higher order terms, one might retain them, placing the linear and quadratic terms on one side of the equation, and obtaining an implicit solution for the augment e in terms of itself by completing the square. When applied to a (specific) quartic equation, Halley notes that this implicit method quadruples the number of correct decimals in the expansion for the root.

Abraham Sharp's contribution

One reaction to Halley's 1694 article on root approximations came from Abraham Sharp, assistant to the Astronomer Royal and noted calculator. Sharp, in correspondence with Euclid Speidell and John Parsons, extended Halley's ideas, and showed how to apply them to computing roots of high index (such as the 2^{47}th root of 1.024, the key step in finding the logarithm of 2). Sharp's letter has not been reprinted, and I have not seen it, but several responses to him *have* been republished in a number of sources (including [4] and [12]), and from them I have arrived at the following reconstruction.

Halley had limited his applications of his method to polynomials of degree 8 or less, and appended to his article a table showing the result of multiplying out $(a+b)^2$, $(a+b)^3$, ..., $(a+b)^8$, for use in expanding the powers of $a+e$ into a polynomial in e. Sharp notes that if one uses the binomial theorem, this limitation of degree is removed, and one can apply Halley's idea to arbitrarily large powers. Sharp then shows how Halley's technique can be used to find the 2^{47}th root of 1.024 (relatively) directly. We do know that during this time period Sharp produced the logarithms of the primes up to 19 to sixty decimal places (c.f., [10, p. 63]), and it appears quite likely that he used his extension of Halley's methods to do so.

To find the 2^{47}th root of 1.024, Sharp would have proceded as follows: let $c = 140737488355328 (= 2^{47})$, and define constants $d = \frac{c-1}{2}$, $f = \frac{c-2}{3}$, $g = \frac{c-3}{4}$, etc.... Taking 1 as our first approximation to the root of $x^c = 1.024$, let $x = 1 + e$ with e small. Then for $(1 + e)^{140737488355328} = 1.024$, by the binomial theorem we have

$$1 + c \cdot e + cd \cdot e^2 + cdf \cdot e^3 + cdfg \cdot e^4 + \cdots = 1.024$$

If we discard terms involving cubic (and higher) powers of e as negligible, we can solve the resulting quadratic by completing the square, resulting in the approximation

$$e = -\frac{1}{2d} + \sqrt{\frac{1}{4d^2} + \frac{.024}{cd}} \approx 0.00000000000000000168531580624021144$$

If we do not discard the higher order terms, we find that

$$cd \cdot e^2 + c \cdot e = 0.024 - cdf \cdot e^3 - cdfg \cdot e^4 - \cdots$$

which upon completing the square yields

$$e = -\frac{1}{2d} + \sqrt{\frac{1}{4d^2} + \frac{.024}{cd} - f \cdot e^3 - fg \cdot e^4 - \cdots}$$

Substituting the previously found approximate value for e, we find an improved value of

$$e \approx 0.00000000000000168516057053949752$$

so that the 2^{47}th root of 1.024 is $1 + e \approx 1.00000000000000168516057053949752$, a result that agrees with that found by Briggs to as many decimal places as Briggs had considered. Thus the work of extracting 47 successive square roots has been replaced with a modest amount of arithmetic, and two square root extractions, a significant advance.

Sharp's letter found its way into Halley's hands, and on March 9th, 1694/5, he wrote the following to Sharp:

> I have seen your curious improvement of the method I published in the *Transactions* of May last, where you have apply'd Mr. Newton's invention of the unciæ [i.e., binomial coefficients] affixt to the members of very high powers, to so good purpose that I cannot believe it can be carried further, and I congratulate you on your happy discovery. But since in your letter you mention the making the [sic] logarithms by this means, give me leave to observe to you, what perhaps you had overlookt, that if instead of 140737488355328 for the index of your power, you use 10000, &c., taken as infinite, and extract by this method the root-bearing unity, the remainder will be Napier's, or the hyperbolick logarithm for that number whose root you extracted. And if you extract the root of the power whose index is assumed 23025851, &c., which is Napier's logarithm of 10, that root unity shall be Briggs his logarithm of the number whose root you extract, wherein you will observe that the only difference between this and the method you lay down will be, that instead of c, d, f, g, &c., you may use c, $\frac{1}{2}c$, $\frac{1}{3}c$, $\frac{1}{4}c$, &c.; and if c be unity with ciphers, then $1 + e + \frac{1}{2}ee + \frac{1}{6}eee + \frac{1}{24}eeee + \frac{1}{120}eeeee + \frac{1}{720}e^6$, being put equal to any number, e shall be Napier's logarithm thereof, which I find results to the same with what Mercator has with the help of Gregory's improvements done in the Quadrature of the Hyperbola and the construction of the logarithms, as you will easily perceive. [4, p. 25] (Also reprinted in [12].)

Halley would go on to publish an article along these lines in the *Philosophical Transactions* of March–May, 1695, essentially contemporaneous to the composition of the above letter to Sharp.

Edmond Halley's power series derivations

Edmond Halley's article "A most compendious and facile Method for Constructing the Logarithms, exemplified and demonstrated from the Nature of Numbers, without any regard to the Hyperbola, with a speedy Method for finding the number from the Logarithm given," appeared in the *Philosophical Transactions* in the March-April-May issue of 1695, shortly after he would have seen Abraham Sharp's letter to John Parsons and Euclid Speidell.

The article specifically sets out to give a non-geometric method of constructing logarithms, and is based on the methods employed when working arithmetically to construct logarithmic tables. The extent to which it succeeded might be inferred by Edmond Stone's comment:

> Dr. Halley…has given their [logarithms] Nature and Construction (after a sort) without any mention of the Hyperbola; tho' it is evident, that all the while he had the Hyperbola and the Mensuration of the asymptotical Spaces under consideration; but rather than expressly mention them, because he will not use Geometrical Figures in an Affair purely Arithmetical (as Mr. Jones, in his Synopsis, says) he perplexes and strains his Reader's Imagination with several almost unintelligible Ways of Expression.... (quoted in [15, p. 300])

It seems likely that Stone's criticisms are aimed at the early parts of Halley's paper, in which he gives an opaque discussion leading to something akin to the equation $\log(1+q) = m \cdot ((1+q)^{1/m} - 1)$, where m is infinite. (Halley doesn't quite get this equation—he leaves off the leading multiplier m—and notes that his result will depend on the choice of infinite m. Halley believes that by varying the choice of m, one will obtain power series for the different species of logarithm. From a modern perspective, he appears to be confounding the roles of the infinite number n and the constant C in the equation $\log(1+x) = C \cdot n\left((1+x)^{1/n} - 1\right)$.)

Having argued for such a representation, Halley points out that computing an infinite root is actually easier than computing a large but finite root:

> Now, though the Notion of an Infinite Power may seem very strange, and to those that know the difficulty of the Extraction of the Roots of High Powers, perhaps impracticable; yet by the help of that admirable Invention of Mr. *Newton*, whereby he determines the *Unciæ* or Numbers prefixt to the Members composing Powers (on which chiefly depends the Doctrine of Series) the Infinity of the Index contributes to render the Expression much more easie: For if the Infinite Power to be resolved be put (after Mr. *Newton*'s Method) $\overline{p+pq}$, $\overline{p+pq}\,|^{\frac{1}{m}}$, or $\overline{1+q}\,|^{\frac{1}{m}}$, instead of

$$1 + \frac{1}{m}q + \frac{1-m}{2mm}qq + \frac{1-3m+2mm}{6m^3}q^3 + \frac{1-6m+11mm-6m^3}{24m^4}q^4 \,\&\text{c.}$$

(which is the Root when m is finite,) becomes

$$1 + \frac{1}{m}q - \frac{1}{2m}qq + \frac{1}{3m}q^3[-]\frac{1}{4m}q^4 + \frac{1}{5m}q^5, \,\&\text{c.}$$

> *mm* being *infinite* infinite, and consequently whatever is divided thereby vanishing.[4]

Halley retains the factor $1/m$ in his expansion for the logarithm, an artifact of his belief that the choice of infinite number m will correspond to a change of base. Subsequent sections of Halley's article derive more rapidly converging series expansions (such as that for $\log(\frac{1+x}{1-x})$) and illustrations of their use.

Finally, Halley examines the converse to the problem of computing logarithms:

---

[4]The original has $+\frac{1}{4m}q^4$, apparently a typographic error.

From the Logarithm given to find what *ratio* it expresses, is a Problem that has not been so much considered as the former, but which is solved with the like ease, and demonstrated by a like Process, from the same general Theorem of Mr. *Newton*: For as the Logarithm of the *ratio* of 1 to $1 + q$ was proved to be $\overline{1+q}\Big|^{\frac{1}{m}} - 1$, and that of the *ratio* of 1 to $1 - q$ to be $1 - \overline{1-q}\Big|^{\frac{1}{m}}$: so the Logarithm, which we will from henceforth call L, being given, $1 + L$ will be equal to $\overline{1+q}\Big|^{\frac{1}{m}}$ in the one case; and $1 - L$ will be equal to $\overline{1-q}\Big|^{\frac{1}{m}}$ in the other: Consequently $\overline{1+L}\Big|^{m}$ will be equal to $1 + q$, and $\overline{1-L}\Big|^{m}$ to $1 - q$; that is, according to Mr. *Newton*'s said Rule,

$$1 + mL + \tfrac{1}{2}m^2L^2 + \tfrac{1}{6}m^3L^3 + \tfrac{1}{24}m^4L^4 + \tfrac{1}{120}m^5L^5 \&\text{c. will be} = 1 + q, \text{ and}$$
$$1 - mL + \tfrac{1}{2}m^2L^2 - \tfrac{1}{6}m^3L^3 + \tfrac{1}{24}m^4L^4 - \tfrac{1}{120}m^5L^5 \&\text{c. will be equal to } 1 - q,$$

m being any infinite Index whatsoever, which is a full and general Proposition from the Logarithm given to find the Number, be the *Species* of Logarithm what it will. But if *Napeir*'s [sic] Logarithm be given, the Multiplication by m is saved, (which Multiplication is indeed no other than the reducing the other *Species* to his) and the *Series* will be more simple, *viz.* $1 + L + \tfrac{1}{2}LL + \tfrac{1}{6}L^3 + \tfrac{1}{24}L^4 + \tfrac{1}{120}L^5 \&\text{c. or}$ $1 - L + \tfrac{1}{2}LL - \tfrac{1}{6}L^3 + \tfrac{1}{24}L^4 - \tfrac{1}{120}L^5 \&\text{c.}$

In simplifying the earlier expansion for the logarithm, Halley called attention to the fact that he was disregarding those parts of each coefficient that were negligible. In the present calculation he makes no such explicit comment.

Commentaries on Halley

Halley's paper was quite influential in its time, and a number of other authors followed his method of deriving the logarithmic and exponential series, notably William Jones [11] and Roger Cotes. Halley's claim, that while many of these series results had been anticipated by others, their derivations "never till now perfected without the consideration of the Hyperbola, which in a matter purely Arithmetical as this is, cannot so properly be applyed," [10, p. 64] met with approval in many circles, for providing an arithmetic foundation for the logarithm separate from geometric considerations.

Halley's paper was reprinted in Sherwin's *Tables* through the fourth edition. Commenting on their omission from the fifth edition of 1771, Samuel Clark noted that Halley's methods "... at the Time of their Publication were doubtless the most compendious of any then extant...," but had made way for simpler methods and more rapidly converging expansions. [14, p. v]

Francis Maseres reprinted Halley's paper in his *Scriptores logarithmici* [13] (published 1791–1807), as well as writing a commentary on it. Maseres, however, offered commentary only on Halley's derivations of more rapidly converging series (such as $\log(\frac{1+x}{1-x})$), given the logarithmic series. Maseres comments:

The reader will, however, observe that I have made no notes on some of the most important parts of this discourse, to wit, those parts in which the author gives us the investigation of the two logarithmic series [series for $\log(1 + x)$ and $\log(1 - x)$] ..., and the two antilogarithmic series [the series for e^L and e^{-L}].... The reason for my omitting to make notes on these important passages, is, that I never have been able perfectly to understand them. [13, p. 92]

From Halley to Euler

Halley's 1695 article presents a radically new approach to obtaining power series for the logarithmic and exponential functions. While Halley had claimed to derive power series expansions for these functions independent of any geometric considerations, this came at great cost. Halley's exposition of the foundations of the logarithm is highly opaque, and his arguments extremely difficult to follow, as the quotes from Maseres (above) and Stone (p. 152) attest. That Halley was inspired by Briggs' root extraction method only becomes clear in light of Halley's correspondence with Sharp, where the computation of the 2^{47}th root of 1.024 is mentioned in connection with the logarithm, and which consideration is known to have immediately preceded Halley's 1695 article.

In contrast, Euler's exposition of this content is lucid and relatively straightforward. Euler does not start with the logarithm, but rather with a study of exponential functions in general. [Cajori [3] credits William Gardiner with the first published treatment, in 1742, of a complete theory of logarithms based on properties of exponentiation, and suggests Gardiner's approach originated in work of William Jones (although this approach is not to be found in [11], which is clearly based on Halley's 1695 exposition).] Applying the arithmetic of infinite and infinitesimal numbers, Euler is able to relate powers of the base to powers of binomials, and hence by applying the binomial theorem arrives at power series representations for the exponential functions. Further, from the representation of a^x as an infinite power of a binomial, Euler inverts the equation and instead finds a logarithm as an infinite root of a binomial.

By starting his analysis with the exponential functions rather than the logarithmic, Euler is able to base his discussion on the reader's understandings of exponentiation, rather than having to appeal to geometric or computational understandings of the logarithm. Euler also has the advantage over Halley of having a clear understanding of the arithmetic of infinite and infinitesimal numbers, which he used to great advantage throughout much of the *Introductio*.

It is the clarity of Euler's exposition, his successful presentation of the foundations of the logarithm and exponential functions independent of geometric considerations, and the prominent appearance of these arguments in so highly celebrated a text as the *Introductio in analysin infinitorum*, that has caused Euler's presentation of these power series derivations to eclipse that of Halley.

References

[1] *Addenda to the third volume of The Statutes at Large, beginning with the fourth year of the reign of Queen Anne, and continuing to the end of the last session of Parliament, April 1 1708*, C. 27, §17.

[2] Henry Briggs, *Arithmetica Logarithmica*, London, 1624.

[3] Florian Cajori, "History of the exponential and logarithmic concepts" [part 2 of 7], *American Mathematical Monthly* **20** (1913) 35–47.

[4] William Cudworth, *Life and Correspondence of Abraham Sharp*, S. Low, Marston, Searle & Rivington, 1889.

[5] Thomas Fantet de Lagny, Nouvelle méthode de Mr. T. F. de Lagny pour l'approximation des racines cubiques, *Journal des Sçavans* **19** (1692), no. 17, 14 Mai 1691, 200–202.

[6] Leonhard Euler, De summis serierum reciprocarum (E41), *Commentarii Academiæ Scientiarum Imperialis Petropolitanæ* **7** (1734/5), 1740, 123–134, Reprinted in *Opera Omnia*, series 1, volume 14, pp. 73–86.

[7] ——, Consideratio progressionis cuiusdam ad circuli quadraturam inveniendam idoneae (E125), *Commentarii Academiae Scientiarum Imperialis Petropolitanæ* **11** (1739) 1750, 116–127, Reprinted in *Opera Omnia*, series 1, volume 14, pp. 350–363.

[8] ——, *Introductio in analysin infinitorum* (E101), Lausanne, 1748. Translated by John Blanton, *Introduction to Analysis of the Infinite, Book I*, Springer-Verlag, New York, 1988.

[9] Edmond Halley, Methodus nova accurata & facilis inveniendi radices æquationum quarumcumque generaliter, sine prævia reductione, *Philosophical Transactions of the Royal Society of London* **18** (1694), 136–148.

[10] ——, A most compendious and facile method for constructing the logarithms, exemplified and demonstrated from the nature of numbers, without any regard to the hyperbola, with a speedy method for finding the number from the logarithm given, *Philosophical Transactions of the Royal Society of London* **19** (1695/7), 58–67.

[11] William Jones, *Synopsis Palmariorum Matheseos*, London, 1706.

[12] E. F. MacPike, *Correspondence and Papers of Edmond Halley*, Oxford, 1932.

[13] Francis Maseres, Notes on some of the more difficult passages of the foregoing discourse of Dr. Edmund Halley, *Scriptores Logarithmici*, vol. 2, London, 1791–1807, pp. 92–122.

[14] Henry Sherwin, *Sherwin's Mathematical Tables*, 5th ed., London, 1771, Revised, corrected and improved by Samuel Clark.

[15] Edmund Stone, *A New Mathematical Dictionary*, London, 1743, Excerpt reprinted in *The History of Mathematics: A Reader* (John Fauvel and Jeremy Gray, eds.), Macmillan Press, 1987.

[16] John Wallis, *A Treatise of Algebra, both Historical and Practical*, London, 1685.

Taylor and Euler:
Linking the Discrete and Continuous[1]

Dick Jardine

Introduction

It is clear from Leonhard Euler's works that he had read and extended some of the mathematics that Brook Taylor introduced in *Methodus incrementorum directa et inversa* (1715). The focus of this paper is to address the connections between the mathematics of Taylor and that of Euler. The presentation begins with a biographical sketch of Brook Taylor, followed by a brief description of the *Methodus,* emphasizing two of the subjects in that book that were of particular interest to Euler: the Taylor series and the motion of a vibrating string.

The importance of Taylor series, which first appeared as Proposition VII Theorem 3 Corollary 2 of the *Methodus*, is well known to calculus students. The emphasis that Lagrange placed on Taylor series led some to believe that "The importance of Taylor's theorem remained unrecognized until 1772 when Lagrange proclaimed it the basic principle of the differential calculus" [17]. In fact, the significance of Taylor's series was recognized decades earlier by Euler, who in 1736 wrote (roughly translated from the Latin), "This series... was first produced by the Illust. TAYLOR in *Methodo Increm. inv.* and he adapted it to many excellent uses" [6]. In fact, Euler was among the first to attribute the series to Taylor [18], and others followed his lead. Taylor did put the series to good use, but in the hands of the masterful Euler, the tool was put to many more.

Many are aware of the series that bears his name, but few know of Brook Taylor's significant role at a critical time in the history of mathematics. Taylor's period of scientific productivity was relatively brief. In slightly more than a decade, he produced 13 articles and two groundbreaking books. He was elected to the Royal Society in 1712 and succeeded Edmond Halley as Secretary at the height of the priority dispute between Leibniz and Newton over the discovery of the calculus. Taylor sided with his countryman and was a staunch supporter of Newton and therefore an object of the scorn of Leibniz and Johann Bernoulli.

---

[1]A variation of this paper was presented at the Eastern Sectional Meeting of the American Mathematical Society, Northeastern University, Boston, MA, October 2002.

Figure 1. Frontispiece with Brook Taylor's Image, courtesy of National Portrait Gallery, London

The *Methodus*, the first of his books, is acknowledged to be foundational in the calculus of finite differences. His *Linear Perspective* was an important work in geometry. Although the content of his writing was difficult to understand, Taylor's mathematical publications influenced the mathematics of Maclaurin, Daniel Bernoulli, D'Alembert, Lagrange, and Euler, among others [9, p. 5]. He touched upon a wide range of mathematical topics and applications—finite differences, differential equations, probability, atmospheric pressure, refraction of light, the vibrating string, perspective geometry, among others—but because of health problems, family issues, and other concerns, Taylor was not able to fulfill his mathematical promise.

Brook Taylor (1685–1731)

Brook Taylor was born on August 18, 1685, into a wealthy family that enjoyed connections to minor nobility. He had an interest and aptitude for landscape painting and playing the harpsichord, both of which motivated his later mathematical investigations. He was tutored at Bifrons House, his home in the south of England, in preparation for enrolling at St. John's College, Cambridge, in 1701. He studied the law at Cambridge, obtaining the LL.B. degree in 1709 and the LL.D. degree in 1714. Between earning his legal degrees, he submitted mathematical and scientific work of sufficient merit to earn him admission as a Fellow of the Royal Society in 1712. Shortly after his election to the Royal Society, Taylor—along with Abraham de Moivre and Francis Aston—was chosen to serve on a Royal Society committee to resolve the calculus priority dispute. The committee came to the not surprising conclusion that Newton was first. Taylor's role in the proceedings earned him the wrath of Continental mathematicians, particularly Leibniz and Johann Bernoulli. Fortunately Pierre Rémond de Montmort, a French mathematician, corresponded with both Taylor and Johann Bernoulli and served as a moderating influence in the dispute. Montmort's area of interest was probability, and Taylor is thought to have suggested the knight's tour problem to both Montmort and de Moivre, the two who are credited with early solutions [1].

Among Taylor's early mathematical works was "De motu nervi tensi" (Of the motion of a taut string) which first appeared in the Royal Society's *Philosophical Transactions* in 1713 and reappeared in the *Methodus*, where it was likely to have caught Euler's attention. Taylor's most productive period began in 1715 with the publication of the *Methodus*. In the same year *Linear Perspective* was published, and he authored at least 11 papers over the next 8 years.

Taylor resigned his position with the Royal Society in 1718 due to illness, perhaps exacerbated by the stresses of the calculus priority debate and the criticism of his own work. He made several trips to France for his illness and to spend time with his friend Montmort. His 1721 marriage to a woman who did not meet his father's approval resulted in Taylor's estrangement from his family. His wife died in childbirth, however, and he returned to Bifrons House after that personal tragedy. Taylor remarried in 1725, this time with his father's approval, but his second wife also died in childbirth in 1730 (the child, a daughter, survived). Taylor's health decayed quickly after this second tragic event, and he died in London at age 46 on December 29, 1731.

The *Methodus* (1715)

The *Methodus incrementorum directa et inversa* was published in 1715 at 118 pages plus a short preface. A second edition printed in 1717 did not differ significantly from the first. The *Methodus* was written with the purpose of clarifying Newton's fluxional calculus [15, pp. 426–427] while serving as a vehicle to communicate Taylor's mathematical ideas. To come to a full understanding of Newton's fluxional calculus (continuous mathematics), Taylor decided that he must first develop a full treatment of what he called the method of increments, which in modern terms is the calculus of finite differences or difference equations (discrete mathematics). Whereas Newton's fluxions and fluents were explained by their creator in terms of continuous motion, Taylor's method of increments was principally an algebraic treatment of discrete difference equations. Historians of mathematics

Figure 2. Brook Taylor, courtesy of the National Portrait Gallery, London

have credited the *Methodus* as being a most important text in that Taylor "added a new branch to mathematics, now called 'finite differences,' of which he was the inventor"[4, p. 226].

Taylor's writing style prevented the *Methodus* from being as effective as the author had intended. His friend Montmort compared reading the book to "rowing in the galleys" [9, p. 3]. As the book was written at the height of the calculus priority controversy, it is no surprise that Leibniz and the Bernoullis panned it. Nikolaus Bernoulli, wrote:

> Taylor's book on the Method of Increments has arrived here at last. I have found nothing new in it, but most things already known for a long time, however obscurely set forth and excessively abstract so that I believe them to be understood by

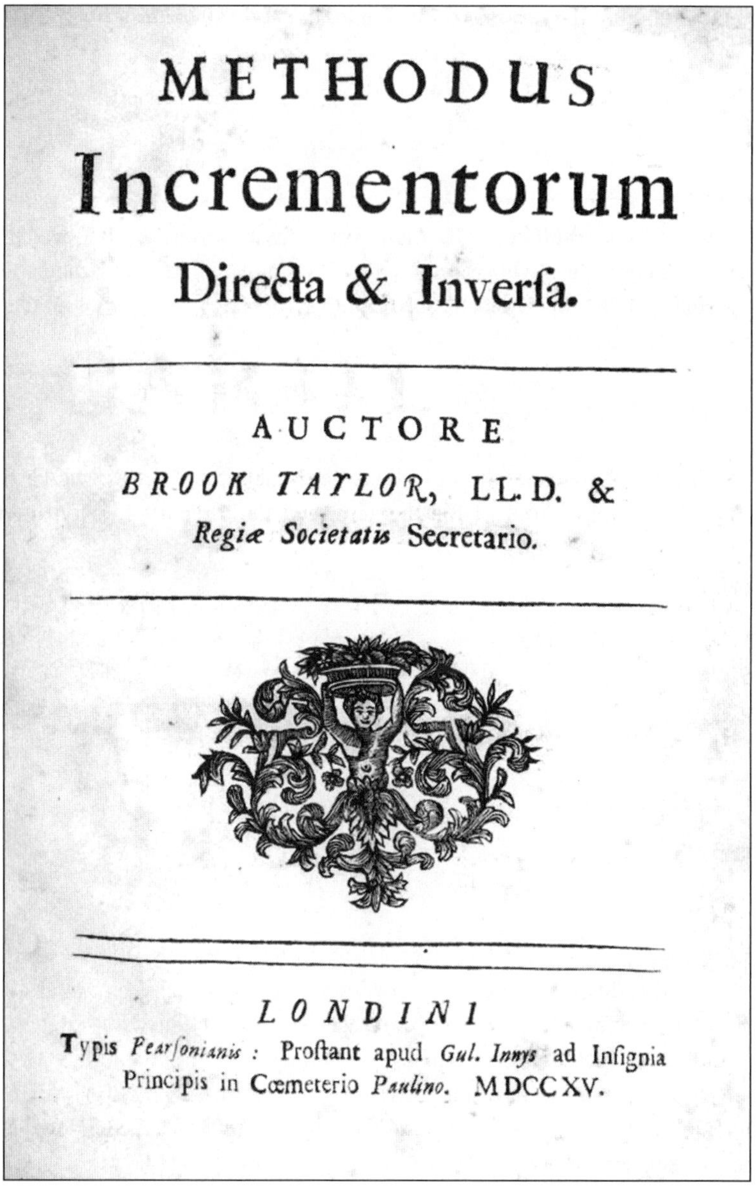
METHODUS

Incrementorum

Directa & Inverſa.

AUCTORE

BROOK TAYLOR, LL. D. &

Regiæ Societatis Secretario.

LONDINI

Typis *Pearſonianis* : Proſtant apud *Gul. Innys* ad Inſignia Principis in Cœmeterio *Paulino*. MDCCXV.

Figure 3. Title page of the *Methodus*, by permission of the Master and Fellows of St. John's College, Cambridge

> few... the whole book is written obscurely enough; I myself do not wonder at this, for how can he pass off as his own things which belong to others, unless he affects obscurity on purpose in order to hide the theft... [2].

The *Methodus* began with a discussion of finite differences, developing procedures using methods that today we would describe as discrete mathematics. Then he made the transition to the continuous fluxions. He included such mathematical innovations as singular solutions to difference and differential equations, formulas relating the fluxion in one variable to the fluxion of the inverse (for example, in modern notation,

$$\frac{d^2x}{dy^2} = -\frac{\frac{d^2y}{dx^2}}{\left(\frac{dy}{dx}\right)^3})$$

[3, p. 429], and many applications.

But the most famous result in the *Methodus* is the Taylor series. It is believed that Taylor first arrived at his conjecture while applying Halley's approximation method to solve the Kepler problem [9]. To begin the discussion of the Taylor series, let's start with the binomial series expansion, in modern notation:

$$(1+x)^n = 1 + nx + \frac{n(n-1)}{2!}x^2 + \frac{n(n-1)(n-2)}{3!}x^3 + \cdots.$$

It is not difficult to see the similarity between that infinite series, which played an important role in Taylor's proof of his theorem, and the Gregory-Newton interpolation formula (using modern notation),

$$f(x+h) = f(x) + \frac{h}{a}\Delta f(x) + \frac{\frac{h}{a}\left(\frac{h}{a}-1\right)}{2!}\Delta^2 f(x) + \frac{\frac{h}{a}\left(\frac{h}{a}-1\right)\left(\frac{h}{a}-2\right)}{3!}\Delta^3 f(x) + \cdots$$

where

$$\Delta f(x) = f(x+a) - f(x)$$
$$\Delta^2 f(x) = \Delta f(x+a) - \Delta f(x) = f(x+2a) - 2f(x+a) + f(x)$$
$$\Delta^3 f(x) = f(x+3a) - 3f(x+2a) + 3(x+a) - f(x)$$
$$\cdots$$

Newton and Gregory each used the interpolation formula in connection with their work with the binomial series [19], and the reader may have noted the binomial coefficients also appear in the coefficients of the difference equations. The Newton-Gregory interpolation formula determines the unknown $f(x+h)$ using the known values of $f(x)$ and $f(x+a)$. Gregory is said to have had Taylor series, but his expression was in terms of finite differences [13, p. 75]. One can see the similarities between the Newton-Gregory formula and Taylor series

$$f(x+h) = f(x) + hf'(x) + \frac{h^2}{2!}f''(x) + \frac{h^3}{3!}f'''(x) + \cdots.$$

Taylor's series, then, is seen as a non-rigorous limiting case of the Gregory-Newton formula as $a \longrightarrow 0$, which was how it was derived by Taylor [19]. Felix Klein did not particularly appreciate this leap from the discrete to the continuous, remarking: "We have here, in fact, a passage to the limit of unexampled audacity." [14, p. 233] But Taylor was not alone in making this jump. Euler did the same in his proof, as we shall see later.

Before discussing Taylor's proof, we take on the daunting task of trying to understand his notation, an important part of this story. Where modern notation (due to Euler) would represent the increment (or difference) of x by Δx, Taylor denoted the first increment by

x, the second increment by $\underset{\cdot\cdot}{x}$, etc. This is similar to Newton's fluxional notation: the first fluxion $\dot{x}$, the second fluxion $\ddot{x}$, etc., which Taylor also used. Newton employed $\overset{'}{x}$ and $\overset{''}{x}$ to represent the first and second fluent (Newton's equivalent to the antiderivative), whereas Taylor chose a couple of notations, to include $\boxed{x}$. For example, in Proposition 11 of the *Methodus* Taylor used this notation for what we have come to call integration by parts:

$$\boxed{\dot{r}s} = rs - \boxed{r\dot{s}}.$$

Taylor was among the first to apply that integration technique. He further obfuscated his text by introducing $\overset{\backslash}{x}$, $\overset{\backslash\backslash}{x}$, x, $\underset{\backslash}{x}$, and $\underset{\backslash\backslash}{x}$ to denote successive values of x obtained by differentiation or integration. The confusion brought about by Taylor's inconsistent notation did not endear him to readers. Even Taylor acknowledged the difficulty, writing to Montmort, "What I have found obscure, & not well explained, I believe others will find so too ..." (quoted on p. 4 of [9]). Taylor was one of those authors who clearly understood the subject matter but was unable to write the mathematics clearly. A lucid exposition would not be available until Euler took up the subject. But the gem to be extracted from doing the difficult work of reading the *Methodus* is one of the most important results in mathematics.

Taylor's theorem is actually just a second corollary to Proposition 7 Theorem III in the *Methodus*. Proposition 7 is a finite difference theorem in which "... in the time that z increases to $z + v$, x will correspondingly increase to

$$x + \dot{x}\frac{v}{1\underset{\cdot}{z}} + \underset{\cdot\cdot}{x}\frac{v\overset{\backslash}{v}}{1\cdot 2\underset{\cdot}{z}^2} + \underset{\cdot\cdot\cdot}{x}\frac{v\overset{\backslash}{v}\overset{\backslash\backslash}{v}}{1\cdot 2\cdot 3\underset{\cdot}{z}^3} + \&c."$$

This result was derived using a table of finite differences (increments) and the binomial series. The variable x depends on the variable z, and Taylor chose v to be the increment ($v = \Delta z$). Then $v - \Delta z = \overset{\backslash}{v}$, $\overset{\backslash}{v} - \Delta z = \underset{\backslash}{v}$, etc. We now describe how to get to that result using the more modern notation of the calculus of finite differences.

The first difference is $\Delta x(z) = x(z + v) - x(z)$. Solving for $x(z + v)$ we obtain

$$x(z + v) = x + \Delta x$$

where $x = x(z)$. The second difference is

$$
\begin{aligned}
\Delta^2 x &= \Delta x(z + v) - \Delta x(z) \\
&= x(z + 2v) - x(z + v) - (x(z + v) - x(z)) \\
&= x(z + 2v) - 2x(z + v) + x(z),
\end{aligned}
$$

and solving for $x(z + 2v)$ we obtain

$$
\begin{aligned}
x(z + 2v) &= 2x(z + v) - x(z) + \Delta^2 x \\
&= x(z) + 2(x(z + v) - x(z)) + \Delta^2 x \\
&= x + 2\Delta x + \Delta^2 x.
\end{aligned}
$$

The process continues producing the results

$$x$$
$$x + \Delta x$$
$$x + 2\Delta x + \Delta^2 x$$
$$x + 3\Delta x + 3\Delta^2 x + \Delta^3 x.$$

Taylor noted the similarity between the coefficients of these difference equations and the coefficients of the binomial expansion, so he wrote the general result

$$x(z + nv) = x + \frac{n}{1}\Delta x + \frac{n(n-1)}{2!}\Delta^2 x + \frac{n(n-1)(n-2)}{3!}\Delta^3 x + \cdots.$$

or, in his notation

$$x + \overset{.}{x}\frac{n}{1} + \overset{..}{x}\frac{n}{1}\cdot\frac{n-1}{2} + \overset{...}{x}\frac{n}{1}\cdot\frac{n-1}{2}\cdot\frac{n-2}{3} + \&c.$$

Continuing Taylor wrote

$$n = \frac{v}{\underset{.}{z}}, \quad \frac{n-1}{2} = \frac{v-\overset{.}{z}}{2\underset{.}{z}} = \frac{\overset{\backslash}{v}}{2\underset{.}{z}}, \quad \frac{n-2}{3} = \frac{\overset{\backslash\backslash}{v}}{3\underset{.}{z}},$$

producing the result:

$$x + \overset{.}{x}\frac{v}{1\underset{.}{z}} + \overset{..}{x}\frac{v\overset{\backslash}{v}}{1\cdot 2\underset{.}{z}^2} + \overset{...}{x}\frac{v\overset{\backslash}{v}\overset{\backslash\backslash}{v}}{1\cdot 2\cdot 3\underset{.}{z}^3} + \&c.$$

Corollary 1 is the analogous formula for when x decreases:

$$x - \overset{.}{x}\frac{v}{1\underset{.}{z}} + \overset{..}{x}\frac{v\overset{\backslash}{v}}{1\cdot 2\underset{.}{z}^2} - \overset{...}{x}\frac{v\overset{\backslash}{v}\overset{\backslash\backslash}{v}}{1\cdot 2\cdot 3\underset{.}{z}^3} + \&c.$$

This brings us to Corollary 2, in which an increasing variable z "flows uniformly" and all the v's "become equal," which leads to the next x becoming

$$x + \overset{.}{x}\frac{v}{1\overset{.}{z}} + \overset{..}{x}\frac{v^2}{1\cdot 2\overset{.}{z}^2} + \overset{...}{x}\frac{v^3}{1\cdot 2\cdot 3\overset{.}{z}^3} + \&c.$$

That latter step is generated Klein's objections concerning the lack of rigor. Taylor went on to the case for the decrease of the increment, in which x becomes

$$x - \overset{.}{x}\frac{v}{1\cdot z} + \overset{..}{x}\frac{v^2}{1\cdot 2\overset{.}{z}^2} - \overset{...}{x}\frac{v^3}{1\cdot 2\cdot 3\overset{.}{z}^3} + \&c. \quad [10]$$

In those last steps, the result that originated with discrete finite differences is transformed into a continuous result in Newtonian fluxional notation. In the notation of Leibniz,

$$\frac{\overset{.}{x}}{\overset{.}{z}} = \frac{dx}{dz}, \quad \frac{\overset{..}{x}}{\overset{.}{z}^2} = \frac{d^2x}{dz^2},$$

etc. Taylor did not address the convergence of the result nor did he provide any remainder term. Those issues were resolved much later by Lagrange and Cauchy.

Taylor used Proposition 7 Theorem III Corollary 2, hereafter Taylor's theorem, and the other results in Proposition 7 to solve both difference equations and differential equations in various examples in the *Methodus*. Some of the differential equations caught the attention of Continental mathematicians, to include Euler and the Bernoullis. The other results in the *Methodus* were overshadowed by Taylor's theorem, particularly after Euler proved the result himself in his "Inventio summae cuiusque seriei ex dato termino generali" (E47). Euler credited Taylor with the series, as quoted earlier [6].

Euler's extensions of the work of Taylor

Late in his life, Euler wrote a brief, handwritten autobiography. It is republished in Emil Fellmann's short biography of Euler. Euler wrote (in German):

> ... I soon found the opportunity to become acquainted with the famous professor Johann Bernoulli, who made it a special pleasure for himself to help me along in the mathematical sciences. Private lessons, however, he categorically ruled out because of his busy schedule: However, he gave me a far more beneficial advice, which consisted in myself taking a look at some of the more difficult mathematical books and work through them with great diligence, and should I encounter some objections or difficulties, he offered me free access to him every Saturday afternoon, and he was gracious enough to comment on the collected difficulties, ... which certainly is the best method of making auspicious progress in the mathematical sciences [11].

Taking Bernoulli's advice, Euler learned to read the mathematics available to him. As the quotation from "Inventio ..." indicates, one of the available works he read was Taylor's *Methodus*. In his eulogy of Euler, the Marquis de Condorcet observed that Euler had transformed the work of Taylor: "A nearly unknown but intelligent work on finite differences by Mr. Taylor was made into an important branch of integral calculus by assigning a simple and workable notation which was found to apply successfully to the theory of series." [5] Euler recognized the merits of Taylor's mathematics and through his subsequent exposition was able to make Taylor's work understood by many. It is not clear exactly what impact Taylor's book had on him, but it is interesting to note that Euler started his introductory book on the calculus, *Institutiones calculi differentialis*, with difference equations, the subject Taylor introduced first in *Methodus*. After developing the calculus of finite differences, Euler moved on to the continuous calculus as Taylor had before him, but Euler's is a far more readable treatment than Taylor produced in *Methodus*. In other works of Euler, we find a proof of Taylor's theorem similar to that of Taylor, and we note that Euler spent significant time and effort extending the mathematical modeling of the vibrating string that Taylor originated in *Methodus*.

In this section we summarize Euler's proof of Taylor's theorem [6]. Euler started with y as a function of x. Using the notation of Leibniz but the same process as Taylor, he computed successive values for y as x increases successively by the infinitesimals dx, ddx, d^3x:

$$y + dy$$
$$y + 2dy + ddy$$
$$y + 3dy + 3ddy + d^3y.$$

Euler noted that these were the coefficients of the binomial expansion just as Gregory, Newton, and Taylor had previously. Substituting $x + m\,dx$ for x, y becomes

$$y + \frac{m}{1}dy + \frac{m(m-1)}{1 \cdot 2}d\,dy + \frac{m(m-1)(m-2)}{1 \cdot 2 \cdot 3}d^3 y + \text{ etc.}$$

Euler then made a similarly unrigorous leap, as Taylor had done before him, letting x become sufficiently large so that the smaller powers of m in each term are relatively negligible. Then he obtained for y

$$y + \frac{m}{1}dy + \frac{m^2}{1 \cdot 2}d\,dy + \frac{m^3}{1 \cdot 2 \cdot 3}d^3 y + \frac{m^4}{1 \cdot 2 \cdot 3 \cdot 4}d^4 y + \text{ etc.}$$

Finally, he substitutes $m = \frac{a}{dx}$ to get the Taylor series:

$$y + \frac{a\,dy}{1\,dx} + \frac{a^2 d\,dy}{1 \cdot 2 \cdot dx^2} + \frac{a^3 d^3 y}{1 \cdot 2 \cdot 3 \cdot dx^3} + \text{ etc.}$$

After proving the result, Euler effectively applied Taylor series as a mathematical tool to solve a wide variety of problems. These included finding roots of equations and solving both difference and differential equations, just as Taylor had before him in the *Methodus*.

We turn our attention now to the vibrating string problem, a differential equation that Taylor addressed in the *Methodus* but that also appeared earlier [22]. Taylor's work "marks the beginning of the modern theory of the vibrating string" [19, p. 177], a theory furthered by the efforts of D'Alembert, Daniel Bernoulli, and Euler. Our discussion will focus on the work of Taylor and Euler.

Taylor's study of the vibrating string was not an effort to find the equations of motion but rather to derive Mersenne's law from mathematical principles and to find the shape of the string. He modeled the string with the fluxional equation $a^2 \ddot{x} = \dot{s} y \dot{y}$ where $\dot{s} = \sqrt{\dot{x}^2 + \dot{y}^2}$, where the differentiation is with respect to time. He arrived at a solution for the shape of the string, in modern notation, $y = k \sin\left(\frac{\pi x}{l}\right)$, where l is the length of the string [19], and at an equation for the fundamental frequency of the string (an expression of Mersenne's law),

$$v = \frac{1}{2l}\sqrt{\frac{T}{\sigma}},$$

where T is tension and σ is the mass per unit length divided by the gravitational acceleration [15]. Taylor also determined that the force on the string was proportional to $\frac{d^2 y}{dx^2}$. Without the benefit of modern notation, Taylor had all the pieces for the wave equation

$$\sigma \frac{\partial^2 y}{\partial t^2} = T \frac{\partial^2 y}{\partial x^2},$$

but it would take others, to include the Bernoullis and Euler, to put the pieces together.

Johann Bernoulli worked on the vibrating string problem and modeled the problem using difference equations [20, p. 351]. He obtained results consistent with Taylor's and communicated his work to his son Daniel. Euler was working on the problem at the same time as the younger Bernoulli, arriving at this equation for the "figure of the string":

$$y = \alpha \sin\left(\frac{\pi x}{a}\right) + \beta \sin\left(\frac{2\pi x}{a}\right) + \gamma \sin\left(\frac{3\pi x}{a}\right) + \cdots .$$

This infinite trigonometric series produced the "eel-like curve" that improved the model for the shape of the string that Taylor had obtained. The Bernoullis and Euler continued their work on the problem from the late 1720s through the 1750s. By 1753 the younger Bernoulli extended the work of his father, Taylor, Euler, and D'Alembert to arrive at a general solution of the wave equation expressed in terms of the infinite trigonometric series

$$y = a_1 \sin\left(\frac{\pi x}{l}\right) \cos\left(\frac{\pi ct}{l}\right) + a_2 \sin\left(\frac{2\pi x}{l}\right) \cos\left(\frac{2\pi ct}{l}\right)$$

$$+ a_3 \sin\left(\frac{3\pi x}{l}\right) \cos\left(\frac{3\pi ct}{l}\right) + \cdots.$$

This work laid the foundation for Fourier's development of the infinite trigonometric series bearing his name that is so very useful in applied mathematics.

Conclusion

Perhaps the relative brevity of the period when Brook Taylor made direct contributions to mathematics diminished the importance of his contributions to our discipline. He will always be remembered for the series and theorem that bear his name but should also be recalled for his other contributions, particularly as a creator of a branch of discrete mathematics (finite differences or difference equations) [4]. He was a pioneer in developing mathematical models using both difference equations and differential equations, thereby bridging the gap between the discrete and the continuous. Despite the weaknesses of his exposition, the strength of his mathematics motivated others to pursue Taylor's interests further. Surely Taylor was not a giant like Euler, but his work was a foundation for the master to extend with great success.

Acknowledgment   I thank Lenore Feigenbaum for her kindness in sharing so very much information about Brook Taylor and the *Methodus*. Additionally, the efforts of the editors and reviewers of this volume are to be commended, as they helped prevent this paper from being as unreadable as Taylor's work.

References

[1] W.W.R. Ball, *Mathematical Recreations and Essays*, Macmillan, London, 1912.

[2] N. Bernoulli quoted in [9], p. 27.

[3] C.B. Boyer and U. Merzbach, *A History of Mathematics*, 2nd ed., John Wiley and Sons, New York, 1991.

[4] F. Cajori, *A History of Mathematics*, Chelsea, New York, 1991.

[5] M. Condorcet, "Eulogy to Mr. Euler," History of the Royal Academy of Sciences 1783, Paris 1786, 37–68, translated by J. Glaus and accessed from www.math.dartmouth.edu/ ~euler/, March 2006.

[6] L. Euler, "Inventio summae cuiusque seriei ex dato termino generali" (E47), *Commentarii academiae scientiarum Petropolitanae* v. 8, (1736), 1741, 9–22.

[7] ——, translated by E. Sandifer, "Inventio summae cuiusque seriei ex dato termino generali" (E47), *Commentarii academiae scientiarum Petropolitanae* v. 8, (1736), 1741.

[8] ——, *Institutiones Calculi Differentialis* (E212), translated by J.D. Blanton, *Foundations of the Differential Calculus*, Springer-Verlag, New York, 2000.

[9] L. Feigenbaum, "Brook Taylor and the Method of Increments," *Archive for History of Exact Sciences*, v. 34, number 1/2, 1985, 1–140.

[10] ——, *Brook Taylor's "Methodus incrementorum": A Translation with Mathematical and Historical Commentary.* Doctoral Dissertation, Yale University, 1981.

[11] E. Fellman, *Leonhard Euler*, translated by E. Gautschi and W. Gautschi, Birkhäuser, Basel, 2007, p.5.

[12] C. Gillispie, ed., "Brook Taylor" in *Dictionary of Scientific Biography*, Scribner, New York, 1978.

[13] H.H. Goldstine, *A History of Numerical Analysis from the 16th through the 19th Century*, Springer-Verlag, New York, 1977.

[14] F. Klein, *Elementary Mathematics from an Advanced Standpoint: Arithmetic, Algebra, Analysis*, Dover, New York, 2004.

[15] M. Kline, *Mathematical Thought from Ancient to Modern Times.* Oxford University Press, New York, 1972.

[16] R.E. Langer, "An Excerpt from the Works of Euler," *The American Mathematical Monthly*, v. 64, Part 2: to Lester R. Ford on His Seventieth Birthday (Oct. 1957), 37–44.

[17] J.J. O'Connor, E.F. Robertson, "Brook Taylor," *The MacTutor History of Mathematics Archive*, www-groups.dcs.st-and.ac.uk/~history/Mathematicians/Taylor.html, accessed January 2006.

[18] E. Sandifer, "Estimating the Basel Problem," *How Euler Did It*, MAA Online, www.maa.org /editorial/euler/HowEulerDidIt02EstimatingtheBaselProblem.pdf, accessed January 2006.

[19] J. Stillwell, *Mathematics and Its History.* Springer-Verlag, New York, 1989.

[20] D. Struik, *A Source Book in Mathematics, 1200–1800.* Harvard University Press, Cambridge, MA, 1969.

[21] B. Taylor, *Methodus incrementorum directa et inversa*, London, (1715), 1717.

[22] ——, "De motu Nervi tensi," *Philosophical Transactions* v. 28, 1713, 26–32.

Dances between continuous and discrete: Euler's summation formula[1]

David J. Pengelley[2]

I Introduction

Leonhard Euler (1707–1783) discovered his powerful "summation formula" in the early 1730s. He used it in 1735 to compute the first 20 decimal places for the precise sum of all the reciprocal squares — a number mathematicians had competed to determine ever since the surprising discovery that the alternating sum of reciprocal odd numbers is $\pi/4$. This reciprocal squares challenge was called the "Basel problem," and Euler achieved his 20-place approximation using only a few terms from his diverging summation formula. In contrast, if sought as a simple partial sum of the original slowly converging series, such accuracy would require more than 10^{20} terms. With his approximation, Euler probably became convinced that the sum was $\pi^2/6$, which spurred his first solution of the Basel problem in the same year [7, volume 16, section 2, pp. VIIff, volume 14][19, 27].

We are left in awe that just a few terms of a diverging formula can so closely approximate this sum. Paradoxically, Euler's formula, even though it usually diverges, provides breathtaking approximations for partial and infinite sums of many slowly converging or diverging series. My goal here is to explore Euler's own mature view of the summation formula and a few of his more diverse applications, largely in his own words from the *Institutiones calculi differentialis (Foundations of Differential Calculus)* of 1755. I hope that readers will be equally impressed at some of his other applications.

In the *Calculi differentialis*, Euler connected his summation formula to Bernoulli numbers and proved the sums of powers formulas that Jakob Bernoulli had conjectured. He also applied the formula to harmonic partial sums and the related gamma constant, and to sums of logarithms, thereby approximating large factorials (Stirling's asymptotic approximation) and binomial coefficients with ease. He even made an approximation of π that he

---

[1] Based on a talk given at the Euler 2K+2 conference, Rumford, Maine, 2002.
[2] Dedicated to the memory of my parents, Daphne and Ted Pengelley, who inspired a love of history.

himself commented was hard to believe so accurate for so little work. Euler was a wizard at finding these connections, at demonstrating patterns by generalizable examples, at utilizing his summation formula only "until it begins to diverge," and at determining the relevant "Euler-Maclaurin constant" in each application. His work also inaugurated study of the zeta function [2, 25]. Euler's accomplishments throughout this entire arena are discussed from different points of view in many modern books [5; 12, pp. 119–136; 13, II.10; 14, chapter XII; 16, pp. 197ff; 20, chapter XIV; 27, pp. 184, 257–285; 29, pp. 338ff].

Euler included all of these discoveries and others in beautifully unified form in Part Two[3] of the *Calculi differentialis* [7, volume 10; 8], portions of which I have translated for an undergraduate course based on original sources [21, 22, 23], and for selective inclusion[4] in a companion book built around annotated primary sources [19]. The chapter *The Bridge Between Continuous and Discrete* [19, 23] follows the entwining of the quest for formulas for sums of numerical powers with the development of integration, via sources by Archimedes, Fermat, Pascal, Jakob Bernoulli, and finally from Euler's *Calculi differentialis*. I have also written an article [24] providing an independent exposition of this broader story.

Here I will first discuss the Basel problem and briefly outline the progression of ideas and sources that led to the connection in Euler's work between it and sums of powers. Then I will illustrate a few of Euler's achievements with his summation formula via selected translations. I present Euler's derivation of the formula, discuss his analysis of the resulting Bernoulli numbers, show his application to sums of reciprocal squares, to large factorials and binomial coefficients, and mention other applications. A more detailed treatment can be found in [19]. I will also raise and explore the question of whether large factorials can be determined uniquely from Euler's formula.

2   The Basel problem

In the 1670s, James Gregory (1638–1675) and Gottfried Leibniz (1646–1716) discovered that

$$1 - \frac{1}{3} + \frac{1}{5} - \frac{1}{7} + \cdots = \frac{\pi}{4},$$

as essentially had the mathematicians of Kerala in southern India two centuries before [17, pp. 493ff, 527]. Because, aside from geometric series, very few infinite series then had a known sum, this remarkable result enticed Leibniz and the Bernoulli brothers Jakob (1654–1705) and Johann (1667–1748) to seek sums of other series, particularly the reciprocal squares

$$\frac{1}{1} + \frac{1}{4} + \frac{1}{9} + \frac{1}{16} + \frac{1}{25} + \cdots = ?,$$

a problem first raised by Pietro Mengoli (1626–1686) in 1650. Jakob expressed his eventual frustration at its elusive nature in the comment "If someone should succeed in finding what till now withstood our efforts and communicate it to us, we shall be much obliged to him" [29, p. 345].

---

[3] Part One has recently appeared in English translation [9], but not Part Two.
[4] See [10] for my most extensive translation from Euler's Part Two (albeit more lightly annotated).

Euler proved that the sum is exactly $\pi^2/6$, in part by a broadening of the context to produce his "summation formula" for $\sum_{i=1}^{n} f(i)$, with n possibly infinite. His new setting thus encompassed both the Basel problem, $\sum_{i=1}^{\infty} 1/i^2$, and the quest for closed formulas for sums of powers, $\sum_{i=1}^{n} i^k \approx \int_0^n x^k \, dx$, which had been sought since antiquity for area and volume investigations. The summation formula helped Euler resolve both questions. This is a fine pedagogical illustration of how generalization and abstraction can lead to the combined solution of seemingly independent problems.

3 Sums of powers and Euler's summation formula: historically interlocked themes

Our story (told more completely elsewhere [19, 24]) begins in ancient times with the Greek approximations used to obtain areas and volumes by the method of exhaustion. The Pythagoreans (sixth century B.C.E.) knew that

$$1 + 2 + 3 + \cdots + n = \frac{n(n+1)}{2},$$

and Archimedes (third century B.C.E.) proved an equivalent to our modern formula

$$1^2 + 2^2 + 3^2 + \cdots + n^2 = \frac{n(n+1)(2n+1)}{6},$$

which he applied to deduce the area inside a spiral: "The area bounded by the first turn of the spiral and the initial line is equal to one-third of the first circle" [1, Spirals].

Summing yet higher powers was key to computing other areas and volumes, and one finds the formula for a sum of cubes in work of Nicomachus of Gerasa (first century B.C.E.), Āryabhaṭa in India (499 C.E.), and al-Karajī in the Arab world (circa 1000) [4; 15, p. 68f; 17, pp. 212f, 251ff] The first evidence of a general relationship between various exponents is in the further Arabic work of Abū ʿAlī al-Ḥasan ibn al-Haytham (965–1039), who needed a formula for sums of fourth powers to find the volume of a paraboloid of revolution. He discovered a doubly recursive relationship between exponents [17, p. 255f].

By the mid-seventeenth century Pierre de Fermat (1601–1665) and Blaise Pascal (1623–1662) had realized the general connection between the figurate (equivalently binomial co-efficient) numbers and sums of powers, motivated by the drive to determine areas under "higher parabolas" (i.e., $y = x^k$) [17, p. 481ff]. Fermat called the sums of powers challenge "what is perhaps the most beautiful problem of all arithmetic," and he claimed a recursive solution using figurate numbers. Pascal used binomial expansions and telescoping sums to obtain the first simply recursive relationship between sums of powers for varying exponents [4].

Jakob Bernoulli, during his work in the nascent field of probability, was the first to conjecture a general pattern in sums of powers formulas, simultaneously introducing the Bernoulli numbers into mathematics[5]. In his posthumous book of 1713, *The Art of Conjecturing* [3, volume 3, pp. 164–167], appears a section on *A Theory of Permutations and*

---

[5]The evidence suggests that around the same time, Takakazu Seki (1642?–1708) in Japan also discovered the same numbers [26, 28].

Combinations. Here one finds him first listing the formulas for *Sums of Powers* up to exponent ten (using the notation $\int$ for the discrete sum from 1 to n), and then claiming a pattern, to wit[6]:

❁❁❁❁❁❁

$$\int n = \frac{1}{2}nn + \frac{1}{2}n.$$

$$\int nn = \frac{1}{3}n^3 + \frac{1}{2}nn + \frac{1}{6}n.$$

$$\int n^3 = \frac{1}{4}n^4 + \frac{1}{2}n^3 + \frac{1}{4}nn.$$

$$\int n^4 = \frac{1}{5}n^5 + \frac{1}{2}n^4 + \frac{1}{3}n^3 * -\frac{1}{30}n.$$

$$\int n^5 = \frac{1}{6}n^6 + \frac{1}{2}n^5 + \frac{5}{12}n^4 * -\frac{1}{12}nn.$$

$$\int n^6 = \frac{1}{7}n^7 + \frac{1}{2}n^6 + \frac{1}{2}n^5 * -\frac{1}{6}n^3 * +\frac{1}{42}n.$$

$$\int n^7 = \frac{1}{8}n^8 + \frac{1}{2}n^7 + \frac{7}{12}n^6 * -\frac{7}{24}n^4 * +\frac{1}{12}nn.$$

$$\int n^8 = \frac{1}{9}n^9 + \frac{1}{2}n^8 + \frac{2}{3}n^7 * -\frac{7}{15}n^5 * +\frac{2}{9}n^3 * -\frac{1}{30}n.$$

$$\int n^9 = \frac{1}{10}n^{10} + \frac{1}{2}n^9 + \frac{3}{4}n^8 * -\frac{7}{10}n^6 * +\frac{1}{2}n^4 * -\frac{3}{20}nn.$$

$$\int n^{10} = \frac{1}{11}n^{11} + \frac{1}{2}n^{10} + \frac{5}{6}n^9 * -1n^7 * +1n^5 * -\frac{1}{2}n^3 * +\frac{5}{66}n.$$

Indeed, a pattern can be seen in the progressions herein which can be continued by means of this rule: Suppose that c is the value of any power; then the sum of all n^c or

$$\int n^c = \frac{1}{c+1}n^{c+1} + \frac{1}{2}n^c + \frac{c}{2}An^{c-1} + \frac{c \cdot c - 1 \cdot c - 2}{2 \cdot 3 \cdot 4}Bn^{c-3}$$

$$+ \frac{c \cdot c - 1 \cdot c - 2 \cdot c - 3 \cdot c - 4}{2 \cdot 3 \cdot 4 \cdot 5 \cdot 6}Cn^{c-5}$$

$$+ \frac{c \cdot c - 1 \cdot c - 2 \cdot c - 3 \cdot c - 4 \cdot c - 5 \cdot c - 6}{2 \cdot 3 \cdot 4 \cdot 5 \cdot 6 \cdot 7 \cdot 8}Dn^{c-7} \dots,$$

where the value of the power n continues to decrease by two until it reaches n or nn. The uppercase letters A, B, C, D, etc., in order, denote the coefficients of the final term of $\int nn$, $\int n^4, \int n^6, \int n^8$, etc., namely

$$A = \frac{1}{6}, \ B = -\frac{1}{30}, \ C = \frac{1}{42}, \ D = -\frac{1}{30}.$$

These coefficients are such that, when arranged with the other coefficients of the same order, they add up to unity: so, for D, which we said signified $-\frac{1}{30}$, we have

$$\frac{1}{9} + \frac{1}{2} + \frac{2}{3} - \frac{7}{15} + \frac{2}{9}(+D) - \frac{1}{30} = 1.$$

---

[6]Bernoulli's asterisks in the table indicate missing monomial terms. Also, there is an error in the original published Latin table of sums of powers formulas. The last coefficient in the formula for $\int n^9$ should be $-\frac{3}{20}$, not $-\frac{1}{12}$; we have corrected this here.

∞∞∞∞∞∞∞

At this point we modern readers could conceivably exhibit great retrospective pre-science, anticipate Euler's broader context of $\sum_{i=1}^{n} f(i)$, for which Bernoulli's claimed summation formula above provides test functions of the form $f(x) = x^c$, and venture a rash generalization:

$$\sum_{i=1}^{n} f(i) \approx C + \int^{n} f(x)dx + \frac{f(n)}{2} + A\frac{f'(n)}{2!} + B\frac{f'''(n)}{4!} + \cdots.$$

This formula is what Euler discovered in the early 1730s (although he was apparently unaware of Bernoulli's claim until later). Euler's summation formula captures the delicate details of the general connection between integration and discrete summation, and sub-sumes and resolves the two-thousand year old quest for sums of powers formulas as a simple special case. In what follows I will focus on just a few highlights from Euler.

4   The Basel problem and the summation formula

"Euler calculated without any apparent effort, just as men breathe, as eagles sustain them-selves in the air." Arago [29, p. 354]

Around the year 1730, the 23-year old Euler, along with his frequent correspondents Christian Goldbach (1690–1764) and Daniel Bernoulli (1700–1782), developed ways to find increasingly accurate fractional or decimal estimates for the sum of the reciprocal squares. But highly accurate estimates were challenging, since the series converges very slowly. They were likely trying to guess the exact value of the sum, hoping to recognize that their approximations hinted something familiar, perhaps involving π, like Leibniz's series, which had summed to $\pi/4$. Euler hit gold with the discovery of his summation for-mula. One of its first major uses was in a paper[7] submitted to the St. Petersburg Academy of Sciences on the 13th of October, 1735, in which he approximated the sum correctly to twenty decimal places. Only seven and a half weeks later Euler astonished his contem-poraries with another paper[8], solving the famous Basel problem by demonstrating with a completely different method that the precise sum of the series is $\pi^2/6$: "Now, however, quite unexpectedly, I have found an elegant formula for $1 + \frac{1}{4} + \frac{1}{9} + \frac{1}{16} +$ etc., depending upon the quadrature of the circle [i.e., upon π]" [27, p. 261]. Johann Bernoulli reacted "And so is satisfied the burning desire of my brother [Jakob] who, realizing that the investigation of the sum was more difficult than anyone would have thought, openly confessed that all his zeal had been mocked. If only my brother were alive now" [29, p. 345].

Much of Euler's *Calculi differentialis*, written two decades later, focused on the rela-tionship between differential calculus and infinite series, unifying his many discoveries in a single exposition. He devoted Chapters 5 and 6 of Part Two to the summation formula and a treasure trove of applications. In Chapter 5 Euler derived his summation formula, analyzed the generating function for Bernoulli numbers in terms of transcendental functions, derived several properties of Bernoulli numbers, showed that they grow supergeometrically, proved Bernoulli's formulas for sums of powers, and found the exact sums of all infinite series of

---

[7]E 47 in the Eneström Index [11].
[8]E 41.

reciprocal even powers in terms of Bernoulli numbers. Chapter 6 applied the summation formula to approximate harmonic partial sums and the associated "Euler" constant γ, sums of reciprocal powers, π, and sums of logarithms, leading to approximations for large factorials and binomial coefficients.

I will guide the reader through a few key passages from the translation. The reader may find more background, annotation, and exercises in our book [19] or explore my more extensive translation on the web [10]. The passages below contain Euler's derivation, the relation to Bernoulli numbers, application to reciprocal squares, and to sums of logarithms, large factorials, and binomials, with mention of other omitted passages. Each application uses the summation formula in a fundamentally different way. The complete glory of Euler's chapters is still available only in the original Latin [7, volume 10] or an old German translation [8] (poorly printed in Fraktur); I encourage the reader to revel in the original.

5   Euler's derivation

Euler's derivation of his summation formula rests on two ideas. First, he used Taylor series from calculus to relate the sum of the values of a function at finitely many successive integers to similar sums involving the derivatives of the function.

∞∞∞∞∞∞∞∞∞∞

Leonhard Euler, from
Foundations of Differential Calculus
Part Two, Chapter 5
On Finding Sums of Series from the General Term

105. Consider a series whose general term, belonging to the index x, is y, and whose preceding term, with index $x - 1$, is v; because v arises from y, when x is replaced by $x - 1$, one has[9]

$$v = y - \frac{dy}{dx} + \frac{d\,dy}{2dx^2} - \frac{d^3 y}{6dx^3} + \frac{d^4 y}{24dx^4} - \frac{d^5 y}{120dx^5} + \text{etc.}$$

If y is the general term of the series

$$
\begin{array}{ccccccc}
1 & 2 & 3 & 4 & \cdots & x-1 & x \\
a + & b + & c + & d + & \cdots + & v & + y
\end{array}
$$

and if the term belonging to the index 0 is A, then v, as a function of x, is the general term of the series

$$
\begin{array}{ccccccc}
1 & 2 & 3 & 4 & 5 & \cdots & x \\
A + & a + & b + & c + & d + & \cdots + & v \ ,
\end{array}
$$

so if Sv denotes the sum of this series, then $Sv = Sy - y + A$.

106. Because

$$v = y - \frac{dy}{dx} + \frac{d\,dy}{2dx^2} - \frac{d^3 y}{6dx^3} + \text{etc.,}$$

---

[9]Euler expressed the value v of his function at $x - 1$ in terms of its value y at x and the values of all its derivatives, also implicitly evaluated at x. This uses Taylor series with increment -1. Of course he was tacitly assuming that this all makes sense, i.e., that his function is infinitely differentiable, and that the Taylor series converges and equals its intended value. Note also that the symbols x and y are being used, respectively, to indicate the final value of an integer index and the final value of the function evaluated there, as well as more generally as a variable and a function of that variable. Today we would find this much too confusing to dare write this way.

one has, from the preceding,

$$Sv = Sy - S\frac{dy}{dx} + S\frac{d\,dy}{2dx^2} - S\frac{d^3y}{6dx^3} + S\frac{d^4y}{24dx^4} - \text{etc.,}$$

and, because $Sv = Sy - y + A$,

$$y - A = S\frac{dy}{dx} - S\frac{d\,dy}{2dx^2} + S\frac{d^3y}{6dx^3} - S\frac{d^4y}{24dx^4} + \text{etc.,}$$

or equivalently

$$S\frac{dy}{dx} = y - A + S\frac{d\,dy}{2dx^2} - S\frac{d^3y}{6dx^3} + S\frac{d^4y}{24dx^4} - \text{etc.}$$

Thus if one knows the sums of the series, whose general terms are

$$\frac{d\,dy}{dx^2}, \quad \frac{d^3y}{dx^3}, \quad \frac{d^4y}{dx^4}, \quad \text{etc.,}$$

one can obtain the summative term of the series whose general term is $\frac{dy}{dx}$. The constant A must then be such that the summative term $S\frac{dy}{dx}$ disappears when $x = 0 \ldots$

∞∞∞∞∞∞∞∞∞∞∞

Euler next applied this equation recursively, in §107–108, to demonstrate how one can obtain individual sums of powers formulas, because in these cases the derivatives will eventually vanish. He then continued with his second idea, which produced the summation formula.

∞∞∞∞∞∞∞∞∞∞∞

109. … if one sets $\frac{dy}{dx} = z$, then

$$Sz = \int z\,dx + \frac{1}{2}S\frac{dz}{dx} - \frac{1}{6}S\frac{d\,dz}{dx^2} + \frac{1}{24}S\frac{d^3z}{dx^3} - \text{etc.,}$$

adding to it a constant value such that when $x = 0$, the sum Sz also vanishes. …

110. But if in the expressions above one substitutes the letter z in place of y, or if one differentiates the preceding equation, which yields the same, one obtains

$$S\frac{dz}{dx} = z + \frac{1}{2}S\frac{d\,dz}{dx^2} - \frac{1}{6}S\frac{d^3z}{dx^3} + \frac{1}{24}S\frac{d^4z}{dx^4} - \text{etc.;}$$

but using $\frac{dz}{dx}$ in place of y one obtains

$$S\frac{d\,dz}{dx^2} = \frac{dz}{dx} + \frac{1}{2}S\frac{d^3z}{dx^3} - \frac{1}{6}S\frac{d^4z}{dx^4} + \frac{1}{24}S\frac{d^5z}{dx^5} - \text{etc.}$$

… and so forth indefinitely. …

111. Now when these values for

$$S\frac{dz}{dx}, \quad S\frac{d\,dz}{dx^2}, \quad S\frac{d^3z}{dx^3}$$

are successively substituted in the expression

$$Sz = \int z\,dx + \frac{1}{2}S\frac{dz}{dx} - \frac{1}{6}S\frac{d\,dz}{dx^2} + \frac{1}{24}S\frac{d^3z}{dx^3} - \text{etc.,}$$

one finds an expression for Sz, composed of the terms $\int z\,dx$, z, $\frac{dz}{dx}$, $\frac{ddz}{dx^2}$, $\frac{d^3z}{dx^3}$ etc., whose coefficients are easily obtained as follows. One sets

$$Sz = \int z\,dx + \alpha z + \frac{\beta\,dz}{dx} + \frac{\gamma\,ddz}{dx^2} + \frac{\delta\,d^3z}{dx^3} + \frac{\varepsilon\,d^4z}{dx^4} + \text{etc.,}$$

and substitutes for these terms the values they have from the previous series, yielding

$$\int z\,dx = Sz - \frac{1}{2}S\frac{dz}{dx} + \frac{1}{6}S\frac{ddz}{dx^2} - \frac{1}{24}S\frac{d^3z}{dx^3} + \frac{1}{120}S\frac{d^4z}{dx^4} - \text{etc.}$$

$$\alpha z = \quad + \alpha S\frac{dz}{dx} - \frac{\alpha}{2}S\frac{ddz}{dx^2} + \frac{\alpha}{6}S\frac{d^3z}{dx^3} - \frac{\alpha}{24}S\frac{d^4z}{dz^4} + \text{etc.}$$

$$\frac{\beta\,dz}{dx} = \qquad\qquad \beta S\frac{ddz}{dx^2} - \frac{\beta}{2}S\frac{d^3z}{dx^3} + \frac{\beta}{6}S\frac{d^4z}{dx^4} - \text{etc.}$$

$$\frac{\gamma\,ddz}{dx^2} = \qquad\qquad\qquad \gamma S\frac{d^3z}{dx^3} - \frac{\gamma}{2}S\frac{d^4z}{dx^4} + \text{etc.}$$

$$\frac{\delta\,d^3z}{dx^3} = \qquad\qquad\qquad\qquad \delta\,S\frac{d^4z}{dx^4} - \text{etc.}$$

$$\text{etc.}$$

Since these values, added together, must produce Sz, the coefficients $\alpha, \beta, \gamma, \delta$ etc. are ...

112. ...

$$\alpha = \frac{1}{2}, \quad \beta = \frac{\alpha}{2} - \frac{1}{6} = \frac{1}{12}, \quad \gamma = \frac{\beta}{2} - \frac{\alpha}{6} + \frac{1}{24} = 0,$$

$$\delta = \frac{\gamma}{2} - \frac{\beta}{6} + \frac{\alpha}{24} - \frac{1}{120} = -\frac{1}{720}, \quad \varepsilon = \frac{\delta}{2} - \frac{\gamma}{6} + \frac{\beta}{24} - \frac{\alpha}{120} + \frac{1}{720} = 0 \text{ etc.,}$$

and if one continues in this fashion one finds that alternating terms vanish.

6 Connection to Bernoulli numbers and sums of powers

Before Euler showed how to apply his summation formula to derive new results, in §112–120 he intensively studied the coefficients $\alpha, \beta, \gamma, \ldots$, and discovered that their generating function relates directly to the transcendental functions of calculus, especially the cotangent. In particular, Euler proved that every second coefficient vanishes, and that those that remain alternate in sign, by investigating a power series solution to the differential equation satisfied by the cotangent function by dint of its derivative formula. Euler also explored number theoretic properties of the coefficients, including the growth and prime factorizations of their numerators and denominators, some of which we will see below.

Caution: In the process of distilling the summation formula in terms of Bernoulli numbers, Euler switched the meaning of the Greek letters $\alpha, \beta, \gamma, \delta, \ldots$, and the formula now takes revised form:

∞∞∞∞∞∞∞∞∞∞

121. ... If one finds the values of the [redefined] letters $\alpha, \beta, \gamma, \delta$, etc. according to this rule, which entails little difficulty in calculation, then one can express the summative term of

any series, whose general term $= z$ corresponding to the index x, in the following fashion:

$$Sz = \int z\,dx + \frac{1}{2}z + \frac{\alpha\,dz}{1\cdot2\cdot3\,dx} - \frac{\beta\,d^3z}{1\cdot2\cdot3\cdot4\cdot5\,dx^3} + \frac{\gamma\,d^5z}{1\cdot2\cdots7\,dx^5}$$

$$- \frac{\delta\,d^7z}{1\cdot2\cdots9\,dx^7} + \frac{\varepsilon\,d^9z}{1\cdot2\cdots11\,dx^9} - \frac{\zeta\,d^{11}z}{1\cdot2\cdots13\,dx^{11}} + \text{etc.}\dots$$

122. These numbers have great use throughout the entire theory of series. First, one can obtain from them the final terms in the sums of even powers, for which we noted above (in §63 of part one) that one cannot obtain them, as one can the other terms, from the sums of earlier powers. For the even powers, the last terms of the sums are products of x and certain numbers, namely for the 2nd, 4th, 6th, 8th, etc., $\frac{1}{6}$, $\frac{1}{30}$, $\frac{1}{42}$, $\frac{1}{30}$ etc. with alternating signs. But these numbers arise from the values of the letters α, β, γ, δ, etc., which we found earlier, when one divides them by the odd numbers 3, 5, 7, 9, etc. These numbers are called the Bernoulli numbers after their discoverer Jakob Bernoulli, and they are

$$\frac{\alpha}{3} = \frac{1}{6} = \mathfrak{A} \qquad \frac{\iota}{19} = \frac{43867}{798} = \mathfrak{I}$$

$$\frac{\beta}{5} = \frac{1}{30} = \mathfrak{B} \qquad \frac{\varkappa}{21} = \frac{174611}{330} = \mathfrak{K} = \frac{283\cdot617}{330}$$

$$\frac{\gamma}{7} = \frac{1}{42} = \mathfrak{C} \qquad \frac{\lambda}{23} = \frac{854513}{138} = \mathfrak{L} = \frac{11\cdot131\cdot593}{2\cdot3\cdot23}$$

$$\frac{\delta}{9} = \frac{1}{30} = \mathfrak{D} \qquad \frac{\mu}{25} = \frac{236364091}{2730} = \mathfrak{M}$$

$$\frac{\varepsilon}{11} = \frac{5}{66} = \mathfrak{E} \qquad \frac{\nu}{27} = \frac{8553103}{6} = \mathfrak{N} = \frac{13\cdot657931}{6}$$

$$\frac{\zeta}{13} = \frac{691}{2730} = \mathfrak{F} \qquad \frac{\xi}{29} = \frac{23749461029}{870} = \mathfrak{O}$$

$$\frac{\eta}{15} = \frac{7}{6} = \mathfrak{G} \qquad \frac{\pi}{31} = \frac{8615841276005}{14322} = \mathfrak{P}$$

$$\frac{\theta}{17} = \frac{3617}{510} = \mathfrak{H} \qquad \text{etc.}$$

Euler's very first application of the Bernoulli numbers, in §124–125, was to solve a problem dear to his heart, determining the precise sums of all infinite series of reciprocal even powers. His result (using today's notation $\mathfrak{A} = B_2$, $\mathfrak{B} = -B_4$, $\mathfrak{C} = B_6$, ...) was:

$$\sum_{i=1}^{\infty} \frac{1}{i^{2n}} = \frac{(-1)^{n+1} B_{2n} 2^{2n-1}}{(2n)!} \pi^{2n} \text{ for all } n \geq 1.$$

Because these sums approach one as n grows, he also obtained, in §129, an asymptotic understanding of how Bernoulli numbers grow:

$$\frac{B_{2n+2}}{B_{2n}} \approx -\frac{(2n+2)(2n+1)}{4\pi^2} \approx -\frac{n^2}{\pi^2}.$$

Thus he commented that they "form a highly diverging sequence, which grows more strongly than any geometric sequence of growing terms."

This completed Euler's analysis of the Bernoulli numbers. Now he was ready to turn his summation formula towards applications. He ended Chapter 5 with applications in which the summation formula is finite (§131), including that of a pure power function, which proved the formulas for sums of powers discovered by Bernoulli (§132).

7 "Until it begins to diverge"

Chapter 6 applies the summation formula to make approximations even when it diverges, which it does in almost all interesting situations.

Part Two, Chapter 6
On the summing of progressions via infinite series

140. The general expression, that we found in the previous chapter for the summative term of a series, whose general term corresponding to the index x is z, namely

$$Sz = \int z dx + \frac{1}{2} z + \frac{\mathfrak{A} dz}{1 \cdot 2 dx} - \frac{\mathfrak{B} d^3 z}{1 \cdot 2 \cdot 3 \cdot 4 dx^3} + \frac{\mathfrak{C} d^5 z}{1 \cdot 2 \cdots 6 dx^5} - \text{etc.},$$

actually serves to determine the sums of series, whose general terms are integral rational functions[10] of the index x, because in these cases one eventually arrives at vanishing differentials. On the other hand, if z is not such a function of x, then the differentials continue without end, and there results an infinite series that expresses the sum of the given series up to and including the term whose index $= x$. The sum of the series, continuing without end, is thus given by taking $x = \infty$, and one finds in this way another infinite series equal to the original....

142. Since when a constant value is added to the sum, so that it vanishes when $x = 0$, the true sum is then found when x is any other number, then it is clear that the true sum must likewise be given, whenever a constant value is added that produces the true sum in any particular case. Thus suppose it is not obvious, when one sets $x = 0$, what value the sum assumes and thus what constant must be used; one can substitute other values for x, and through addition of a constant value obtain a complete expression for the sum. Much will become clear from the following.

For a particular choice of antiderivative $\int z dx$, the constant of interest is today called the "Euler-Maclaurin constant" for the function z and a chosen antiderivative $\int z dx$.

There follow Euler's §142a–144, in which he made the first application of his summation formula to an infinite series, the diverging harmonic series $\sum_{i=1}^{\infty} 1/i$. For this series, the Euler-Maclaurin constant in his summation formula will be the limiting difference between $\sum_{i=1}^{x} 1/i$ and $\ln x$. Today we call this particular number the "Euler-Mascheroni constant," and denote it by γ. It is arguably the third most important constant in mathematics after π and e. Euler showed how to extract from the summation formula an approximation of γ accurate to 15 places and then easily obtained the sum of the first thousand terms of the diverging harmonic series to 13 places (see [10]). In fact it is clear from what he wrote that one could use his approach to approximate γ to whatever accuracy desired, and then apply the summation formula to find the value of arbitrarily large finite harmonic sums to that same accuracy. I will discuss in a moment the paradox that he can obtain arbitrarily accurate approximations for the Euler-Maclaurin constant of a function and a chosen antiderivative from a diverging summation!

We continue on to see exactly how Euler applied the summation formula to that old puzzle, the Basel problem.

[10] By this he means polynomials.

ᴄᴅᴄᴅᴄᴅᴄᴅᴄᴅᴄᴅᴏ

148. After considering the harmonic series we wish to turn to examining the series of reciprocals of the squares, letting

$$s = 1 + \frac{1}{4} + \frac{1}{9} + \frac{1}{16} + \cdots + \frac{1}{xx}.$$

Since the general term of this series is $z = \frac{1}{xx}$, then $\int z\,dx = \frac{-1}{x}$, the differentials of z are

$$\frac{dz}{2dx} = -\frac{1}{x^3}, \quad \frac{d\,dz}{2 \cdot 3 dx^2} = \frac{1}{x^4}, \quad \frac{d^3 z}{2 \cdot 3 \cdot 4 dx^3} = -\frac{1}{x^5} \quad \text{etc.,}$$

and the sum is

$$s = C - \frac{1}{x} + \frac{1}{2xx} - \frac{\mathfrak{A}}{x^3} + \frac{\mathfrak{B}}{x^5} - \frac{\mathfrak{C}}{x^7} + \frac{\mathfrak{D}}{x^9} - \frac{\mathfrak{E}}{x^{11}} + \text{etc.,}$$

where the added constant C is determined from one case in which the sum is known. We therefore wish to set $x = 1$. Since then $s = 1$, one has

$$C = 1 + 1 - \frac{1}{2} + \mathfrak{A} - \mathfrak{B} + \mathfrak{C} - \mathfrak{D} + \mathfrak{E} - \text{etc.,}$$

but this series alone does not give the value of C, since it diverges strongly.

ᴄᴅᴄᴅᴄᴅᴄᴅᴄᴅᴄᴅᴏ

On the face of it, these formulas seem both absurd and useless. The expression Euler obtains for the Euler-Maclaurin constant C is clearly a divergent series. In fact the summation formula here diverges for every x because of the supergeometric growth established for Bernoulli numbers. Euler, however, was not fazed: he has a plan for obtaining from such divergent series highly accurate approximations for both very large finite and infinite series.

Euler's idea was to add up the terms in the summation formula only *"until it begins to diverge."* For those unfamiliar with the theory of divergent series, this seems preposterous, but in fact it has sound theoretical underpinnings. Euler's approach was ultimately vindicated by the modern theory of asymptotic series [13, 14, 16, 20]. Euler himself was probably confident of his results, despite the apparently shaky foundations in divergent series, because he was continually checking and rechecking his answers by a variety of theoretical and computational methods, boosting his confidence in their correctness from many different angles. Let us see how Euler continues analyzing the sum of reciprocal squares, begun above.

First he recalled that for this particular function, he already knew the value of C by other means.

ᴄᴅᴄᴅᴄᴅᴄᴅᴄᴅᴄᴅᴏ

Above we demonstrated that the sum of the series to infinity is $= \frac{\pi\pi}{6}$, and therefore setting $x = \infty$, and $s = \frac{\pi\pi}{6}$, we have $C = \frac{\pi\pi}{6}$, because then all other terms vanish. Thus it follows that

$$1 + 1 - \frac{1}{2} + \mathfrak{A} - \mathfrak{B} + \mathfrak{C} - \mathfrak{D} + \mathfrak{E} - \text{etc.} = \frac{\pi\pi}{6}.$$

ᴄᴅᴄᴅᴄᴅᴄᴅᴄᴅᴄᴅᴏ

Next Euler imagined that he didn't already know the sum of the infinite series of reciprocal squares, and approximated it using his summation formula, thereby performing a cross-check on both methods.

∞◁▷◁▷◁▷◁▷◁▷∞

149. If the sum of this series were not known, then one would need to determine the value of the constant C from another case, in which the sum were actually found. To this aim we set $x = 10$ and actually add up ten terms, obtaining[11]

$$s = 1,549767731166540690.$$

Further, add $\quad \dfrac{1}{x} = 0,1$

subtr. $\quad \dfrac{1}{2xx} = 0,005$

$$\overline{1,644767731166540690}$$

add $\quad \dfrac{\mathfrak{A}}{x^3} = 0,000166666666666666$

$$\overline{1,644934397833207356}$$

subtr. $\quad \dfrac{\mathfrak{B}}{x^5} = 0,000000333333333333$

$$\overline{1,644934064499874023}$$

add $\quad \dfrac{\mathfrak{C}}{x^7} = 0,000000002380952381$

$$\overline{1,644934066880826404}$$

subtr. $\quad \dfrac{\mathfrak{D}}{x^9} = 0,000000000033333333$

$$\overline{1,644934066847493071}$$

add $\quad \dfrac{\mathfrak{E}}{x^{11}} = 0,000000000000757575$

$$\overline{1,644934066848250646}$$

subtr. $\quad \dfrac{\mathfrak{F}}{x^{13}} = 0,000000000000025311$

$$\overline{1,644934066848225335}$$

add $\quad \dfrac{\mathfrak{G}}{x^{15}} = 0,000000000000001166$

subtr. $\quad \dfrac{\mathfrak{H}}{x^{17}} = \qquad\qquad 71$

$$\overline{1,644934066848226430} = C.$$

This number is likewise the value of the expression $\frac{\pi\pi}{6}$, as one can find by calculation from the known value of π. From this it is clear that, although the series $\mathfrak{A}$, $\mathfrak{B}$, $\mathfrak{C}$, etc. diverges, it nevertheless produces a true sum.

∞◁▷◁▷◁▷◁▷◁▷∞

So, on the one hand the summation formula diverges for every x, and yet on the other it can apparently be used to make very close approximations, in fact arbitrarily close approximations, to C. How can this be?

Note that the terms Euler actually calculated appear to decrease rapidly, giving the initial appearance, albeit illusory, that the series converges. Examining the terms more closely, one can see evidence that their decrease is slowing in a geometric sense, which hints at the fact that the series actually diverges. Recall that Euler intended to sum only *"until it begins to diverge."* How did he decide when this occurs? Notice that the series alternates in sign, and thus the partial sums bounce back and forth, at first apparently converging, then

---

[11] Euler used commas (as is still done in Europe today) rather than points, for separating the integer and fractional parts of a decimal.

diverging as the terms themselves eventually increase due to rapid growth of the Bernoulli numbers. Euler knew to stop before the smallest bounce, with the expectation that the true sum he sought lies between any partial sum and the next one, and is thus bracketed most accurately if one stops just before the smallest term is included.

Much later, through the course of the nineteenth century, mathematicians would wrestle with the validity, theory and usefulness of divergent series. Two (divergent) views reflected this struggle, and exemplified the evolution of mathematics:

"The divergent series are the invention of the devil, and it is a shame to base on them any demonstration whatsoever. By using them, one may draw any conclusion he pleases and that is why these series have produced so many fallacies and so many paradoxes.... I have become prodigiously attentive to all this, for with the exception of the geometrical series, there does not exist in all of mathematics a single infinite series the sum of which has been determined rigorously. In other words, the things which are most important in mathematics are also those which have the least foundation.... That most of these things are correct in spite of that is extraordinarily surprising. I am trying to find a reason for this; it is an exceedingly interesting question." Niels Abel (1802–1829), 1826 [18, p. 973f].

"The series is divergent; therefore we may be able to do something with it." Oliver Heaviside (1850–1925) [18, p. 1096].

Euler, long before this, was confident in proceeding according to his simple dictum *"until it begins to diverge."* Indeed, it is astounding but true that the summation formula does behave exactly as Euler used it for many functions, including all the ones Euler was interested in. Today we know for certain that such "asymptotic series" indeed bracket the desired answer, and diverge more and more slowly for larger and larger values of x, making them extremely useful for approximations [14; 16; 18, chapter 47; 20].

One can explore the interplay of calculation versus accuracy achieved by different choices for x. A smaller choice for x will cause the summation formula to begin to diverge sooner, and with a larger final bounce, yielding less accuracy. On the other hand, a larger x will ensure much more rapid achievement of a given level of accuracy, and greater bounding accuracy (as small as desired) for the answer, at the expense of having to compute a longer partial sum on the left-hand side to get the calculation off the ground. Asymptotic series have become important in applications of differential equations to physical problems [18, chapter 47].

Euler's next application of the summation formula, in §150–153, was to approximate the sums of reciprocal odd powers. I remarked above that Euler's very first application of the Bernoulli numbers was to determine the precise sums of all infinite series of reciprocal even powers. Naturally he also would have loved to find formulas for the reciprocal odd powers, and he explored this at length using the summation formula. He produced highly accurate decimal approximations for sums of reciprocal odd powers all the way through the fifteenth, hoping to see a pattern analogous to the even powers, namely simple fractions times the relevant power of π. The first such converging series is the sum of reciprocal cubes $\sum_{i=1}^{\infty} 1/i^3$. Euler computed it accurately to seventeen decimal places. He was disappointed, however, to find that it is not near an obvious rational multiple of π^3, nor did he have better luck with the other odd powers. Even today we know little about these sums of odd powers, although not for lack of trying.

Following this, in §154–156 Euler approximated π to seventeen decimal places using the inverse tangent and cotangent functions with the summation formula. He actually expressed his own amazement that one can approximate π so accurately with such an easy calculation!

8   How to determine (or not) factorials

I will showcase next Euler's efficacious use of the summation formula to approximate finite sums of logarithms, and thus by exponentiating, to approximate very large factorials via the formula now known as Stirling's asymptotic approximation. Notice particularly Euler's ingenious determination of the Euler-Maclaurin constant in the summation formula, from Wallis' infinite product for π.

I will also briefly explore whether the summation formula can determine a factorial precisely, yielding surprising results.

To set the stage for Euler, notice that to estimate a factorial, one can estimate $\log(x!) = \log 1 + \log 2 + \cdots + \log x$, using any base, provided one also knows how to find antilogarithms.

∞◇◇◇◇◇◇◇◇◇∞

157. Now we want to use for z transcendental functions of x, and take $z = lx$ for summing hyperbolic[12] logarithms, from which the ordinary can easily be recovered, so that

$$s = l1 + l2 + l3 + l4 + \cdots + lx.$$

Because $z = lx$,

$$\int z\, dx = xlx - x,$$

since its differential is $dx\, lx$. Then

$$\frac{dz}{dx} = \frac{1}{x}, \quad \frac{d\,dz}{dx^2} = -\frac{1}{x^2}, \quad \frac{d^3 z}{1\cdot 2 dx^3} = \frac{1}{x^3},$$

$$\frac{d^4 z}{1\cdot 2\cdot 3 dx^4} = -\frac{1}{x^4}, \quad \frac{d^5 z}{1\cdot 2\cdot 3\cdot 4 dx^5} = \frac{1}{x^5}, \quad \text{etc.}$$

One concludes that

$$s = xlx - x + \frac{1}{2}lx + \frac{\mathfrak{A}}{1\cdot 2x} - \frac{\mathfrak{B}}{3\cdot 4x^3} + \frac{\mathfrak{C}}{5\cdot 6x^5} - \frac{\mathfrak{D}}{7\cdot 8x^7} + \text{etc.} + \text{Const.}$$

But for this constant one finds, when one sets $x = 1$, because then $s = l1 = 0$,

$$C = 1 - \frac{\mathfrak{A}}{1\cdot 2} + \frac{\mathfrak{B}}{3\cdot 4} - \frac{\mathfrak{C}}{5\cdot 6} + \frac{\mathfrak{D}}{7\cdot 8} - \text{etc.,}$$

a series that, due to its great divergence, is quite unsuitable even for determining the approximate value of C.

158. Nevertheless we can not only approximate the correct value of C, but can obtain it exactly, by considering Wallis's expression for π provided in the *Introductio* [6, volume 1, chapter 11]. This expression is

$$\frac{\pi}{2} = \frac{2\cdot 2\cdot 4\cdot 4\cdot 6\cdot 6\cdot 8\cdot 8\cdot 10\cdot 10\cdot 12\cdot \text{ etc.}}{1\cdot 3\cdot 3\cdot 5\cdot 5\cdot 7\cdot 7\cdot 9\cdot 9\cdot 11\cdot 11\cdot \text{ etc.}}.$$

---

[12]Euler called "hyperbolic" logarithms what we today call "natural" logarithms.

Taking logarithms, one obtains from this

$$l\pi - l2 = 2l2 + 2l4 + 2l6 + 2l8 + 2l10 + l12 + \text{ etc.}$$
$$-l1 - 2l3 - 2l5 - 2l7 - 2l9 - 2l11 - \text{ etc.}$$

Setting $x = \infty$ in the assumed series, we have

$$l1 + l2 + l3 + l4 + \cdots + lx = C + \left(x + \frac{1}{2}\right)lx - x,$$

thus

$$l1 + l2 + l3 + l4 + \cdots + l2x = C + \left(2x + \frac{1}{2}\right)l2x - 2x$$

and

$$l2 + l4 + l6 + l8 + \cdots + l2x = C + \left(x + \frac{1}{2}\right)lx + xl2 - x,$$

and therefore

$$l1 + l3 + l5 + l7 + \cdots + l(2x - 1) = xlx + \left(x + \frac{1}{2}\right)l2 - x.$$

Thus because

$$l\frac{\pi}{2} = 2l2 + 2l4 + 2l6 + \cdots + 2l2x - l2x$$
$$- 2l1 - 2l3 - 2l5 - \cdots - 2l(2x - 1),$$

letting $x = \infty$ yields

$$l\frac{\pi}{2} = 2C + (2x + 1)lx + 2xl2 - 2x - l2 - lx - 2xlx - (2x + 1)l2 + 2x,$$

and therefore

$$l\frac{\pi}{2} = 2C - 2l2, \quad \text{thus} \quad 2C = l2\pi \quad \text{and} \quad C = \frac{1}{2}l2\pi,$$

yielding the decimal fraction representation

$$C = 0,9189385332046727417803297,$$

thus simultaneously the sum of the series

$$1 - \frac{\mathfrak{A}}{1 \cdot 2} + \frac{\mathfrak{B}}{3 \cdot 4} - \frac{\mathfrak{C}}{5 \cdot 6} + \frac{\mathfrak{D}}{7 \cdot 8} - \frac{\mathfrak{E}}{9 \cdot 10} + \text{ etc.} = \frac{1}{2}l2\pi.$$

159. Since we now know the constant $C = \frac{1}{2}l2\pi$, one can exhibit the sum of any number of logarithms from the series $l1 + l2 + l3 +$ etc. If one sets

$$s = l1 + l2 + l3 + l4 + \cdots + lx,$$

then

$$s = \frac{1}{2}l2\pi + \left(x + \frac{1}{2}\right)lx - x + \frac{\mathfrak{A}}{1 \cdot 2x} - \frac{\mathfrak{B}}{3 \cdot 4x^3} + \frac{\mathfrak{C}}{5 \cdot 6x^5} - \frac{\mathfrak{D}}{7 \cdot 8x^7} + \text{ etc.}$$

if the proposed logarithms are hyperbolic; if however the proposed logarithms are common, then one must take common logarithms also in the terms $\frac{1}{2}l2\pi + (x + \frac{1}{2})lx$ for $l2\pi$ and lx, and multiply the remaining terms

$$-x + \frac{\mathfrak{A}}{1 \cdot 2x} - \frac{\mathfrak{B}}{3 \cdot 4x^3} + \text{ etc.}$$

of the series by $0,434294481903251827 = n$. In this case the common logarithms are

$$l\pi = 0,497149872694133854351268$$
$$l2 = 0,301029995663981195213738$$
$$l2\pi = 0,798179868358115049565006$$
$$\frac{1}{2}l2\pi = 0,399089934179057524782503.$$

Example.

Find the sum of the first thousand common logarithms

$$s = l1 + l2 + l3 + \cdots + l1000.$$

So $x = 1000$, and

$$lx = \quad 3,0000000000000,$$
and thus $xlx = 3000,0000000000000$
$$\frac{1}{2}lx = \quad 1,5000000000000$$
$$\frac{1}{2}l2\pi = \quad 0,3990899341790$$
$$\overline{3001,8990899341790}$$

subtr. $nx = \quad 434,2944819032518$
$$\overline{2567,6046080309272.}$$

Then
$$\frac{n\mathfrak{A}}{1\cdot2x} = \quad 0,0000361912068$$
subtr. $\frac{n\mathfrak{B}}{3\cdot4x^3} = \quad 0,0000000000012$
$$\overline{0,0000361912056}$$

add $\quad 2567,6046080309272$
the sum sought $s = 2567,6046442221328.$

Now because s is the logarithm of a product of numbers

$$1 \cdot 2 \cdot 3 \cdot 4 \cdot 5 \cdot 6 \cdots 1000,$$

it is clear that this product, if one actually multiplies it out, consists of 2568 figures, beginning with the figures 4023872, with 2561 subsequent figures.

∞∞∞∞∞∞∞∞∞

One wonders how accurate such factorial approximations from the summation formula can actually be. Exponentiating Euler's summation formula above for a sum of logarithms produces the Stirling asymptotic approximation:

$$x! \approx \frac{\sqrt{2\pi x}\,x^x}{e^x}e^{\left(\mathfrak{A}/(1\cdot2x)-\mathfrak{B}/(3\cdot4x^3)+\mathfrak{C}/(5\cdot6x^5)-\mathfrak{D}/(7\cdot8x^7)+\cdots\right)}.$$

Because the summation formula diverges for each x, the accuracy of this approximation is theoretically limited. Yet the value sought always lies between those of successive partial sums. Moreover, from the asymptotic growth rate of Bernoulli numbers obtained earlier, we see that approximately the first πx terms in the exponent might be expected to decrease (recall that for $x = 1000$ Euler used only two terms), with divergence occurring after that.

To explore the accuracy achievable with this formula, let us denote by $S(x, m)$ the approximation to $x!$ using the first m terms in the exponent. Note that the discussion above tells us to expect this approximation to "start to diverge" after using around $x\pi$ terms in the exponent, i.e., near $S(x, \pi x)$. Beginning modestly with $x = 10$, calculations with Maple show that 3628800 is the only integer between $S(10, 2)$ and $S(10, 3)$, thus determining 10! on the nose. So although the summation formula has limited accuracy, it suffices to determine easily the integer 10! uniquely.

And for $x = 50$, one finds that
30414093201713378043612608166064768844377641568960512000000000000
is the only integer between $S(50, 26)$ and $S(50, 27)$, thus producing all 65 digits of 50!. This striking accuracy, and using so few of the roughly πx terms that in each case we expect to provide ever better approximations, leads us to ask:

Question: Can one obtain the exact value of any factorial this way?

There is an interplay here as x grows. Certainly the exponent becomes more accurately known for larger x, using a given number of terms, and moreover even more precisely known from the diverging series generally, which improves for around $x\pi$ terms. On the other hand, it is then being exponentiated, and finally, multiplied times something growing, to produce the factorial approximation. So it is not so clear whether the factorial itself will always be sufficiently trapped to determine its integer value.

Continuing experimentally, let us compare with $x = 100$. First, note that 100! is approximately 9.33×10^{157}. Using the same number of terms, 27, as was needed above to determine uniquely all 65 digits of 50!, one finds that $S(100, 27)$ agrees with 100! for the first 82 digits. Thus it is giving more digits than when $x = 50$, but does not yet determine all the digits of 100!. Further calculation shows that 100! is however the unique integer first bracketed by $S(100, 74)$ and $S(100, 75)$. In fact, from above one expects improvement for 100π terms. While one still seems to have lots of terms to spare, one worries that, as x increases, with the number of decreasing terms in the summation only increasing linearly with x, i.e., as πx, the number of terms needed to bracket the factorial uniquely may be growing faster than this. In particular, when one doubled x from 50 to 100, the number of terms needed to determine the factorial increased from 27 to 75, more than doubling.

Both my theoretical analysis and further Maple computations ultimately confirm this fear, eventually answering the question in the negative. But the size of the factorials that are actually uniquely determined as integers by Euler's summation formula, before it finally cannot keep up with all the digits, is staggering. For instance, Euler showed above that 1000! possesses 2568 digits, of which he calculated the first seven. My theoretical analysis shows that the Stirling approximation based on Euler's summation formula will determine every one of those 2568 digits before it diverges.

9   Large binomials

In our final excerpt, Euler applied the summation formula to estimate the size of large binomial coefficients. I translate just one of his methods here, in which he merged two summation series term by term. As a sample application, Euler studied the ratio $\binom{100}{50}/2^{100}$, despite the huge size of its parts, thus closely approximating the probability that if one tosses 100 coins, exactly equal numbers will land heads and tails.

⊂⊃⊂⊃⊂⊃⊂⊃⊂⊃⊂⊃⊂⊃

160. By means of this summation of logarithms, one can approximate the product of any number of factors, that progress in the order of the natural numbers. This can be especially helpful for the problem of finding the middle or largest coefficient of any power in the binomial $(a + b)^m$, where one notes that, when m is an odd number, one always has two equal middle coefficients, which taken together produce the middle coefficient of the next even power. Thus since the largest coefficient of any even power is twice as large as the middle coefficient of the immediately preceding odd power, it suffices to determine the middle largest coefficient of an even power. Thus we have $m = 2n$ with middle coefficient expressed as

$$\frac{2n\,(2n-1)\,(2n-2)\,(2n-3)\cdots(n+1)}{1 \cdot 2 \cdot 3 \cdot 4 \cdots n}.$$

Setting this $= u$, one has

$$u = \frac{1 \cdot 2 \cdot 3 \cdot 4 \cdot 5 \cdots 2n}{(1 \cdot 2 \cdot 3 \cdot 4 \cdots n)^2},$$

and taking logarithms

$$lu = l1 + l2 + l3 + l4 + l5 + \cdots l2n$$
$$- 2l1 - 2l2 - 2l3 - 2l4 - 2l5 - \cdots - 2ln.$$

161. The sum of hyperbolic logarithms is

$$l1 + l2 + l3 + l4 + \cdots + l2n = \frac{1}{2}l2\pi + \left(2n + \frac{1}{2}\right)ln + \left(2n + \frac{1}{2}\right)l2 - 2n$$
$$+ \frac{\mathfrak{A}}{1 \cdot 2 \cdot 2n} - \frac{\mathfrak{B}}{3 \cdot 4 \cdot 2^3 n^3} + \frac{\mathfrak{C}}{5 \cdot 6 \cdot 2^5 n^5} - \text{etc.}$$

and

$$2l1 + 2l2 + 2l3 + 2l4 + \cdots + 2ln$$
$$= l2\pi + (2n+1)ln - 2n + \frac{2\mathfrak{A}}{1 \cdot 2n} - \frac{2\mathfrak{B}}{3 \cdot 4n^3} + \frac{2\mathfrak{C}}{5 \cdot 6n^5} - \text{etc.}$$

Subtracting this expression from the former yields

$$lu = -\frac{1}{2}l\pi - \frac{1}{2}ln + 2nl2 + \frac{\mathfrak{A}}{1 \cdot 2 \cdot 2n} - \frac{\mathfrak{B}}{3 \cdot 4 \cdot 2^3 n^3} + \frac{\mathfrak{C}}{5 \cdot 6 \cdot 2^5 n^5} - \text{etc.}$$
$$- \frac{2\mathfrak{A}}{1 \cdot 2n} + \frac{2\mathfrak{B}}{3 \cdot 4n^3} - \frac{2\mathfrak{C}}{5 \cdot 6n^5} + \text{etc.},$$

and collecting terms in pairs[13]

$$lu = l\frac{2^{2n}}{\sqrt{n\pi}} - \frac{3\mathfrak{A}}{1 \cdot 2 \cdot 2n} + \frac{15\mathfrak{B}}{3 \cdot 4 \cdot 2^3 n^3} - \frac{63\mathfrak{C}}{5 \cdot 6 \cdot 2^5 n^5} + \frac{255\mathfrak{D}}{7 \cdot 8 \cdot 2^7 n^7} - \text{etc.}$$

162. ...

Second Example

Find the ratio of the middle term of the binomial $(1 + 1)^{100}$ to the sum 2^{100} of all the terms.

---

[13] Note that Euler's notation leaves us to keep track of the scope of the square root symbol.

For this we wish to use the formula we found first,

$$lu = l\frac{2^{2n}}{\sqrt{n\pi}} - \frac{3\mathfrak{A}}{1\cdot2\cdot2n} + \frac{15\mathfrak{B}}{3\cdot4\cdot2^3n^3} - \frac{63\mathfrak{C}}{5\cdot6\cdot2^5n^5} + \text{ etc.,}$$

from which, setting $2n = m$, in order to obtain the power $(1 + 1)^m$, and after substituting the values of the letters $\mathfrak{A}$, $\mathfrak{B}$, $\mathfrak{C}$, $\mathfrak{D}$ etc., one has

$$lu = l\frac{2^m}{\sqrt{\frac{1}{2}m\pi}} - \frac{1}{4m} + \frac{1}{24m^3} - \frac{1}{20m^5} + \frac{17}{112m^7} - \frac{31}{36m^9} + \frac{691}{88m^{11}} - \text{ etc.}$$

Since the logarithms here are hyperbolic, one multiplies by

$$k = 0,434294481903251,$$

in order to change to tables, yielding

$$lu = l\frac{2^m}{\sqrt{\frac{1}{2}m\pi}} - \frac{k}{4m} + \frac{k}{24m^3} - \frac{k}{20m^5} + \frac{17k}{112m^7} - \frac{31k}{36m^9} + \text{ etc.,}$$

Now since u is the middle coefficient, the ratio sought is $2^m : u$, and

$$l\frac{2^m}{u} = l\sqrt{\frac{1}{2}m\pi} + \frac{k}{4m} - \frac{k}{24m^3} + \frac{k}{20m^5} - \frac{17k}{112m^7} + \frac{31k}{36m^9} - \frac{691k}{88m^{11}} + \text{ etc.}$$

Now, since the exponent $m = 100$,

$$\frac{k}{m} = 0,0043429448, \quad \frac{k}{m^3} = 0,0000004343, \quad \frac{k}{m^5} = 0,0000000000,$$

yielding

$$\frac{k}{4m} = 0,0010857362$$
$$\frac{k}{24m^3} = 0,0000000181$$
$$\overline{0,0010857181}.$$
$$\text{Further } l\pi = 0,4971498726$$
$$l\tfrac{1}{2}m = 1,6989700043$$
$$l\tfrac{1}{2}m\pi = 2,1961198769$$
$$l\sqrt{\tfrac{1}{2}m\pi} = 1,0980599384$$
$$\frac{k}{4m} - \frac{k}{24m^3} + \text{ etc.} = 0,0010857181$$
$$1,0991456565 = l\frac{2^{100}}{u}.$$

Thus $\frac{2^{100}}{u} = 12{,}56451$, and the middle term in the expanded power $(1 + 1)^m$ is to the sum of all the terms 2^{100} as 1 is to 12,56451.

∞∞∞∞∞∞

So the probability that 100 coin tosses will result in exactly 50 each of heads and tails is between one in twelve and one in thirteen.

References

[1] Archimedes, *Works*, T. L. Heath (editor), Dover, New York, and in Great Books of the Western World (editor R. Hutchins), volume 11, Encyclopaedia Britannica, Chicago, 1952.

[2] R. Ayoub, "Euler and the zeta function," *American Mathematical Monthly*, 81 (1974) 1067–1086.

[3] J. Bernoulli, *Die Werke von Jakob Bernoulli*, Naturforschende Gesellschaft in Basel, Birkhäuser Verlag, Basel, 1975.

[4] C. Boyer, "Pascal's formula for the sums of powers of the integers," *Scripta Mathematica*, 9 (1943) 237–244.

[5] W. Dunham, *Euler: The Master of Us All*, Mathematical Association of America, Washington D.C., 1999.

[6] L. Euler, *Introduction to Analysis of the Infinite, volume I*, translation by John D. Blanton of *Introductio in analysin infinitorum*, Lausanne, 1748, (E101), Springer-Verlag, New York, 1988.

[7] ——, *Opera Omnia*, series I, B.G. Teubner, Leipzig and Berlin, 1911– .

[8] ——, *Vollständige Anleitung zur Differenzial-Rechnung*, translation by Johann Michelsen of *Institutiones calculi differentialis* . . . , St. Petersburg, 1755, (E212), Berlin, 1790, reprint of the 1798 edition by LTR-Verlag, Wiesbaden, 1981.

[9] ——, *Foundations of Differential Calculus*, translation by John D. Blanton of Part I of *Institutiones calculi differentialis* . . . , St. Petersburg, 1755, (E212), Springer Verlag, New York, 2000.

[10] ——, "Excerpts on the Euler-Maclaurin summation formula," translation by David Pengelley from *Institutiones calculi differentialis* . . . , St. Petersburg, 1755, (E212), at `www.math.nmsu.edu/~davidp`, New Mexico State University, 2000, and at *The Euler Archive*, `www.math.dartmouth.edu/~euler/`, 2004.

[11] *The Euler Archive*, `www.EulerArchive.org`.

[12] H. H. Goldstine, *A History of Numerical Analysis from the 16th through the 19th Century*, Springer Verlag, New York, 1977.

[13] E. Hairer and G. Wanner, *Analysis by Its History*, Springer Verlag, New York, 1996.

[14] G. H. Hardy, *Divergent Series*, Chelsea Publishing, New York, 1991.

[15] T. L. Heath, *A Manual of Greek Mathematics*, Dover, New York, 1963.

[16] F. B. Hildebrand, *Introduction to Numerical Analysis*, 2nd edition, McGraw-Hill, New York, 1974.

[17] V. Katz, *A History of Mathematics*, 2nd edition, Addison-Wesley, Reading, Mass., 1998.

[18] M. Kline, *Mathematical Thought from Ancient to Modern Times*, Oxford University Press, New York, 1972.

[19] A. Knoebel, R. Laubenbacher, J. Lodder, D. Pengelley, *Mathematical Masterpieces: Further Chronicles by the Explorers*, Springer Verlag, New York, in press. See `www.math.nmsu.edu/~history` for a detailed table of contents.

[20] K. Knopp, *Theory and Application of Infinite Series*, Dover Publications, New York, 1990.

[21] R. Laubenbacher, D. Pengelley, M. Siddoway, "Recovering motivation in mathematics: Teaching with original sources," *Undergraduate Mathematics Education Trends,* 6, No. 4 (September, 1994) 1,7,13 and at `www.math.nmsu.edu/~history`.

[22] R. Laubenbacher, D. Pengelley, "Mathematical masterpieces: teaching with original sources," pp. 257–260 in *Vita Mathematica: Historical Research and Integration with Teaching,* R. Calinger, ed., Mathematical Association of America, Washington, D.C., 1996, and at `www.math.nmsu.edu/~history`.

[23] ——, *Teaching with Original Historical Sources in Mathematics,* a resource web site, `www.math.nmsu.edu/~history`, New Mexico State University, Las Cruces, 1999–.

[24] D. Pengelley, "The bridge between the continuous and the discrete via original sources," pp. 63–73 in *Study the Masters: The Abel-Fauvel Conference,* Kristiansand, 2002, Otto Bekken et al., eds., National Center for Mathematics Education, University of Gothenburg, Sweden, 2003 and at `www.math.nmsu.edu/~davidp`.

[25] G. Schuppener, *Geschichte der Zeta-Funktion von Oresme bis Poisson,* Deutsche Hochschulschriften 533, Hänsel-Hohenhausen, Egelsbach, Germany, 1994.

[26] K. Shen, "Seki Takakazu and Li Shanlan's formulae on the sum of powers and factorials of natural numbers. (Japanese)," *Sugakushi Kenkyu,* 115 (1987) 21–36.

[27] A. Weil, *Number theory: An Approach Through History: From Hammurapi to Legendre,* Birkhäuser, Boston, 1983.

[28] K. Yosida, "A brief biography on Takakazu Seki (1642?–1708)," *Math. Intelligencer,* 3 (1980/81, no. 3) 121–122.

[29] R. M. Young, *Excursions in Calculus: An Interplay of the Continuous and the Discrete,* Mathematical Association of America, Washington, DC, 1992.

Some Combinatorics in Jacob Bernoulli's *Ars Conjectandi*

Stacy G. Langton

Abstract. In 2002, at the first Euler Society Conference, David Pengelley spoke on the Euler-Maclaurin Summation Formula. The coefficients in this formula are the Bernoulli numbers. They appear for the first time (so far as I know) in Jacob Bernoulli's *Ars Conjectandi* (published posthumously, 1713). In this talk, I will describe some of the combinatorics in Bernoulli's book, and in particular I will try to explain how he found the Bernoulli numbers and the associated formula for sums of powers of integers.

In 2002, at the first Euler Society Conference, David Pengelley spoke about the Euler-Maclaurin Summation Formula.[1] This formula involves a sequence of numbers called the *Bernoulli numbers*,[2] which appear in Jacob Bernoulli's *Ars Conjectandi*, published posthumously in 1713.[3]

The *Ars Conjectandi* was edited for publication by Bernoulli's nephew Nicholas.[4] It is divided into four parts. The first part is a reprint of Christiaan Huygens's book *De Ratiociniis in Ludo Aleae*, annotated by Jacob. The second part is an introduction to what

---

[1] "Dances between continuous and discrete: Euler's summation formula," pp. 169–189 in this volume. See also his paper, "The bridge between the continuous and the discrete via original sources."

[2] According to A. W. F. Edwards, *Pascal's Arithmetical Triangle*, p. 128, the term "Bernoulli numbers" is due to de Moivre, in *Miscellanea analytica de seriebus et quadraturis*, 1730. I haven't seen this work of de Moivre, but in the *Doctrine of Chances*, 3rd ed. (1756), p. 95, de Moivre refers to these numbers as "being the numbers of Mr. *James Bernoulli* in his excellent Theorem for the Summing of Powers." I haven't seen the first two editions of the *Doctrine of Chances*. Euler, in his *Institutiones Calculi Differentialis*, part 2, §122 (1755) mentions the numbers "qui ab inventore Iacobo Bernoullio vocari solent Bernoulliani." The word "solent" suggests that Euler is not naming them himself.

Edwards, *ibid.*, suggests that the numbers should have been named after Johann Faulhaber (1580–1635). However, Donald Knuth, "Johann Faulhaber and sums of powers," p. 287, writes, "Faulhaber never discovered the Bernoulli numbers."

According to Kôsaku Yosida, "A Brief Biography of Takakazu Seki (1642?–1708)," the Bernoulli numbers appear in Seki's book *Katsuyô Sampô*, vol. 1, published in 1712—also posthumously.

[3] An English translation has recently appeared: *The Art of Conjecturing*, tr. by Edith Dudley Sylla.

[4] This is Nicholas Bernoulli (1687–1754), sometimes called "Nicholas I," the son of Jacob's brother Nicholas, not to be confused with Daniel's brother Nicholas (1695–1726), sometimes called "Nicholas II," the son of Johann. Nicholas I wrote a doctoral dissertation on the application of probabilities to law, became Professor of Mathematics at the University of Padua, and eventually returned to Basel.

Jacob Bernoulli

we would call elementary combinatorics, the theory of permutations and combinations. Bernoulli's formula for the sums of powers, in which the Bernoulli numbers appear, is found in this part. The third part gives applications of the theory of permutations and combinations to problems in probability. The fourth part—perhaps the most important for the history of probability—discusses applications of probability theory to social and economic questions, and contains Bernoulli's proof of a version of the Law of Large Numbers.[5] The present paper will be devoted to the second part.

This part begins with a treatment of the elementary properties of permutations and combinations. Bernoulli uses the same words for these concepts that we use today.[6] He finds

---

[5] In Part Four, Bernoulli contrasts his "Art of Conjecturing" with the "Art of Thinking" given in *La Logique ou l'Art de penser* of 1662—in Bernoulli's Latin, *Ars Cogitandi*—a manual of logic written by Antoine Arnauld and Pierre Nicole, two leaders of the Port Royal religious movement. This is the movement that Pascal was associated with.

[6] Bernoulli notes in *Ars Conjectandi*, p. 83, that, strictly speaking, the word "com*b*inations" ought to refer to selections of just *two* things. He suggests that for selections of 3 or 4 things one might use the terms "con3nations," "con4nations," and so forth! The usual portraits of Bernoulli don't suggest that he had a sense of humor.

Tabula

Combinationum, feu Numerorum Figuratorum.

Exponentes Combinationum.

Numeri Rerum Combinandarum.

	I.	II.	III.	IV.	V.	VI.	VII.	VIII.	IX.	X.	XI.	XII.
1.	1	0	0	0	0	0	0	0	0	0	0	0
2.	1	1	0	0	0	0	0	0	0	0	0	0
3.	1	2	1	0	0	0	0	0	0	0	0	0
4.	1	3	3	1	0	0	0	0	0	0	0	0
5.	1	4	6	4	1	0	0	0	0	0	0	0
6.	1	5	10	10	5	1	0	0	0	0	0	0
7.	1	6	15	20	15	6	1	0	0	0	0	0
8.	1	7	21	35	35	21	7	1	0	0	0	0
9.	1	8	28	56	70	56	28	8	1	0	0	0
10.	1	9	36	84	126	126	84	36	9	1	0	0
11.	1	10	45	120	210	252	210	120	45	10	1	0
12.	1	11	55	165	330	462	462	330	165	55	11	1

Figure 1.

the number of permutations of n distinct objects in the usual way, then works out the case in which the objects are not all distinct just as we do: first suppose that the repeated objects are in fact distinct, then divide by the number of ways of permuting these hypothetically distinct objects among themselves. For example, the number of permutations of the letters in the word *studiosus* is the number 362880 of permutations of 9 letters, divided by 2, the number of permutations of the 2 u's, and by 6, the number of permutations of the three s's, giving 30240.

At this point, we might anticipate that Bernoulli would also find the number of *combinations* of n things taken k at a time the same way we do: first find the number of *permutations* of n things taken k at a time, then divide by the number of permutations of those k things. But this is not what Bernoulli does. Instead, he bases his treatment of combinations on the properties of (what we call) Pascal's triangle (*Ars Conjectandi*, p. 87).

Bernoulli refers to the entries in this triangle—that is, the binomial coefficients—as "figurate numbers." Specifically, the entries in the first column (that is, the values $\binom{n}{0}$) are just the unit; the entries in the second column (that is, $\binom{n}{1}$) are the "side numbers" (*series Lateralium*); in the third column ($\binom{n}{2}$) the "triangular numbers"; in the fourth column ($\binom{n}{3}$) the "pyramidal numbers," and so forth. The triangular numbers, of course, are very ancient and perhaps go back to the Pythagoreans. The pyramidal numbers are found in Nicomachus.[7]

It is easier to recreate the gist of Bernoulli's treatment in modern notation. If $\{u_n\}$ is a sequence of numbers, define the *difference operator* Δ by $\Delta u_n = u_{n+1} - u_n$. Then for the

---

[7] Nicomachus of Gerasa, *Introduction to Arithmetic*, Book II, Chapter XIII, par. 8.

binomial coefficients we have

$$\Delta_n \binom{n}{k} = \binom{n+1}{k} - \binom{n}{k} = \binom{n}{k-1},$$

where the subscript n on the Δ indicates that we are here treating n as the "independent variable." Of course, this is nothing but the rule for the formation of Pascal's triangle.

Then —using a "telescoping sum"— we can get a formula for the sums of binomial coefficients:

$$\sum_{a \le n < b} \binom{n}{k} = \sum_{a \le n < b} \Delta_n \binom{n}{k+1}$$

$$= \binom{n}{k+1} \Bigg]_{n=a}^{b}$$

$$= \binom{b}{k+1} - \binom{a}{k+1}.$$

This formula (with $a = 0$) is one of Bernoulli's basic tools. In his set-up, it gives the sums of the values in the *columns* of the arithmetical triangle. Bernoulli does not give any proof of the formula —he seems to have taken it as being well-known— but he does devote several pages to deriving some fairly trivial consequences of it.

If I may make a digression here, I'd like to sketch a way of looking at these results which, I think, ought to be part of our standard curriculum, but which in fact doesn't seem to be very well known.

Let us define the kth *falling power* of a number n by

$$n^{\underline{k}} = \overbrace{n(n-1)\cdots(n-k+1)}^{k \text{ factors}},$$

if k is a natural number. This notation has been popularized by Knuth.[8] Then the binomial coefficient is just

$$\binom{n}{k} = \frac{n^{\underline{k}}}{k!}.$$

The rule for Pascal's triangle becomes $\Delta_n n^{\underline{k}} = k n^{\underline{k-1}}$, a pretty analogue of the corresponding elementary differentiation formula. Bernoulli's summation formula then becomes

$$\sum_{a \le n < b} n^{\underline{k}} = \frac{n^{\underline{k+1}}}{k+1} \Bigg]_{a}^{b}.$$

---

[8] See Donald Knuth, *Fundamental Algorithms*, p. 50. Knuth attributes the analogous notation for *rising* powers to Capelli, 1893. Of course, $n^{\underline{k}}$ is just the number of *permutations* of n things taken k at a time. Bernoulli goes on to work out this formula in Chapter VII of Part Two of the *Ars Conjectandi*.

We can carry the analogue with calculus further. If $\{u_n\}$ and $\{v_n\}$ are two sequences, write

$$\Delta(u_n v_n) = u_{n+1} v_{n+1} - u_n v_n$$

$$= u_{n+1} v_{n+1} - u_n v_{n+1} + u_n v_{n+1} - u_n v_n$$

$$= (u_{n+1} - u_n) v_{n+1} + u_n (v_{n+1} - v_n).$$

If we define the *shift operator* $\mathbf{E}$ by $\mathbf{E} v_n = v_{n+1}$,[9] then we have the "product rule" for finite differences:

$$\Delta(u_n v_n) = (\Delta u_n)(\mathbf{E} v_n) + u_n \Delta v_n.$$

Just as in ordinary calculus the product rule for derivatives implies the rule for integration by parts, so here the product rule for differences gives the rule for *summation by parts*:

$$\sum_{a \le n < b} u_n \Delta v_n = \sum_{a \le n < b} [\Delta(u_n v_n) - (\Delta u_n)(\mathbf{E} v_n)]$$

$$= u_n v_n \Big]_a^b - \sum_{a \le n < b} (\mathbf{E} v_n)(\Delta u_n).$$

This rule, usually stated in a less perspicuous notation, is often called *Abel's Partial Summation Formula*. Abel used it as a tool for studying conditional convergence in his great 1826 paper on the binomial series.[10]

Let's return now to Bernoulli's *Ars Conjectandi*. Using the formula for the sums of binomial coefficients, Bernoulli shows how to derive formulas for the sums of powers. For example, take the formula

$$\sum_{0 \le j \le n} \binom{j}{3} = \binom{n+1}{4}.$$

Bernoulli knows how to express the right-hand side as a polynomial in n. On the other hand, the left-hand side is

$$\sum_{0 \le j \le n} \frac{j(j-1)(j-2)}{6} = \frac{1}{6} \sum_{0 \le j \le n} (j^3 - 3j^2 + 2j).$$

Bernoulli has already found formulas for $\sum_{0 \le j \le n} j$ and $\sum_{0 \le j \le n} j^2$, so he can use this equation to get a formula for $\sum_{0 \le j \le n} j^3$. Of course, the process can be repeated, recursively, to find $\sum_{0 \le j \le n} j^p$ for higher values of p.

In this way, Bernoulli computes a table (*Ars Conjectandi*, p. 97) of $\sum_{0 \le j \le n} j^p$ for $1 \le p \le 10$.[11]

---

[9]For this notation, see George Boole, *A Treatise on the Calculus of Finite Differences*, 2nd edition, p. 16. In the first edition, Boole uses the letter D for this operation. Since the second edition takes D to stand for differentiation (p. 18, footnote), it seems plausible that Moulton, the editor of the second edition, simply took the next letter of the alphabet to represent the shift operator.

[10]"Recherche sur la série $1 + \frac{m}{1} x + \frac{m(m-1)}{1 \cdot 2} x^2 + \frac{m(m-1)(m-2)}{1 \cdot 2 \cdot 3} x^3 + \cdots$," Théorème III, p. 222.

[11]The final coefficient $-\frac{1}{12}$ in the penultimate row is incorrect. It should be $-\frac{3}{20}$.

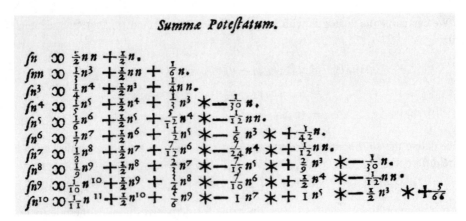

Figure 2.

After displaying this table, Bernoulli comments, "Quin imò qui legem progressionis inibi attentius inspexerit, eundem etiam continuare poterit" —"whoever studies carefully the pattern in this table will be able to continue it further"! And this is no idle boast; for he then writes down the general formula for sums of cth powers.

How did Bernoulli find the general rule? He doesn't say. Several writers have commented on the abruptness of Bernoulli's presentation here. For Michael Spivak, the problem of finding the pattern "may be regarded as a super-perspicacity test."[12] Jekuthiel Ginsburg writes, "Nor is the element of puzzle and mystery lacking. Regardless of the fact that the discovery is more than 200 years old, mathematicians have not been able as yet to find by what process Bernoulli derived the properties of his numbers which he gives in these pages."[13] Anders Hald remarks merely that, "Bernoulli does not explain how he got the idea of introducing the binomial coefficients as factors in the expansion."[14]

Of course, given that Bernoulli does not explain how he found the general formula, there is no way we can know for sure. Still, it seems to me that the following suggestion is at least very plausible.

In order to make it easier to compare Bernoulli's results with their expression in modern notation, let me do something Bernoulli would not have done (compare his table of binomial coefficients on *Ars Conjectandi*, p. 87): let's number the columns of Bernoulli's table of sums of powers starting from 0.

The pattern of coefficients in column 0 is surely clear: the coefficient in the pth row is $\frac{1}{p+1}$. The pattern in column 1 is even easier! So what about column 2? It takes only a few moments' thought to see that each coefficient in this column is just the previous coefficient, plus $\frac{1}{12}$. Another way to say this is that if we take the *differences* of successive coefficients in this column, the differences are constant, namely, $\frac{1}{12}$. (Note, by the way, how natural it is now to look for patterns in the *columns*.)

The coefficients in the next column are all 0—indicated in Bernoulli's text by asterisks. So now look at column 4. Since taking *differences* gave a nice pattern in column 2, what

---

[12]*Calculus*, 2nd edition, p. 30.

[13]David Eugene Smith, *A Source Book in Mathematics*, vol. 1, p. 85.

[14]*A History of Probability and Statistics and Their Applications before 1750*, p. 233.

could be more natural than to apply this idea here? Thus:[15]

$$-\frac{1}{30} \quad -\frac{1}{12} \quad -\frac{1}{6} \quad -\frac{7}{24} \quad -\frac{7}{15} \quad -\frac{7}{10} \quad -1$$

$$\Delta: \quad -\frac{1}{20} \quad -\frac{1}{12} \quad -\frac{1}{8} \quad -\frac{7}{40} \quad -\frac{7}{30} \quad -\frac{3}{10}$$

Unfortunately, the resulting differences don't appear to have a simple pattern.

Would this have stumped Bernoulli? I don't think so. Even *I* can think of an obvious thing to do here: take *higher* differences. Doing so, we find that the second differences form a simple arithmetic sequence; in other words, the *third* differences are constant:

$$-\frac{1}{30} \quad -\frac{1}{12} \quad -\frac{1}{6} \quad -\frac{7}{24} \quad -\frac{7}{15} \quad -\frac{7}{10} \quad -1$$

$$\Delta: \quad -\frac{1}{20} \quad -\frac{1}{12} \quad -\frac{1}{8} \quad -\frac{7}{40} \quad -\frac{7}{30} \quad -\frac{3}{10}$$

$$\Delta^2: \quad -\frac{1}{30} \quad -\frac{1}{24} \quad -\frac{1}{20} \quad -\frac{7}{120} \quad -\frac{1}{15}$$

$$\Delta^3: \quad -\frac{1}{120} \quad -\frac{1}{120} \quad -\frac{1}{120} \quad -\frac{1}{120}.$$

Knowing this, we can reconstruct the pattern of the coefficients in column 4. Letting u_p be the coefficient in Bernoulli's row p, we have to solve the equation

$$(*) \qquad\qquad \Delta^3 u_p = -\frac{1}{120}.$$

The general solution to this third-order difference equation is

$$u_p = -\frac{1}{120}\binom{p}{3} + C_1\binom{p}{2} + C_2\binom{p}{1} + C_3\binom{p}{0},$$

where C_1, C_2, C_3 are constants to be determined from the initial conditions. In fact, it turns out that in the present case $C_1 = C_2 = C_3 = 0$, so that $u_p = -\frac{1}{120}\binom{p}{3}$.

It should be noted here that Bernoulli was perfectly familiar with higher differences, and would certainly have been able to solve equation $(*)$ in the general case. In fact, on the very next page of the *Ars Conjectandi* (p. 98) he sketches the theory of difference equations of this type.[16]

Having reconstructed the pattern of coefficients in column 4, it is easy to guess the pattern in the next (nontrivial) column, number 6: we naturally expect that the *fifth* differences

---

[15]To save space, I have displayed Bernoulli's column 4 as a *row*.

[16]Finite differences were a basic topic of 17th-century mathematics. Thomas Harriot used higher differences for interpolation around 1600. Newton, apparently unaware of Harriot's work, also used finite differences for the same purpose. Leibniz too studied finite differences; his work with them formed the basis of his infinitesimal calculus. For a discussion of work on finite differences in the 17th century, see D. T. Whiteside, *The Mathematical Papers of Isaac Newton*, vol. IV, pp. xi–xx.

In *Pascal's Arithmetical Triangle*, pp. 127–128, A. W. F. Edwards suggests another way in which Bernoulli could have found his formula: just put the coefficients in each column over a common denominator, and notice that the resulting numerators are figurate numbers. This is of course perfectly possible. Still, it seems to me that the use of differences is more typical of 17th-century mathematics.

will be constant, which is in fact the case. (Bernoulli's table has only 5 coefficients in this column, not enough to compute even *one* fifth difference, so he could not have checked this guess against his computed results. Nevertheless, he guessed correctly.)

In general, then, we might conjecture, as did Bernoulli, that the pth coefficient in column k will be a constant multiple of $\binom{p}{k-1}$. We see from Bernoulli's table that the first non-zero entry in this column (if it has one) will occur in row k. Starting in column 2, and ignoring columns of zeros, Bernoulli denoted these entries by $A, B, C, D, \ldots$. They are now called *Bernoulli numbers*, the Bernoulli number from column k being denoted by b_k. If column k consists entirely of zeros, we let $b_k = 0$.[17] Thus, the entry in column k and row p will be $\left(\frac{b_k}{k}\right)\binom{p}{k-1}$.

In modern treatments, it is customary to work with the sum $\sum_{0 \leq j < n} j^p$ instead of Bernoulli's $\sum_{0 \leq j \leq n} j^p$. This has the effect of subtracting n^p from the formulas given by Bernoulli, so that the constant coefficient in column 1 of his table becomes $-\frac{1}{2}$ instead of $+\frac{1}{2}$.

In this notation, then, we have

$$\sum_{0 \leq j < n} j^p = \frac{n^{p+1}}{p+1} + \sum_{1 \leq k \leq p} \binom{p}{k-1} \frac{b_k}{k} n^{p-(k-1)},$$

which, with a slight alteration of notation, is precisely the formula Bernoulli gives on *Ars Conjectandi*, p. 97.[18]

In order to complete Bernoulli's formula for sums of powers, it is necessary to determine the values of the Bernoulli numbers. It is not hard to see that $b_0 = 1$,[19] $b_1 = -\frac{1}{2}$, and, as Bernoulli notes on pp. 97–98, $b_2 = \frac{1}{6}, b_4 = -\frac{1}{30}, b_6 = \frac{1}{42}, b_8 = -\frac{1}{30}$. Bernoulli's table also shows that $b_{10} = \frac{5}{66}$.

It's a little ironic, actually, that Bernoulli stopped his table at the tenth row. Some years later, in his 1736 paper "Inventio summae cuiusque seriei ex dato termino generali" (E47, §23), Euler recomputed Bernoulli's table. Euler carried the table up to the sums of sixteenth powers. From Euler's table, we see that $b_{12} = -\frac{691}{2730}$. It's not likely that the sequence of Bernoulli numbers could be described by a simple formula!

No doubt this was already clear to Bernoulli. At any rate, on *Ars Conjectandi*, p. 98, he explains how his numbers can be computed *recursively*: just use the fact that the sum of the coefficients in each row must be 1. Why is that? Bernoulli doesn't say, but it is easy to see. We get the sum of the coefficients in a given row by substituting $n = 1$. But the corresponding sum $\sum_{0 \leq j \leq 1} j^p$ is 1 (if $p > 0$). It is not hard to check that Bernoulli's rule

---

[17]Not all modern authors use this numbering for the Bernoulli numbers. See, for example, J.-P. Serre, *A Course in Arithmetic*, p. 91.

[18]With a little algebra, this formula can be put into the more symmetric form

$$\sum_{0 \leq j < n} j^p = \frac{1}{p+1} \sum_{0 \leq k < p+1} \binom{p+1}{k} b_k n^{p+1-k}.$$

See, for example, Graham, Knuth and Patashnik, *Concrete Mathematics*, second edition, p. 283.

[19]This is the coefficient in the row representing $\sum_{0 \leq j < n} j^0$, which is not included in Bernoulli's table. Of course, this is "row 0."

is equivalent to the standard modern recurrence relation for the Bernoulli numbers:

$$\sum_{0 \le j < p} \binom{p}{j} b_j = 0, \quad \text{if } p > 1.$$

Of course, it has to be!

A few pages earlier in the *Ars Conjectandi* (p. 95), Bernoulli had criticized Faulhaber, Johann Remmelini of Ulm (1583–1632), Wallis, Mercator, and Jean Prestet (1648–1690) for treating the properties of the binomial coefficients without giving rigorous proofs. According to him, their demonstrations were simply "by induction"; in other words, in our terminology, they just worked out some terms of the sequence until they thought they saw a pattern. In view of this criticism of his predecessors, it seems fair to ask, did Bernoulli himself have a proof of his formula for sums of powers?

Well, Bernoulli does not give any proof. If he had one, it would probably have had to be based on a recurrence relation for the sums of powers. Now, such a relation had already been found by Pascal, probably in 1654. Pascal's analysis, which is purely verbal, with no algebraic symbolism, amounts to the following:[20]

$$n^p - 1 = \sum_{0 \le j < n} [(j+1)^p - j^p]$$

$$= \sum_{0 \le j < n} \left[\sum_{0 \le k \le p} \binom{p}{k} j^k - j^p \right]$$

$$= \sum_{0 \le j < n} \sum_{0 \le k < p} \binom{p}{k} j^k$$

$$= \sum_{0 \le k < p} \binom{p}{k} \sum_{0 \le j < n} j^k.$$

Using this recurrence relation, it is indeed possible to give a proof of Bernoulli's formula. But the proof involves rather complicated algebraic manipulations. Written in modern notation, it requires changing the order of summation in a double sum.[21] Of course, as we have just seen, Pascal was able to do this kind of thing, so I think that Bernoulli probably could have found the proof. But the proof is sufficiently difficult that, it seems to me, if Bernoulli had in fact worked it out, he would have said so. Consequently, it seems most likely to me that Bernoulli did not actually have the proof.

Having found his formula, however, Bernoulli cannot resist a little boasting. On p. 98, he claims that "in less than half of a quarter of an hour" he was able to calculate

$$\sum_{0 \le j \le 1000} j^{10} = 91{,}409{,}924{,}241{,}424{,}243{,}424{,}241{,}924{,}242{,}500.$$

---

[20] See "Potestatum numericarum summa," paragraph "Summa potestatum." There are many editions of Pascal's works. I found this in *Œuvres Complètes*, Éditions Gallimard, 1954, p. 170.

[21] See, for example, Graham, Knuth, and Patashnik, *Concrete Mathematics*, pp. 284–285.

This computational feat gives him occasion to denigrate Ismael Boulliau (1605–1694), whose book *Arithmetica Infinitorum*—according to Bernoulli—contains nothing but tables of sums of powers up to the sixth power.

It should be observed that Bernoulli chose the parameters for this calculation rather carefully. For $n = 1000$, the several powers of n required by his formula are very easy to get. Moreover, when $p = 10$, the corresponding coefficients have comparatively few unpleasant denominators. Still, I was curious whether Bernoulli could really have done this computation in the time he claimed, so I carried out the same computation myself, using just pencil and paper. It took me just under 9 minutes (July 16, 2004).[22] Since Bernoulli was probably better at arithmetic than I am, his claim appears to be plausible. (The value that Bernoulli gives is correct.)

In 1740, Euler found what we now call the "exponential generating function" for the Bernoulli numbers:[23]

$$\sum_{0 \le k < \infty} \frac{b_k}{k!} x^k = \frac{x}{e^x - 1}$$

$$= -\frac{1}{2}x + \frac{x}{2} \coth \frac{x}{2}.$$

This formula is actually equivalent to Bernoulli's recurrence relation for the Bernoulli numbers.[24] But this way of expressing the relation is much more powerful. For example, since $(x/2) \coth(x/2)$ is an *even* function, it follows that all the odd-numbered Bernoulli numbers, except b_1, must be 0. Of course, Bernoulli must have observed this from the columns of zeros in his table, but it seems unlikely that he could have found the proof.

In the same paper (§29), Euler computes special values of what we now call the *Riemann zeta-function*, $\zeta(s) = \sum_{1 \le j < \infty} 1/j^s$. Euler gives a table of the values of $\zeta(2n)$ for $1 \le n \le 6$; he also gives *approximate* values for $\zeta(2n + 1)$ for $1 \le n \le 5$. Of course, this table includes his famous evaluation $\zeta(2) = \pi^2/6$. But the value of $\zeta(12)$ is also worthy of note. Euler gets

$$\zeta(12) = \frac{\pi^{12}}{924041 \frac{544}{691}}.$$

We recognize the remarkable denominator 691 as the numerator of b_{12}. This is surely no accident; there must be a relation between the zeta-function and the Bernoulli numbers. In

---

[22] My calculator takes about 3 seconds.

[23] "De seriebus quibusdam considerationes" (E130); see §27.

[24] Let $B(x) = \sum_{0 \le k < \infty} b_k(x^k/k!)$ be the exponential generating function for the Bernoulli numbers. Also, define $h_k = \delta_{k,1}$ and $c_k = 1 - \delta_{k,0}$, where δ_{ij} is the Kronecker delta. Then the exponential generating function for the sequence $\{c_k\}$ is $C(x) = e^x - 1$, and the exponential generating function for the sequence $\{h_k\}$ is $H(x) = x$. The recurrence relation for the Bernoulli numbers may be written in the form

$$\sum_{0 \le j \le p} \binom{p}{j} b_j c_{p-j} = h_p, \quad \text{for } p \ge 0,$$

where the left-hand side is now the so-called *binomial convolution* of the sequences $\{b_k\}$ and $\{c_k\}$ (Graham, Knuth, and Patashnik, *Concrete Mathematics*, p. 365). It follows then from the theory of exponential generating functions that the recurrence relation is equivalent to the relation $B(x)C(x) = H(x)$; in other words, $B(x)(e^x - 1) = x$. See Wilf, *generatingfunctionology*, pp. 41–42, and *Concrete Mathematics*, pp. 364–365.

fact, Euler essentially has the relation

$$\zeta(2n) = (-1)^{n-1}\frac{2^{2n-1}\pi^{2n}b_{2n}}{(2n)!}.$$

(See §24.) Since $\zeta(2n) > 0$, it follows that the *nonzero* Bernoulli numbers must alternate in sign, another fact that must have been clear "inductively" to Bernoulli.

Well, there are many other fascinating things in the *Ars Conjectandi*. I hope that I have whetted your interest in this important book.

This paper is based on a talk given at The Euler Society 2004 Conference, Roger Williams University Conference Center, Portsmouth, Rhode Island, 10 August 2004.

References

[1] Niels Henrik Abel, "Recherche sur la série $1 + \frac{m}{1}x + \frac{m(m-1)}{1\cdot2}x^2 + \frac{m(m-1)(m-2)}{1\cdot2\cdot3}x^3 + \cdots$," L. Sylow and S. Lie, eds., *Œuvres complètes de Niels Henrik Abel*, nouvelle édition, tome premier, Christiania, 1881 (reprinted, Johnson Reprint Corporation, 1965), pp. 219–250.

[2] Jacob Bernoulli, *Ars Conjectandi*, Basel, 1713. English translation: *The Art of Conjecturing*, tr. by Edith Dudley Sylla, Johns Hopkins University Press, 2005. Page references in this article are to the 1713 Basel edition. The pagination of this edition is indicated in Sylla's translation.

[3] George Boole, *A Treatise on the Calculus of Finite Differences*, 1st edition, Macmillan, 1860; 2nd (posthumous) edition, edited by John F. Moulton, Macmillan, 1872, reprinted by Dover, 1960.

[4] Abraham de Moivre, *The Doctrine of Chances*, 3rd edition, London, 1756; reprinted by Chelsea, New York, 1967.

[5] A. W. F. Edwards, *Pascal's Arithmetical Triangle*, Charles Griffin, London, 1987, reprinted by Johns Hopkins University Press, 2002.

[6] Leonhard Euler, "Inventio summae cuiusque seriei ex dato termino generali" (E47), *Commentarii academiae scientiarum Petropolitanae*, **8** (1736), pp. 9–22; reprinted in *Opera Omnia*, I.14, pp. 108–123.

[7] ——, "De seriebus quibusdam considerationes" (E130), *Commentarii academiae scientiarum Petropolitanae*, **12** (1750), pp. 53–96; reprinted in *Opera Omnia*, I.14, pp. 407–462.

[8] ——, *Institutiones calculi differentialis* (E212), St. Petersburg, 1755; *Opera Omnia*, I.10.

[9] Ronald L. Graham, Donald E. Knuth, and Oren Patashnik, *Concrete Mathematics*, second edition, Addison-Wesley, 1994.

[10] Anders Hald, *A History of Probability and Statistics and Their Applications before 1750*, Wiley, 1990.

[11] Donald Knuth, *The Art of Computer Programming*, vol. 1, *Fundamental Algorithms*, 3rd edition, Addison-Wesley, 1997.

[12] ——, "Johann Faulhaber and sums of powers," *Mathematics of Computation*, **61** (1993) pp. 277–294.

[13] Nicomachus of Gerasa, *Introduction to Arithmetic*. Translation by Martin Luther D'Ooge, University of Michigan Press, 1926; reprinted by Encyclopedia Britannica, *Great Books of the Western World*, 1952, vol. 11.

[14] Blaise Pascal, "Potestatum numericarum summa," *Œuvres Complètes*, Éditions Gallimard, 1954, p. 170.

[15] David Pengelley, "Dances between continuous and discrete: Euler's summation formula," this volume, pp. 169–189.

[16] ———, "The bridge between the continuous and the discrete via original sources," *Study the Masters: The Abel–Fauvel Conference, 2002*, ed. Otto Bekken *et al.*, National Center for Mathematics Education, University of Gothenburg, Sweden, 2003, pp. 63–73.

[17] J.-P. Serre, *A Course in Arithmetic*, Springer-Verlag, 1973.

[18] David Eugene Smith, *A Source Book in Mathematics*, Dover reprint, 1959.

[19] Michael Spivak, *Calculus*, 2nd edition, Publish or Perish, 1980.

[20] D. T. Whiteside, *The Mathematical Papers of Isaac Newton*, vol. IV (Cambridge, 1971).

[21] Herbert S. Wilf, *generatingfunctionology*, 2nd ed., Academic Press, 1994.

[22] Kôsaku Yosida, "A Brief Biography of Takakazu Seki (1642?–1708)," *Mathematical Intelligencer*, **3** (1980/81), no. 3, pp. 121–122.

The Genoese Lottery and the Partition Function[1]

Robert E. Bradley

Abstract. In 1749, King Frederick the Great sought Euler's mathematical counsel concerning the establishment of a state lottery. The combinatorial issues involved in the analysis of this game of chance, known as the Genoese Lottery, piqued Euler's curiosity. As a consequence, he wrote four memoirs over the course of his career examining questions arising from this lottery. These papers are surveyed, with particular attention paid to the use of the partition function in the second one.

1 Introduction

Leonhard Euler was one of the most productive mathematicians of all time. The Eneström index [Eneström 1913] catalogs more than 800 of his papers and books. With such an extensive publication record, it is not surprising that Euler revisited a number of topics on various occasions throughout his long career. Sometimes he came back to generalize an earlier result, other times he took an old problem as the starting point but headed off in a new direction. On yet other occasions, his aim was to gave a new proof to a result he had already proved—something he did, for example, with the Basel Problem, showing in different ways [Euler 1740, Euler 1743a, Euler 1743b] that

$$1 + \frac{1}{4} + \frac{1}{9} + \frac{1}{16} + \text{ etc. } = \frac{\pi^2}{6}.$$

In this paper we examine two problems, each of which Euler discussed on four occasions, and the surprising connection between the two. The first problem involves probability theory and qualifies as applied mathematics, insofar as it comes from real life and was brought to Euler's attention when his royal patron, King Frederick II (the Great) of Prussia asked him to analyze a proposal for the establishment of a state lottery. The second topic is from number theory and is familiar to almost anyone who has had an introduction to that most abstract branch of pure mathematics: the problem of partitioning a natural number.

---

[1] Based on talks given at the meetings of the Canadian Society for History and Philosophy of Mathematics, June 4, 2005 and of The Euler Society, August 9, 2005.

Euler's application of the partition function to the Genoese lottery probably counts as the first practical application of number theory in the history of mathematics.

Except where otherwise indicated, the notation used when describing the contents of Euler's papers is his own.

2   The Genoese Lottery

Euler's incredible catalog of publications, including many posthumous works, has been collected in his *Opera Omnia* [Euler 1911–]. This was one of the great publishing projects of the last century. The Euler Commission was established in Euler's bicentennial year to oversee the publication of his works. Volumes in the series began appearing in 1911, and the last of the 72 volumes of his works appeared only recently, in 2004. The Commission is also seeing to the publication of Euler's correspondence and unpublished manuscripts, but it will be many years before that task is completed.

In the taxonomy of the *Opera Omnia*, Euler's papers on the Genoese lottery belong to series I, volume 7, *Commentationes algebraicae ad theoriam combinationum et probabilitatum pertinentes* [Euler 1923]. This volume was published in 1923 and edited by Louis Gustave du Pasquier. It contains Euler's papers on recreational mathematics, probability theory, and various statistical topics, including life insurance. This is where one can find the papers on the Bridges of Königsberg, the Knight's Tour and Græco-Latin Squares. Of eight papers Euler wrote on probability theory, five concerned lotteries and four of those were about a particular lottery called the Genoese lottery.

The Genoese Lottery is the ancestor of a wide variety of "number lotteries," which are very popular in our time. Lotto 6/49, Powerball and the New York State Lottery are just a few examples. In all of these games, n numbered balls or tickets are placed in an urn or a wheel, and m are drawn at random. Players try to guess which numbers will be drawn, and a huge jackpot is paid to anyone who correctly guesses all m of them. Many of the modern versions feature bonus numbers and other complicating features, but the orginal number lottery, about which Euler wrote, had no such wrinkles. In the Genoese lottery, $n = 90$ and $m = 5$ and players could choose to bet on fewer than 5 numbers if they wished. Some variants permitted bets on only one, two or three numbers, called *estratto*, *ambo* and *terno*. In most modern number lotteries, players may play m numbers only.

The preface [Du Pasquier 1923] of volume I.7 of the *Opera Omnia* is in many ways a valuable document, providing background for the eighteen articles and various fragments that follow. However, du Pasquier's account of the origins of the Genoese Lottery has recently been shown to be of questionable accuracy.

The lottery seems to have originated in Genoa in the seventeenth century. The legend surrounding its origin was firmly established long before du Pasquier wrote his preface. Allegedly, the game grew out of the election procedure of this city state. Du Pasquier reported that five governors were drawn by lot from a group of ninety councillors, in order to share power with the Doge of Genoa in a ruling executive committee. Allegedly, the people of Genoa took to gambling on the outcome of this drawing, and eventually a lottery was born as an abstraction of the election process. Du Pasquier attributed the invention to Benedetto Gentile in 1620. This legend is so pervasive that even as fine a historian as Daston repeated the story [Daston 1988, p. 143], setting the date of the establishment as 1610.

However, recent research [Bellhouse 1991] reveals that the Genoese election procedure was more likely a matter of choosing two councillors from a group of 120 and that such elections by lot occurred significantly later than the popular account. Bellhouse even cited some weak evidence that a numbers lottery in Genoa possibly predated elections by lot. In any case, he revealed the story of Gentile's invention as being subject to serious doubt.

Whatever its origin, this type of lottery was popular in many Italian cities by the early eighteenth century and spread throughout Europe during the decades that followed. In September 1749, an Italian entrepreneur named Roccolini approached Frederick II with a scheme for a state lottery involving the drawing of five numbers between 1 and 90. The king sent the proposal to Euler, who was the director of the Mathematics Class of the Berlin Academy, for comment. Two days later, on September 17, 1749, Euler wrote back with his analysis of the scheme. Both letters are preserved in the *Opera Omnia* [Euler 1986, pp. 316–320], but unfortunately Roccolini's proposal appears not to have survived.

Euler's analysis of Roccolini's proposal reveals that it was a typical number lottery with $n = 90$ and $m = 5$, but one in which players could wager on one, two or three numbers only. The odds favored the bank, with profits to the state of 31%, 49% and 71%, respectively. For more about Euler's analysis of Roccolini's proposal, see [Bradley 2004].

Already in his letter to Fredrick, Euler had considered an abstraction of the Genoese lottery to arbitrary number of balls in the wheel and an arbitrary number drawn, sketching a lottery with $n = 100$, $m = 10$ and payoffs for the *estratto*, *ambo*, *terno* and *quaterna*. Du Pasquier also reported [Du Pasquier 1923, p. xxiii–xxiv] that Euler filled a number of pages of his notebook H5, believed to cover the period 1748–50, with calculations relevant to the Genoese lottery.

3 Euler's Papers on The Genoese Lottery

The Berlin lottery, a classic Genoese-style lottery, was established in 1763. Euler wrote four articles concerning the Genoese lottery beginning at about this time:

E812 "Reflections on a singular type of lottery, called the Genoese Lottery" [Euler 1862b]. Euler read this paper to the Berlin Academy on 10 March 1763, but did not publish it. It appeared in his *Opera postuma* in 1862.

E338 "On the probability of runs in the Genoese lottery" [Euler 1767]. This paper was contained in the *Mémoires* of the Berlin Academy for 1765, which appeared in 1767. I will argue that Euler read it to the Berlin Academy on 21 February 1765, although du Pasquier claims it was "drafted in 1767" [Du Pasquier 1923, p. xxv].

E600 "Solution to various difficult questions in the probability calculus" [Euler 1785]. This was read to the St. Petersburg Academy on 8 October 1781 and appeared in Euler's *Opuscula analytica* in 1785.

E813 "Analysis of a problem in the probability calculus" [Euler 1862c]. Very little can be said with confidence about when this article was written. It seems never to have been presented either to the Berlin or the St. Petersburg Academy. It was included in Euler's *Opera postuma* in 1862.

(The numbers E812, E338, etc., were assigned to Euler's publications by Eneström in his index of Euler's works [Eneström 1913].)

Euler didn't submit his first paper on the lottery for inclusion in the *Mémoires* of the Berlin Academy, nor is it clear that he had ever intended to. It was typical of Euler's work schedule during his Berlin years (1741–1766) that he would submit the final version of a paper for publication two years or so after first reading it to the Academy, although there are plenty of exceptions. Therefore the possibility exists that he originally intended the paper to be published, but substituted E338 instead, shortly before leaving Berlin to return to St. Petersburg in the spring of 1766.

A similar sequence of events definitely occurred with Euler's papers on logarithms of negative and complex numbers. He prepared a first paper on the subject [Euler 1862a], which he read to the Academy on 7 September 1747. This paper did not appear until 1862, when it was published in Euler's *Opera postuma*, along with papers E812 and E813 on the Genoese lottery. Instead, Euler substituted a significantly different paper [Euler 1751b] in the 1749 volume of the *Mémoires*, which appeared in 1751. If Euler did indeed substitute E338 for E812, then the schedule ran precisely in parallel to that of the logarithm papers, 16 years later.

Whatever Euler's intentions for the publication of E812, it is a fairly straightforward paper on the mechanics of the Genoese lottery. He calculates the probabilities of winning for arbitrary n and m and presents some rules of thumb for establishing prize levels in such a way as to make the game attractive to players while still insulating the bank from catastrophic losses. The paper is described in some detail in [Bradley 2004].

The probability that a player who has chosen to bet on k numbers, where $1 \leq k \leq m$, will actually match i of them has a hypergeometric distribution: the player is essentially sampling k balls without replacement from an urn containing n balls, m of which are special because they are the ones that will eventually be chosen in the draw. Although other mathematicians, including Daniel Bernoulli and de Moivre, had solved probability problems involving number lotteries before Euler [Hald 1990, pp. 377, 422], the hypergeometric distribution did not have the status of a standard topic, as it does today. Thus, Euler had to describe the distribution to his audience, even if it was not an original discovery. However, Euler did treat the probability calculations in a novel, recursive way that is both elegant and efficient. He even gave guidelines for the use of log tables to simplify the calculations.

Also notable was his use of something akin to subscripts. Subscripting did not become general mathematical practice until the 19th century and, typically for his time, Euler used the letters A, B, C, etc., to represent probabilities connected with bets placed on $k = 1, 2, 3$, etc., numbers. However, he then used a superscript on the capital letter to represent the number $i \leq k$ of the chosen numbers that actually appeared in the drawing. For example, he denoted the probability that a player who had bet on 4 numbers actually matched two of them by $6D^2$, and that of a player matching one out of five numbers by $5E^1$. In general, he denoted the probability that a player who bet on k numbers actually matched i of them by:

$$\binom{k}{i} [k\text{th capital letter}]^i ,$$

where the i is not an exponent but rather an index that is used in the recursive formula for calculating the probability.

The above notation for the binomial coefficient did not appear in Euler's paper E812. At that time, he had no shorthand for the binomial coefficient, and so his papers of this period were filled with expressions like

$$\frac{n(n-1)(n-2)\cdots(n-m+1)}{1\cdot 2\cdot 3\cdots m}.$$

However, by the time he wrote E600, Euler had developed notation for the binomial coefficient. He used either

$$\left(\frac{n}{m}\right) \quad \text{or} \quad \left[\frac{n}{m}\right]$$

in the papers he wrote at this period in his career.

In the same paper E600, Euler considered the following problem: suppose that a Genoese-style lottery has been repeated d times, where d is an integer satisfying $dm > n$, so that it is possible that each of the n numbers in the lottery has been selected in at least one of the drawings. What is the probability that all of the n numbers have actually been drawn?

Euler let Δ be the total number of possible d-fold drawings, that is

$$\Delta = \binom{n}{m}^d.$$

He also let A, B, C, etc., represent the number of possible drawings in which only $n-1$, $n-2, n-3$, etc., of the n numbers actually appear. The jth of these is therefore equal to

$$\binom{n}{j}\binom{n-j}{m}^d.$$

Of course, each of these cases was already counted in Δ, so Euler needed a principle of inclusion-exclusion to determine the number of possible d-fold drawings in which all n numbers actually appear. That number is

$$\Delta - A + B - C + D - \text{etc.}$$

Euler did not attempt to give a closed formula for this number but showed how to use it to approximate the value of the probability that all n numbers are drawn:

$$\Pi = 1 - \frac{A}{\Delta} + \frac{B}{\Delta} - \frac{C}{\Delta} + \frac{D}{\Delta} - \text{etc.}$$

These ratios are easily calculated with the help of logarithms and, when the number d of drawings is large, the alternating sum will converge quickly. Euler showed by example that for the classic lottery parameters of $n = 90$ and $m = 5$, one needs only 4 terms to give this probability to 4 decimal places when $d = 100$. He calculated the probability as 0.7411, although careful attention to rounding gives 0.7410 as a more accurate value. If $d = 200$, then Euler needed only the first term to find that the probability is 0.99902.

Euler completed E600 by showing that one may use the same machinery to calculate the probabilities that $n-1, n-2, n-3$, etc., numbers appear in the d repeated drawings. Those probabilities are:

$$1 - \frac{B}{\Delta} + 2\frac{C}{\Delta} - 3\frac{D}{\Delta} + 4\frac{E}{\Delta} - \text{etc.,}$$

$$1 - \frac{C}{\Delta} + 3\frac{D}{\Delta} - 6\frac{E}{\Delta} + 10\frac{F}{\Delta} - \text{etc.,}$$

and so on. The letters B, C, D, ... here represent the same quantities they did in the case of drawing all n numbers, whereas the coefficients of the terms with Δ in the denominator, in the formula corresponding to the case where $n - k$ numbers are drawn, are

$$\binom{k}{k}, \binom{k+1}{k}, \binom{k+2}{k}, \text{etc.}$$

In particular, when $n = 90$, $m = 5$ and $d = 100$, the probability that at least 89 numbers will appear is 0.9655 and the probability that at least 88 numbers will appear is 0.9972.

Euler also considered the case of repeated drawings in a Genoese-style lottery in his posthumous paper E813. The date of its composition is unknown. The paper was written in French, so it was possibly drafted in Berlin, or at least intended for publication in the *Mémoires* of that Academy — with few exceptions, this was the only journal for which he wrote in French. The lack of proofs of the combinatorial propositions in this paper probably explains why he never published it in that form. It is not clear whether he intended to finish it up at some point but was unable to return to it, or simply abandoned it.

The problem considered in E813 is similar to that in E600. However, d need not be as large as n/m. In the paper, Euler studied the distribution of the number of tickets that are *not* drawn over the course of d repeated lottery drawings.

4   Runs in the Genoese Lottery

Of his four papers on the Genoese lottery, E338 is the only one Euler saw published in his own lifetime. Although its title is sometimes more literally but less correctly translated as "On the probability of sequences in the Genoese lottery," I prefer to use the word "run" in place of "sequence." A run is a maximal sequence of consecutive integers in the m numbers drawn in a number lottery. For example, if the numbers 10, 11, 28, 29, 30 and 42 are drawn in Lotto 6/49, there is run of length 1, a run of length 2 and a run of length 3. In E338, Euler considered the probability that runs of various lengths will appear in the numbers drawn in a lottery with parameters n and m.

Eneström's index indicates that the date of the presentation of this paper is unknown [Eneström 1913, p. 77] and Du Pasquier speculated that it was not drafted until 1767 [Du Pasquier 1923, p. xxv]. However, the difficulties in dating this paper seem to derive from a simple transcription error by Samuel Formey, who was Secretary of the Berlin Academy when Euler left Berlin for St. Petersburg in 1766.

The minutes (*Procès Verbaux*) of the Berlin Academy from the period of Euler's tenure have not survived: they were lost at the time of the Napoleonic wars. However, before leaving for St. Petersburg in 1766, Euler asked Formey to make him an abbreviated copy of the minutes of all meetings of the Academy from 1746 up to the time of his departure. These *Régistres* of the Berlin Academy were published on the occasion of Euler's 250th anniversary [Winter 1957]. The abbreviated minutes include the list of those in attendance at each meeting as well as a record of points of business, including the papers that were presented. The *Régistres* were repatriated to Berlin from St. Peterburg by Jacobi, and they were one of the primary sources for Eneström's index.

The 1765 volume of *Mémoires* of the Berlin Academy contains papers by both Euler and Beguelin [Beguelin 1767] concerning runs in the Genoese lottery. Actually, Beguelin's piece consists of a first memoir and a second memoir, published consecutively in the pages of that volume. Beguelin mentioned papers by both Euler and Johann III Bernoulli presented to the Academy. Although Bernoulli had no paper on the lottery included in that volume of the Berlin *Mémoires*, he did have a paper in the 1769 volume with the same title as Beguelin's. In a footnote to that paper, Bernoulli wrote

> This memoir was read in 1765, after the memoir of Mr. Euler on this subject, inserted in the *Mémoires* of the Academy for that year. Since the memoir of Mr. Beguelin, printed following that of Mr. Euler, referred to mine in several places and since the lottery which occasioned it is now more in fashion than ever, I will not hold it back any longer.

To solve the mystery of the composition of E338 then, one need only consult the *Régistres* for 1765. Although there is no mention there of a paper presented by Euler on the lottery, there are two references to lottery papers by Bernoulli: one on February 21 and the other on October 24. However, the title of the paper supposedly read by Bernoulli on February 21 is *"Sur la probabilité des séquences dans la lotterie[2] Génoise,"* which is the title of Euler's paper, whereas the title on October 24 is that of Bernoulli's paper: *"Sur les suites ou séquences dans la lotterie de Gênes."* There can be little doubt, then, that the February 21 presentation was made by Euler, but Formey copied the entry incorrectly into Euler's *Régistres*.

As for the contents of E338, Euler proved two significant theorems about the probability of sequences in the Genoese lottery. He would probably have called his method of proof "induction," but, as with E812 and E600, the induction is not in the form one might see today, but is rather a "Socratic" induction, where the first few cases are worked out in detail, until one clearly spots the pattern. Specifically, Euler considered a lottery with an arbitrary n and worked out the probability of various run patterns when m is 2, 3, 4, and so on. Because there were so many cases to consider, the patterns were not yet evident when Euler finished the case $m = 5$, the parameter for the canonical lottery. However, by the time he had completed the case $m = 6$ he was ready to state general theorems.

Before Euler could even state his results, he had to classify the various patterns of runs that could occur in a lottery with parameters n and m and develop some notation. He defined the *species* of a drawing of m numbers as

$$\alpha(a) + \beta(b) + \gamma(c) + \text{etc.}$$

if the drawing consisted of

α runs of length a,
β runs of length b,
γ runs of length c,
        etc.

---

[2]Euler's article used this alternate spelling, but when Bernoulli's article actually appeared in 1771, *"loterie"* was spelled in the modern way, with a single "t." However, the reference to it in the *Procès Verbaux*, as reproduced in [Winter 1957], employed this alternate spelling, as did the titles of the articles by Beguelin and Euler. By the time Euler's posthumous article [Euler 1862b] appeared, the spelling of this word seems to have become standardized.

In this case, we necessarily have $m = \alpha a + \beta b + \gamma c + \ldots$, and the total number of runs in the drawing is $k = \alpha + \beta + \gamma + \ldots$.

Through what du Pasquier called "marvellous inductions" [Du Pasquier 1923, p. xxv], but what is actually a 34-page catalog of special cases, Euler was drawn to conclude the following two theorems, given here in modern notation.

Theorem 1 *The total number of drawings with species* $\alpha(a) + \beta(b) + \gamma(c) + \ldots$ *is the multinomial coefficient*

$$\binom{n - m + 1}{\alpha, \beta, \gamma, \ldots}.$$

Theorem 2 *The total number of drawings with* k *runs is*

$$\binom{m - 1}{k - 1} \binom{n - m + 1}{k}.$$

We conclude this section with proofs of these propositions. The proofs are not at all in the spirit of Euler's inductions in E338, but rather are modern combinatorial proofs that assume familiarity with the definitions and properties of the binomial and multinomial distributions.

To prove Theorem 1, we observe that two consecutive runs in a drawing must be separated by at least one of the $n - m$ numbers that are not selected in that drawing. These $n - m$ numbers define $n - m + 1$ possible locations for the runs: at the beginning (i.e., a run of $1, 2, \ldots, a$), at the end (i.e., a run of $n - a + 1, n - a + 2, \ldots, n$) or in any of the $n - m - 1$ spaces in between. It is now only a matter of distributing α runs of length a, β runs of length b, γ runs of length c, and so on, in these $n - m + 1$ locations. That is, the multinomial coefficient

$$\binom{n - m + 1}{\alpha, \beta, \gamma, \ldots}.$$

To prove Theorem 2, we observe that there are $n - m + 1$ possible locations for the k runs, as before, which accounts for the second of the binomial coefficients. To determine how the m numbers drawn are to be distributed into k runs in numerical order, one can imagine laying down m tokens in a line. This defines $m - 1$ spaces between consecutive tokens. Distributing $k - 1$ markers into these $m - 1$ spaces determines the distribution of the lengths of the k runs. This accounts for the first binomial coefficient in the statement of Theorem 2.

5   The Partition Function

The problem of enumerating and classifying the various species in the problem of runs in the Genoese lottery is clearly the problem of partitioning the number m. In particular, the number of cases to be considered in Theorem 1 is $p(m)$, the number of ways of writing m as a sum of natural numbers, with repetitions allowed. The number of cases to be considered in Theorem 2 is the number of ways of expressing m as a sum of exactly k natural numbers, again with repetitions permitted. In this paper, we will denote that quantity as $p(m, k)$. We will also use $p_d(m)$ and $p_d(m, k)$ for the number of such partitions with distinct summands. For more on partitions, the standard modern reference is [Andrews 1998].

This correspondence between species and partitions can be illustrated using the following example: Euler's catalog of the 11 species corresponding to $m = 6$ in §22 of E338.

Species	Partition
1(6)	$6 = 6$
1(5) + 1(1)	$6 = 5 + 1$
1(4) + 1(2)	$6 = 4 + 2$
1(4) + 2(1)	$6 = 4 + 1 + 1$
2(3)	$6 = 3 + 3$
1(3) + 1(2) + 1(1)	$6 = 3 + 2 + 1$
1(3) + 3(1)	$6 = 3 + 1 + 1 + 1$
3(2)	$6 = 2 + 2 + 2$
2(2) + 2(1)	$6 = 2 + 2 + 1 + 1$
1(2) + 4(1)	$6 = 2 + 1 + 1 + 1 + 1$
6(1)	$6 = 1 + 1 + 1 + 1 + 1 + 1$

We note that this illustrates that $p(6) = 11$ as well as $p(6, 1) = p(6, 5) = p(6, 6) = 1$, $p(6, 2) = p(6, 3) = 3$ and $p(6, 4) = 2$. We also see that $p_d(6) = 4$, $p_d(6, 1) = p_d(6, 3) = 1$ $p_d(6, 2) = 2$, and $p_d(6, k) = 0$ for other values of k.

In §25 of E338, having just defined the species of a drawing, Euler observed that the number of species is the same as the number of ways in which "it is possible to divide the number m in different ways into parts." He then listed the progression from $p(1)$ through $p(15)$, and referred the reader to "my researches on the partition of numbers." Although Euler did not give exact citations in E338, he was clearly referring to the first three of his four pieces on the subject of partitions:

E158 "Various Analytic Observations about Combinations" [Euler 1751a]. This paper was presented to the St. Petersburg Academy on 6 April 1741, just before Euler left for Berlin. It was published in the *Commentarii* of the Academy for 1741–43, which did not actually appear until 1751.

E101 *Introduction to the Analysis of the Infinite*, vol. 1 [Euler 1748]. Many sources give 1745 as the date of its composition, see [Eneström 1913, p. 25], but the correspondence between Euler and Cramer clearly documents that the manuscript was already at the publisher's in Lausanne in late 1743, see [Bradley 2006]. In any case, Chapter XVI of this book was Euler's second piece on the partition function, although it was the first to appear in print.

E191 "On the Partition of Numbers" [Euler 1753]. This was presented to the St. Petersburg Academy on 26 January 1750 and was published in the Academy's *Novi commentarii* volume for 1750–51, which appeared in 1753.

E394 "On the Partition of Numbers into a Given Number or Kind of Parts" [Euler 1770]. This was presented to the St. Petersburg Academy on 18 August 1768 and was published in the Academy's *Novi commentarii* volume for 1769, which appeared in 1770.

The study of the problem of partitions of numbers is generally said to have originated in two questions posed in a letter by Phillipe Naudé (the younger) to Leonhard Euler on

29 August 1740 [Euler 1975, p. 322] and mentioned by Euler in E158: in how many ways can the number 50 be written as a sum of 7 distinct numbers, or by 7 summands where repetitions are permitted? That is, what are $p_d(50, 7)$ and $p(50, 7)$?

[Dickson 1920, vol. II, p. 101] reported that Leibniz wrote about the partition problem both in an unpublished manuscript of 1674 and in a letter to Johann Bernoulli in 1699, although the date of the letter is incorrectly given as 1669. It is possible that Euler first came across the problem via this route, since he was mentored by Bernoulli in his student days, but there is no compelling reason to entertain such a hypothesis.

Euler solved Naudé's problem in his paper E158, where he invented and first applied the notion of a generating function. As noted above, there was a considerable lag in the publication of this paper, and so it did not appear until after Naudé's death in 1745, although Euler communicated his result to Naudé in September 1740, long before leaving St. Petersburg. Coincidentally, Naudé was a member of the Brandenburg Academy of Sciences, which was the predecessor to Frederick's Academy in Berlin, and the two were colleagues for the last few years of Naudé's life.

E158 was primarily concerned with generating functions, so that the partition problem essentially served as an application of this new tool. By contrast, Euler concentrated squarely on the problem of partitions in his first work to be published on the subject. Chapter XVI of his very influential textbook *Introductio in analysin infinitorum* was titled "On the partition of numbers." Throughout this book Euler used power series as the natural extension of the idea of a polynomial, and he used this intuitive approach to introduce the generating functions

$$(1 + xz)(1 + x^2z)(1 + x^3z) \text{ etc.}$$

and

$$\frac{1}{(1 - xz)(1 - x^2z)(1 - x^3z) \text{ etc.}}$$

in chapter XVI. These are, respectively, the generating functions for $p_d(m, k)$ and $p(m, k)$, in the sense that those quantities are the coefficients of $x^m z^k$ in the formal power series expressions for the corresponding generating functions. Furthermore, the substitution $z = 1$ gives the generating functions of $p_d(m)$ and $p(m)$ respectively.

Although Euler used no special notation for any of these quantities in the *Introductio*, preferring to refer to all of the partition functions in words only, he adopted the notation $m^{(n)}$ in E191 for the number of partitions of m into summands no greater that n, with repetitions permitted. (One should also note, confusingly enough, that Euler used the same notation for $p(m, n)$ in E158.) In the *Introductio*, Euler skillfully manipulated his series expressions to find relations among $p_d(m, k)$, $p(m, k)$ and $m^{(k)}$, thereby reducing all questions about partitions to the calculation $m^{(k)}$. He then proved the recurrence relation:

$$m^{(k)} = m^{(k-1)} + (m - k)^{(k)},$$

which he used to build a table of $m^{(k)}$ for all pairs with $1 \leq m \leq 69$ and $1 \leq k \leq 11$. Using the relationships he had already established, he was able to solve Naudé's problems by looking up the table:

$$p_d(50, 7) = 22^{(7)} = 522 \quad \text{and} \quad p(50, 7) = 43^{(7)} = 8946.$$

Euler concluded the chapter with a variety of other observations, including the result that $p_d(m)$ is the same as the number of partitions of m into odd summands, with repetitions permitted. E191 is primarily a reworking of chapter XVI of the *Introductio* in the style of E158, but there is one very important new result in that paper, namely the recurrence relation

$$p(n) = p(n - 1) + p(n - 2) - p(n - 5) - p(n - 7) + p(n - 12) + p(n - 15) - \text{ etc.}$$

where the quantities subtracted from n on the right-hand side are the pentagonal numbers $(3j^2 \pm j)/2$, with terms added when j is odd and subtracted when j is even. The series always terminates because $p(0) = 1$ and $p(n) = 0$ for negative integers, by definition.

6 Conclusion

With E191, Euler had said pretty much all he could about the partition function. He did not return to the topic, at least in his published work and manuscripts, for a decade and a half. Then in 1765, the problem of runs in the Genoese lottery brought him face to face with a "real world" application of partitions. Even though it was not actually possible to bet on the occurrence of runs in the Berlin Lottery, Beguelin explicitly mentioned the utility of knowing these probabilities "in supposing that one might wish to introduce bets on one species or another of runs in the Genoese lottery." [Beguelin 1767, p. 233]

It seems very likely, then, that it was the problem of runs that induced Euler to return to the study of the partition function after he had settled back into life in St. Petersburg in the late 1760s. Certainly, the problem of runs resonates with the central problem of E394: in how many ways can the number m be written as a sum of k parts, each of which is less than or equal to some natural number n? The answer is, of course, to be found in the properties of the generating function

$$(x + x^2 + \text{ etc. } + x^n)^k.$$

The relevance of this line of inquiry to Theorem 2 of E338 is manifest, although Euler made no reference to that paper, nor to the lottery. In fact, he motivated his research, which was mostly limited to the case $n = 6$, by the question of how many ways the number m can be given as the sum of the spots on k dice.

Euler wrote E394 at a very busy time in his career. He had recently returned to St. Petersburg from Berlin but became ill shortly afterwards and lost his eyesight. Despite this setback, he was in the process of publishing a number of important textbooks on integral calculus, algebra and optics, as well as completing his *Letters to a German Princess*. Somehow, he made a place in his busy schedule to revisit the field of partition theory, even if he evidently did not have a breakthrough to report; at least nothing on the scale of those he had made in his earlier pieces on partitions. Understanding Euler's significant interest in problems arising from the Genoese Lottery, particularly the problem of runs in a lottery drawing, provides a convincing explanation for his return to this problem.

References

[Andrews 1998] Andrews, George E., *The Theory of Partitions*, Cambridge: Cambridge U. Press, 1998.

[Beguelin 1767] Beguelin, Niklaus von, "Sur les suites ou séquences dans la lotterie de Gênes. Premier et second mémoire," *Mémoires de l'académie des sciences de Berlin*, **21** (1765), 1767, pp. 231–280.

[Bellhouse 1991] Bellhouse, David, "The Genoese Lottery," *Statistical Science*, **6**, 1991, pp. 141–148.

[Bernoulli 1771] Bernoulli, Johann (III), "Sur les suites ou séquences dans la loterie de Gênes," *Mémoires de l'académie des sciences de Berlin*, **24** (1769), 1771, pp. 234–280.

[Bradley 2004] Bradley, Robert E., "Euler's Analysis of the Genoese Lottery," *Convergence*, convergence.mathdl.org, 2004.

[Bradley 2006] ——, "The Curious Case of the Bird's Beak," *International J. of Math. Comp. Sci.*, **1**, 2006, pp. 243–268.

[Daston 1988] Daston, Lorraine, *Classical Probability in the Enlightenment*, Princeton: Princeton U. Press, 1988.

[Dickson 1920] Dickson, Leonard E., *History of the Theory of Numbers*, vol. II, 1920, reprinted New York: Chelsea, 1971.

[Du Pasquier 1923] Du Pasquier, L. G., "Préface de l'éditeur," in [Euler 1923], 1923, pp. vii–liii.

[Eneström 1913] Eneström, Gustav, *Die Schriften Eulers chronologisch ...*, *Jahresbericht der Deutschen Mathematiker-Vereinigung*, **22**, 1913, pp. 1–388.

[Euler 1740] Euler, Leonhard, "De summis serierum reciprocarum" (E41), *Commentarii acad. sci. Petrop.*, **7**, 1740, pp. 123–134. Reprinted in [Euler 1911–], vol. I.14, pp. 73–86.

[Euler 1743a] ——, "De summis serierum reciprocarum ex potestatibus numerorum naturalium ..." (E61), *Miscellanea Berolinensia*, **7**, 1743, pp. 172–192. Reprinted in [Euler 1911–], vol. I.14, pp. 138-155.

[Euler 1743b] ——, "Démonstration de la somme de cette suite: $1 + 1/4 + 1/9 + 1/16 ...$" (E63), *Journal littéraire d'Allemagne*, **2:1**, 1743, pp. 115–127. Reprinted in [Euler 1911–], vol. I.14, pp. 177–186.

[Euler 1748] ——, *Introductio in analysin infinitorum*, 2 vols. (E101, E102), Lausanne: Bousquet, 1748. Reprinted in [Euler 1911–], vols. I.8, I.9. English translation: Blanton, John, *Introduction to the Analysis of the Infinite*, New York: Springer-Verlag, 1988 and 1990.

[Euler 1751a] ——, "Observationes analyticae variae de combinationibus" (E158), *Commentarii acad. sci. Petrop.*, **13**, (1741-43), 1751, pp. 64–93. Reprinted in [Euler 1911–], vol. I.2, pp. 163–193.

[Euler 1751b] ——, "De la controverse entre Mrs. Leibniz et Bernoulli sur les logarithmes des nombres négatifs et imaginaires" (E168), *Mémoires de l'academie des sciences de Berlin*, **5** (1749), 1751, pp. 139–179. Reprinted in [Euler 1911–], vol. I.17, pp. 195-232.

[Euler 1753] ——, "De partitione numerorum" (E191), *Novi Commentarii acad. sci. Petrop.*, **3**, (1751), 1753, pp. 125–169. Reprinted in [Euler 1911–], vol. I.2, pp. 254–294.

[Euler 1767] ——, "Sur la probablilité des séquences dans la lotterie Génoise" (E338), *Mémoires de l'académie des sciences de Berlin*, **21** (1765), 1767, pp. 191–230. Reprinted in [Euler 1923], pp. 113–152.

[Euler 1770] ——, "De partitione numerorum in partes tam numero quam specie datas" (E394) *Novi Commentarii acad. sci. Petrop.*, **14**, (1769), 1770, pp. 168–187. Reprinted in [Euler 1911–], vol. I.3, pp. 131–147.

[Euler 1785] ——, "Solutio quarundam quaestionum difficiliorum in calculo probabilium" (E600), *Opuscula Analytica*, vol. 2, St. Petersburg, 1785. Reprinted in [Euler 1923], p. 408–424.

[Euler 1862] ——, *Opera postuma mathematica et physica*, ed. P. H. Fuss & N. Fuss, St. Petersburg, 1862.

[Euler 1862a] ——, "Sur les logarithmes des nombres négatifs et imaginaires" (E807), in [Euler 1862], vol. I, pp. 269–281. Reprinted in [Euler 1911–], vol. I.19, pp. 417–438.

[Euler 1862b] ——, "Réflexions sur une espèce singulière de loterie nommée loterie Génoise" (E812), in [Euler 1862], vol. I, pp. 319–335. Reprinted in [Euler 1923], pp. 466–494.

[Euler 1862c] ——, "Analyse d'une problème du calcul des probabilité" (E813), in [Euler 1862], vol. I, pp. 336–341. Reprinted in [Euler 1923], pp. 495–506.

[Euler 1911–] ——, *Opera Omnia*, multiple volumes, publication in progress, Leipzig: Teubner, Zürich: Orell-Füssli, Basel: Birkhäuser, begun 1911.

[Euler 1923] ——, *Opera Omnia*, vol. I.7, Leipzig: Teubner, 1923.

[Euler 1975] ——. *Leonhardi Euleri Opera Omnia*, vol. IVA.1 (a catalog of Euler's correspondence), Basel: Birkhäuser, 1975.

[Euler 1986] ——. *Leonhardi Euleri Opera Omnia*, vol. IVA.6 (correspondence with Frederick II and du Maupertuis), Basel: Birkhäuser, 1986.

[Hald 1990] Hald, Anders, *A history of probability and statistics and their applications before 1750*, New York: Wiley, 1990.

[Winter 1957] Eduard Winter (Hrsg.), *Die Registres der Berliner Akademie der Wissenschaften 1746–1766*, Berlin, 1957.

Note: English translations of many of Euler's papers referenced above are available at `eulerarchive.org`.

Parallels in the Work of Leonhard Euler and Thomas Clausen

Carolyn Lathrop and Lee Stemkoski

Introduction

Thomas Clausen was a Danish mathematician and astronomer who, while not at the same level of proficiency as the mathematical leaders of his time, was able to produce a number of results building on and paralleling those of Leonhard Euler. Three examples of research that Clausen and Euler shared include the quadrature of lunes, investigation of Graeco-Latin squares, and factorization of Fermat numbers. These results are discussed at length in what follows.

Thomas Clausen: Mathematician and Astronomer

To understand the motivations behind and style of Clausen's work, it is helpful to place it in the greater context of his life. To this end, we begin with a brief biography. The following summary is based on [3], which in turn was mainly based on letters written by Clausen and his contemporaries.

Thomas Clausen, who would eventually publish over 150 papers and become a note-worthy scientific thinker in his time, was born on January 16, 1801 in Snogebaek, Denmark, to a small farmer from South Jutland. At the age of five, he tended cattle for a minister by the name of Georg Holst, who attended to his education, introducing him to reading and writing by sending him to school.

Clausen received an assistantship at the Altona Observatory in 1824. While there he worked for H. C. Schumacher, who made him responsible for various astronomical calculations. By all accounts, Clausen's skill in this field was matched only by his enthusiasm. His adventures and misfortunes ranged from financial problems to almost losing his job after less than a year for accidentally damaging equipment to falling in love with Schumacher's niece. Four years and one broken barometer later, Clausen travelled to Munich to work at the Optical Institute, and he seemed content with this for a while. During his employment there, he was mostly left free to research various topics, working on calculations and experiments with light and optics. He also began research on comets, travelling to Switzerland in 1829 to seek the original observations and documentation concerning the comet of 1770. His later work on this subject (dated 1840, published 1842) won the Copenhagen Academy's prize. Clausen used his leisure time to conduct this research and publish many articles in the *Astronomische Nachrichten* (A.N.) and Crelle's Journal. He gained the attention of such esteemed minds as Carl Friedrich Gauss and Friedrich Wilhelm Bessel, who would continue to admire his work for years to come.

Unfortunately, Clausen began to display the symptoms of a brain inflammation in 1833, and although he initially seemed to continue his work unhindered, the subsequent physical and mental distress eventually sapped his strength and interfered with his duties at the Optical Institute. Clausen disappeared from correspondence between 1834 and 1840, so it is difficult to determine anything about his life during these years.

By 1840 Clausen had recovered, returned to Altona, and experienced a surge in productivity. He continued his research on comets, studied the quadrature of the lune and Bernoulli numbers (producing the theorem which now bears his name) in 1840, investigated Graeco-Latin squares in 1842, and simultaneously pursued many other topics. After 1842, he relocated to Dorpat, Russia (now Tartu, Estonia), working as an observer for J.H. Maedler. In 1844, with Bessel's guidance, he received an honorary doctorate from the University of Koenigsberg. Three years later, he set a record in computing the digits of pi, accurately finding the first 248 decimal digits by calculating the series

$$\frac{\pi}{4} = 4\tan^{-1}\left(\frac{1}{5}\right) - \tan^{-1}\left(\frac{1}{239}\right)$$

and

$$\frac{\pi}{4} = 2\tan^{-1}\left(\frac{1}{3}\right) - \tan^{-1}\left(\frac{1}{7}\right).$$

In 1854, he became a member of the Goettingen Academy; his work with factorization and Fermat numbers occurred around this time. In 1856, he also became a member of the St. Petersburg Academy. Maedler retired in 1865, and Clausen succeeded him as the professor of astronomy and director of the Dorpat Observatory until he retired in 1872. Thomas Clausen died in Dorpat on May 23, 1885.

The article by Biermann also notes that Clausen's typical investigations are characterized by the following:

1. Inspiration by foreign works;

2. A desire to check unproven assumptions (due to his critical attitude);

3. Perseverance and resourcefulness (in particular, calculational ability) often result in solutions derived from peculiar methods;

4. Exploring a new side of a completed problem.

One sees these qualities manifest repeatedly in the following discussions of the three problems mentioned in the introduction.

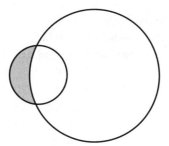

Figure 1. A Lune

The Quadrature of Lunes

This problem begins with Hippocrates of Chios, a geometer born in Greece around 470 B.C. He taught in Athens, and in particular is known for his work on two classical geometric straightedge/compass construction problems: squaring the circle and duplicating the cube (the first asks for a square with the area of a given circle, the second a line segment with length equal to the cube root of two). Work on the first of these two problems led to results on the squaring of lunes. A *lune* is the area cut off by one circle from the interior of a smaller one; see Figure 1.

A description of Hippocrates' results is contained in Eudemus' History of Geometry. The translation by Heath [11] explains that Hippocrates

> ... proceeded to show in what way it was possible to square a lune the outer circumference of which is that of a semicircle. This he affected by circumscribing a semicircle about an isosceles right-angled triangle and a segment of a circle similar to those cut off by the sides. Then, since the segment about the base is equal to the sum of those about the sides, it follows that, when the part of the triangle above the segment about the base is added to both alike, the lune will be equal to the triangle. Therefore the lune, having been proved equal to the triangle, can be squared.

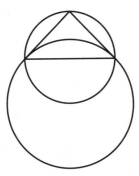

Figure 2. Diagram to accompany Hippocrates' result

Altogether Hippocrates discovered 3 squarable lunes. Throughout history, many mathematicians tried their best to find all such lunes; it turns out there was considerable duplication of effort. According to Heath, all five squarable lunes were given in a dissertation by Martin Johan Wallenius in 1766. According to Eneström [5], Euler's *Considerationes cyclometricae* [7], an 11 page article presented in 1771, is "about quadratic 'Lunulae,' where the 5 known cases will be handled." Clausen made this discovery independently as well and also wrote a short (two page) article [4] about quadrature of lunes in Crelle's Journal in 1840. In this article, Clausen appears to be aware of only one of Hippocrates' lunes; the example detailed above is the only one attributed to the Greek geometer. Although these results had been previously proved by others, at present the Danish Mathematical Society has as its logo one of the diagrams from this paper of Clausen. This particular story remained open until the 1900s, until N. G. Tschebatorew and A. W. Dorodnow proved that these five lunes are in fact the only squarable ones.

Graeco-Latin Squares

The history of Graeco-Latin squares begins with a story about magic squares. There is a Chinese legend that takes place around 2200 B.C., where the Emperor Yu discovers a turtle with spots on its back that appeared in groups arranged as the following:

$$
\begin{array}{ccc}
4 & 9 & 2 \\
3 & 5 & 7 \\
8 & 1 & 6
\end{array}
$$

The Emperor immediately recognized the many patterns and symmetries present, and subsequently believed there was mystical significance in this arrangement, which is sometimes referred to as the *Lo-Shu* square. Each number from 1 to 9 occurs exactly once in the square, and the sum of the numbers in each row, column, and diagonal is the same: 15. Today, a square of side length n, containing the numbers 1 through n^2 and possessing the summation properties described above is called a *magic square* (of order n).

The earliest written records of the Lo-Shu square in China date back to the fourth century B.C.; some of the ascribed meanings included identifying Yin and Yang with the even and odd numbers, respectively, or identifying the elements (Fire, Wind, Water, and Earth) in symmetric positions within the square. The Chinese were not alone in their fascination with this object; cultures that shared this interest included the Mayans and the Hausa of Nigeria [15]. In addition, magic squares have arisen repeatedly in mystical contexts throughout the years. In the eighth century, the Islamic alchemist Jabir ibn Hayyan (known as Geber in Europe) used magic squares in his attempts to derive procedures in his experiments; he assigned elements to the various numbers in the square, and believed that the arrangements of numbers corresponded to formulas that would turn base metal into gold. The astrologist Cornelius Agrippa (1486–1535) created magic squares of orders 3 through 9 and assigned them to planets, to be used in divinations. A magic square even appears in a 1514 painting of Durer [15]. A formal, scholarly investigation of magic squares and their properties did not appear until the Enlightenment and the work of Leonhard Euler. Euler wrote two papers pertaining to magic squares: *Recherches sur une nouvelle espèce de quarrés magiques* (E530), originally published in 1782 [9], and *De quadratis magicis* (E795), published posthumously in 1849 [10]. The Eneström index indicates that the latter of these two works, although published at a later date, was presented to the St. Petersburg Academy on 17 October 1776, while the former was not read to the Academy until March 8, 1779. This, in addition to the content of the articles, suggests that Euler first considered magic squares in *De quadratis magicis*, to which we now turn our attention.

Whether motivated by intellectual curiosity or the legendary powers of magic squares, it is desirable to be able to construct these objects. In E795, a systematic investigation of their patterns and symmetries begin. According to the translation [1], Euler immediately observes that:

> all the numbers from 1 to xx can be represented with this formula: $mx + n$, for if we successively have m take all the values 0, 1, 2, 3, 4 to $x - 1$, and then n take all the values 1, 2, 3, 4, ..., x, it is clear that all the numbers from 1 to xx can be represented by combining each of the values of m with each of the values of n. Furthermore, all the numbers to be inscribed on the square with the formula $mx + n$ are able to be expressed using two parts, always in this order, where we use the Latin letters a, b, c, d etc. for the first part mx, and the Greek letters α, β, γ, δ, etc. for the second part n, where it is clear that for any number x, there is always a Latin and Greek letter that can be equal to x by having the Latin letters be $0x$, $1x$, $2x$, $3x$ to $(x - 1)x$ and the Greek letters take the values 1, 2, 3, 4, ..., x.

Euler then proceeds to write each number in a magic square as a pair consisting of a Latin letter and a Greek letter. He does this for the Lo-Shu square mentioned above, obtaining:

$$
\begin{array}{ccc}
4 & 9 & 2 \\
3 & 5 & 7 \\
8 & 1 & 6
\end{array}
$$

For a paragraph Euler examines the patterns in the square consisting of the Latin letters alone, and similarly for the Greek; in particular, each letter occurs once in every row and column. He notes that every possible pair has appeared, but attributes it to coincidence. Next, Euler analyzes magic squares of orders 4 and 5, assigning a Latin-Greek letter pair to each number. While every possible pair appears in the examples Euler has chosen, for some of these it is not necessarily the case that every Latin and Greek letter appears in every row and column. In the final part of the paper he gives a square of side length 6 similarly consisting of pairs of letters, and closes by stating that while the examples discussed in this paper are somewhat *ad hoc*, such methods exist to construct many magic squares of any size. This comment, combined with the surprising fact that Euler's closing 6 by 6 example actually does not result in a magic square, may have provided the motivation for his second paper dealing with the subject.

In *Recherches sur une nouvelle espèce de quarrés magiques*, Euler opens with a question, which is often (apocryphally) attributed to Catherine the Great: If there are 36 officers from six different regiments, where each officer from a regiment having one of six different ranks, how can they be arranged in a 6×6 square so that one officer from each regiment and one from each rank appears in every row and column? This is often referred to as the *36 officer problem*. To address this question, Euler first defines a *Latin Square of order n* as a square containing n different letters arranged so that every letter appears once in each row and column. For example,

$$
\begin{array}{ccc}
a & b & c \\
c & a & b \\
b & c & a
\end{array}
$$

He goes on to define a *Graeco-Latin square of order n* as a square formed by pairing up the corresponding entries of two Latin squares (one containing Latin letters, the other presumably containing Greek letters) where every possible pair occurs exactly once. For example,

$$(a, \alpha) \quad (b, \beta) \quad (c, \gamma)$$
$$(c, \beta) \quad (a, \gamma) \quad (b, \alpha)$$
$$(b, \gamma) \quad (c, \alpha) \quad (a, \beta)$$

Given a Latin square, Euler refers to the process of finding another Latin square that can be used to create a Graeco-Latin square as *completing* the original Latin square. He goes on to describe a variety of transformations one can perform on a Latin square that preserve its ability to be completed, which allows large sets of squares to be analyzed simultaneously. Euler is able to prove many results on whether special types of Latin squares can be completed, but the opening question of the paper remains unanswered. Euler concludes by mentioning that if there exists a solution to the 36 officer problem, then

> we could derive several others using these transformations that would also satisfy the conditions of the problem. But, having examined a large number of such squares without having encountered a single one, it is most likely that there are none at all.... [W]e see that the number of variations for the case of $n = 6$ cannot be so prodigious that the 50 or 60 that I have examined were but a small part. I observe further here that the exact count of all the possible cases of similar variations would be an object worthy of the attention of Geometers [mathematicians].

Indeed, the problem attracted much attention, but the solution remained elusive for many years.

Thomas Clausen, whose calculational abilities have already been mentioned, apparently took up the problem of finding Graeco-Latin squares while he was still an assistant to Schumacher in Altona. There is a brief correspondence between Schumacher and Gauss focusing on Graeco-Latin squares. Apparently this sparked Clausen's interest, for he seems to have devoted some time to this problem. In a letter dated 10 August 1842 [16], Schumacher reports to Gauss that Clausen had found a solution to this problem. While the work was clearly too long to fully describe in the letter, it is mentioned that the key was organizing these cases into 17 families and then performing an exhaustive analysis on each. Although no record survives of Clausen's actual work, later investigations support the idea that Clausen did have a proof, or at the very least was on the right track.

The earliest *published* proof was produced by Gaston Tarry [17] in 1900. His article was only 33 pages, seemingly short compared to the 100 pages of groundwork that Euler had published years earlier. At the very beginning, Tarry mentions that his proof is based on the organization of all order-6 Latin squares into *17 families* and a case-by-case analysis. His paper is indeed straightforward; there are no "tricks" involved, just a well-developed classification scheme. Hence we know that the proof may be given with large amounts of calculation, a skill Clausen certainly possessed and enjoyed exercising. There is a natural organizational scheme that makes the calculations tractable, which Clausen seems to have discovered; and Clausen had convinced a fellow scientist of the validity of his method, such that it was worthy of announcement to the leading mathematician of the time. The evidence certainly supports the hypothesis that Clausen was in possession of what was probably the first proof of the 36 officer problem that had eluded Euler years ago.

Fermat numbers

Pierre de Fermat, a lawyer who worked on mathematics in his spare time, produced some of the most famous and influential results in number theory, which are still of significance today. The most famous is probably *Fermat's Last Theorem*, that the equation $a^n + b^n = c^n$ has no nontrivial integer solutions when $n \geq 3$, which was only recently proved in [18] and [20]. Among the more fundamental results is *Fermat's little theorem*, that for a given prime p and any integer a not divisible by p we have $a^{p-1} \equiv 1 \pmod{p}$, proved and generalized by Euler [8]. Finally, Fermat also investigated the now-called *Fermat numbers* $F_n = 2^{2^n} + 1$. The first few such numbers are

$$F_0 = 3, F_1 = 5, F_2 = 17, F_3 = 257, F_4 = 65537.$$

Interestingly enough, these Fermat numbers are all prime. Fermat then claimed that for any n, the number F_n is prime, and hence we can systematically produce arbitrarily large prime numbers. This conjecture was initially perhaps little more than an arithmetic curiosity without application.

However, even the best of mathematicians are often attracted by curiosities. In 1732, Euler presented *Observationes de theoremate quodam Fermatiano aliisque ad numeros primos spectantibus* [6], (Observations on a theorem of Fermat and others on looking at prime numbers) (E26), to the St. Petersburg Academy. In this paper, he correctly states that F_5 is divisible by 641, and therefore Fermat's claim is false. However, Euler gives no indication of how he arrived at this result. For this we have to wait another sixteen years.

In 1748, *Theoremata circa divisores numerorum* [8], (Theorems on divisors of numbers) (E134), was presented by Euler to the Academy. This paper contained a second proof of what is now called the Euler-Fermat theorem (the aforementioned generalization of Fermat's little theorem). In addition, according to the translation [2], Euler demonstrated that

> ... the sum of two numbers $a^{2^m} + b^{2^m}$, for which the exponent is a power of two, admits no divisors other than those of the form $2^{m+1} \cdot n + 1$.

This has an immediate consequence to Fermat numbers: on setting $a = 2$ and $b = 1$, we obtain the corollary that every factor of F_n must have the form $k \cdot 2^{n+1} + 1$ for some integer k. For $n = 5$, this means that any factor of

$$F_5 = 4294967297$$

has the form $64k + 1$. It then only required at most 10 trial divisions for Euler to find the factor $641 = 10 \cdot 64 + 1$. At this point he seems content and moves on to other things.

Fermat's claim had been settled in the negative, and thus the study of Fermat numbers may have been regarded as recreational mathematics again, that is, until Gauss drew a connection with the ever-inspirational classic Greek straightedge/compass construction problems.

In Book III, Proposition 30 of the *Elements* [12], Euclid described a method that may be used to double the number of sides of a regular polygon. Since Euclid also gives methods to construct equilateral triangles (Book I, Proposition 1), squares (Book I, Proposition 46), regular pentagons (Book IV, Proposition 11), and regular 15-gons (Book IV, Proposition 16), it follows that an n-gon is constructible when $n = 2^a 3^b 5^c$, where a is a nonnegative integer and b and c are either 0 or 1.

Gauss extended this observation when he proved that if when n is the product of a power of two (including $2^0 = 1$) and any number of distinct Fermat primes, then a regular n-sided polygon with n sides is constructible. (The converse was proved by Wantzel [19].) This relationship between number theory and geometry seems to have renewed interest in the study of Fermat numbers, particularly computing their factors.

The fact that

$$F_6 = 18,446,744,073,709,551,617$$

is composite was first published by Landry [14] in 1880. However, there is a letter from Clausen to Gauss, written in 1855 (the year of Gauss' death), in which the factors of F_6 are given [13]; the smaller factor is 274,177, and the larger factor Clausen (correctly) believed to be the largest prime known at that time. In neither Landry's paper nor Clausen's letter can we determine how these factors were obtained. There are a pair of conjectures as to the method Clausen used. Two years earlier, in a letter dated February 11, 1853, probably directed to an old friend and employer C.A.F. Peters in Koenigsberg, Clausen wrote [3]:

> Perhaps it interested you to learn that I found one method, that I believe to be new, to divide larger numbers into their prime factors; in the decomposition of the number $(10^{17} - 1)/9$ into the two factors 2,071,723 and 5,363,222,357, it worked satisfactorily.

The number $(10^n - 1)/9$ is composed of the digit 1 repeating n times and is often referred to as the nth *repunit*, R_n. As both R_{17} and F_6 are composed of one (relatively) small number and one large number, it is regarded as possible that Clausen used a method similar to Euler's of determining a set of restricted residue classes to which potential factors must belong. Another school of thought notes that Le Lasseur, who was not aware of Clausen's result and factored R_{17} in 1879 [21], used a variant of Fermat's difference of squares technique; perhaps Clausen had used a method similar to this in his work. Regardless of the technique, Clausen is now credited as having taken the next step after Euler in determining the primality of Fermat numbers, an investigation that continues to this day.

Conclusion

Unlike mathematics, history is neither objective nor impartial. Reflecting upon the past, subsequent generations celebrate some aspects of history and historical personalities, but lose sight of others. At first glance, Thomas Clausen may appear to be one such man, lost in the shadow of the great Leonhard Euler. It is true that he may not have matched Euler's dizzying intellect—few, if any, could. However, the results of Clausen do in fact parallel and even extend those of Euler in some cases. For his continuation of the work that Euler had begun, Clausen merits recognition, and here we provide a small portion of the recognition that he has earned.

References

[1] J. Bell, trans., "De quadratis magicis," by L. Euler. Available online at *The Euler Archive*, www.eulerarchive.org

[2] ——, trans., "Theoremata circa divisores numerorum," by L. Euler. Available online at *The Euler Archive*, www.eulerarchive.org

[3] K.R. Biermann, "Thomas Clausen, Mathematiker und Astronom," *J. für die reine und angewandte Mathematik*, 216 (1964) 159–198.

[4] T. Clausen, "Vier neue mondförmige Flächen, deren Inhalt quadrirbar ist," *Crelle J.* 21 (1840) 375–376.

[5] G. Eneström, "Die Schriften Eulers chronologisch nach den Jahren geordnet, in denen sie verfasst worden sind," *Jahresbericht der Deutschen Mathematiker-Vereinigung*, 1913.

[6] L. Euler, "Observationes de theoremate quodam Fermatiano aliisque ad numeros primos spectantibus," (E26), *Commentarii academiae scientiarum Petropolitanae* 6 (1738) 103–107.

[7] ——, "Considerationes cyclometricae," (E432), *Novi Commentarii academiae scientiarum Petropolitanae* 16 (1772) 160–170.

[8] ——, "Theoremata circa divisores numerorum," (E134), *Novi Commentarii academiae scientiarum Petropolitanae* 1 (1750) 20–48.

[9] ——, "Recherches sur une nouvelle espèce de quarrés magiques," (E530), *Verhandelingen uitgegeven door het zeeuwsch Genootschap der Wetenschappen te Vlissingen* 9 (1782) 85–239.

[10] ——, "De quadratis magicis," (E795), *Commentationes arithmeticae* 2 (1849) 593–602.

[11] T.L. Heath, *A History of Greek Mathematics, Vol. 1: From Thales to Euclid*, Dover, 1981.

[12] ——, *The Thirteen Books of Euclid's Elements*, Dover, 1956.

[13] M. Křížek, et al. *17 lectures on Fermat numbers: from number theory to geometry*, Florian Luca, Lawrence Somer, Springer, 2001.

[14] F. Landry, "Note sur la décomposition du nombre $2^{64} + 1$ (Extrait)," *Comptes Rendus Acad. Sci. Paris*, 91 (1880) 138.

[15] C.A. Pickover, *The zen of magic squares, circles, and stars: an exhibition of surprising structures across dimensions*, Princeton University Press, 2002.

[16] Letter from Shumacher to Gauss, regarding Thomas Clausen, August 10, 1842. Gauss, *Werke* Bd. 12, p. 16. Göttingen, Dieterich, (1863).

[17] G. Tarry, "Le problème des 36 officiers," *Comptes Rendus Assoc. France Av. Sci.* 29, part 2 (1900) 170–203.

[18] R. Taylor and A. Wiles, "Ring theoretic properties of certain Hecke algebras," *Annals of Mathematics* 141 (3), (1995) 553–572.

[19] M.L. Wantzel, "Recherches sur les moyens de reconnaître si un problème de géométrie peut se résoudre avec la règle et le compas," *J. Math. pures appliq.* 1 (1836) 366–372.

[20] A. Wiles, "Modular elliptic curves and Fermat's last theorem," *Annals of Mathematics* 141 (3) (1995) 443–551.

[21] H. Williams, *Édouard Lucas and primality testing*, Wiley, 1998.

Three Bodies? Why not Four?
The Motion of the Lunar Apsides[1]

Robert E. Bradley

Abstract. Popular modern accounts of Newton's work frequently give the impression that the problems of planetary motion were solved once and for all in the *Principia*. In fact, giving an account of observed celestial phenomena based entirely on Newton's laws was a problem that engaged the scientific community well into the 18th century. Two thorny three-body problems (Sun-Earth-Moon and Sun-Jupiter-Saturn) were fodder for mid-century prize competitions of the European academies. A theory of the moon was particularly elusive: in 1747 Clairaut even announced that he had demonstrated Newton's gravitational theory to be false, a claim he later retracted.

In this paper, we survey the celestial mechanics of Euler and d'Alembert in the 1740s and 1750s and their attempts to explain the phenomena using Newton's mechanics. Their efforts are illustrated with passages from their correspondence, including a discussion of the possibility that the moon might consist of two disconnected bodies.

1 Introduction

The correspondence between Euler and D'Alembert [Euler 1980] provides a fascinating and highly personal window on scientific practice during the Enlightenment, with expressions of bitter rancor, episodes of political intrigue, and suggestions of academic dishonesty playing themselves out after a friendly and productive initial period [Bradley 2007]. Perhaps the most curious passage during the early collegial period was their discussion of the possibility that the moon might consist of two disjoint globes, one of which remains permanently hidden behind the one that we observe from the earth's surface.

Although neither of the correspondents seems sincerely to have believed that this hypothesis describes the true state of the heavens, the fact that both of them considered such a possibility and calculated its mathematical consequences is a reflection on the state of celestial mechanics in the 1740s. Although Newton had essentially provided all of the ana-

---

[1] This paper is based on a talk given July 10, 2004 at the joint meeting of the Canadian Society for History and Philosophy of Mathematics (CSHPM) and the British Society for History of Mathematics (BSHM) in Cambridge, England.

Isaac Newton

"Drawn and scraped MDCCLX by James Macardel from an original portrait painted by Enoch Seeman."

lytical tools needed in the solution of problems involving the dynamics of heavenly bodies, the true state of affairs twenty years after his death was that there were still many difficult unsolved problems to test the mettle of the mathematical community. Among these were accounting for the nutation of the earth's axis, the motions of Jupiter and Saturn, and the motion of the moon, especially the precession of its apsides.

2   Newton's Lunar Theory

Newton's *Philosophiae Naturalis Principia Mathematica* was first published in 1687, with a second edition in 1713 and a third in 1726. The source used in this paper is the new translation [Newton 1999] by Cohen and Whitman, incorporating the contents of all three editions. The *Principia* is divided into three books, the last of which applies the principles developed in the two preceding ones to what Newton calls "The System of the World," that is, a systematic study of the motion of the heavenly bodies. About a third of this third book is devoted to Newton's theory of the moon's motion.

Cohen considers this "one of the most revolutionary parts of the *Principia* since it introduced a wholly new way of analyzing the moon's motion and thereby set the study of the moon in a wholly new direction which astronomers have largely been following ever since." [Cohen 1999, p. 246] Any theory of the moon's motion before Newton consisted of a model, or geometric description, of the actual lunar phenomena as they had been observed, along with a scheme for drawing up tables to predict the future position of the moon. Newton instead proposed to predict the behavior of the moon based on deductive principles of physics, particularly his inverse square law of gravitation. "That is, Newton set up a wholly new way of studying the moon's motion by introducing physical causes, extending the analysis of the two-body problem of earth and moon to a three-body problem by introducing the gravitational perturbations of the sun." [Cohen 1999, p. 246]

Revolutionary though Newton's program was, he was not able to explain the moon's motion to a satisfactory degree. In fact, his lunar theory was probably the portion of the *Principia* that underwent the most significant change from one edition to the next. Furthermore, during the long gap between the first and second editions of the *Principia*, Newton fashioned a substantially different theory of the moon, which appeared in Latin in David Gregory's 1702 astronomy textbook [Gregory 1702] as well as in an English language pamphlet. I. B. Cohen has had both of these texts reprinted in a modern edition [Newton/Cohen 1975], which also includes a substantial introduction.

It is this 1702 work that is generally meant when mid-18th-century mathematicians speak of "Newton's Lunar Theory." Because his deductive lunar theory could not predict the moon's position to a degree of accuracy which was sufficient for making lunar tables, Newton "had to have recourse to pre-dynamical methods, in particular relying on the system of Jeremiah Horrocks, and in some cases even 'fudging' the numbers in order to gain agreement of theory with observation." [Cohen 1999, p. 247]. The 1702 theory consists of a collection of seven "equations" or corrections to the moon's mean motion which could, according to the claim on the title page of the English pamphlet, give the moon's true position to within two minutes of arc [Newton/Cohen 1975, p. 91].

Euler and d'Alembert both made use of Newton's 1702 equations during the 1740s, when testing the accuracy their own attempts at a deductive lunar theory. Although less accurate than actual observations, they were considerably easier to use than real astronomical data: it's much simpler to perform a few calculations in one's study than to enlist the collaboration of an observational astronomer. Although Newton's equations gave sufficiently accurate data for verifying the precision of a new theory, d'Alembert did not accept the optimistic claims of accuracy to within two minutes. In his letter to Euler of 30 March 1748, he said "I take it as a given that the tables of Mr. Newton agree with observations within 5 minutes, as is recognized by all astronomers." [Euler 1980, p. 284]

3   The Lunar Apsides

The orbit of the moon around the earth is approximately elliptical in shape, with perturbations caused by the gravitational pull of the sun. It was well known to Newton and to later astronomers that the mean distance from the earth to the moon is about 30 earth diameters. The apparent size of the moon varies sufficiently between perigee (its closest approach to the earth) and apogee (its greatest distance) so that the difference is discernible to the naked eye. At apogee the moon's apparent diameter is about $33\frac{1}{2}$ minutes of arc, some 14% larger than the figure of $29\frac{1}{3}$ minutes at perigee, causing a difference of 30% in apparent area. All of this is a consequence of the fact that the distance from the earth to the moon at apogee is about 14% larger than at perigee: modern techniques give these at approximately 406,700 km and 356,400 km respectively. The apogee and perigee of the orbit are called its *apsides*, and the line joining them is the *apsidal line*, although some authors seem to use the singular *apsis* as a synonym for this line of the apsides.

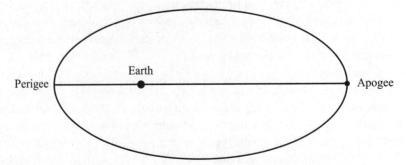

Figure 1. The apsidal line, with the moon at apogee

If the earth and moon truly constituted a two-body system, then over the course of a full revolution from apogee to apogee, the moon would return to the same location with respect to the fixed stars. However, because of the perturbing effect of the sun on the moon's orbit, the moon completes somewhat more than a full revolution in the time if takes for it to return to the apogee. The mean precession of the apsidal line, as illustrated (and exaggerated) in Figure 2, is about 3° per revolution, or about 40° annually. The actual motion is far from simple, and varies from a maximum precession of about 5 times the mean rate, to a regression at a rate equivalent to about 9° per month [Smith 1999, p. 257].

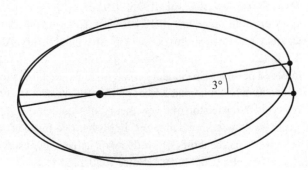

Figure 2. The precession of the apsidal line

In Book 3 of the *Principia* Newton has some real success in deducing certain aspects of the moon's motion from physical principles, such as the variations in its angular speed (greater at the syzygies and less at the quadratures) and changes in its inclination with respect to the ecliptic [Smith 1999, p. 257]. However, Smith continues, "conspicuously absent from the quantitative analysis in book 3 is the motion of the lunar apsis." In Book 1, Proposition 45, Newton does consider the problem of finding "the motions of the apsides of orbits that differ very little from circles." [Newton 1999, p. 539] In the corollaries to this proposition, he works out numerical approximations and concludes that "in each revolution, the upper apsis will move forward through $1°31'28''$. The apsis of the moon is about twice as swift." [Newton 1999, p. 545] However, this final sentence only appears in the third edition of the *Principia*. Smith observes that "nothing is even said to indicate that the result is pertinent to the moon" in the earlier editions [Smith 1999, p. 258].

Thus Newton's celestial mechanics has managed to account for only half of the observed motion of the lunar apsides. The failure to give a full accounting is the result of the difficulty of the general three-body problem. The task of accounting for the rest of the phenomenon was therefore bequeathed to future generations.

4   Clairaut, D'Alembert and Euler

Newton's *Principia* became widely known on the Continent, both among the scientific community and, thanks to Voltaire's 1734 *Lettres Philosophiques sur les Anglais*, also among the broader public. By the 1740s, Continental scientists were grappling with deep problems in Newtonian celestial mechanics. For example, d'Alembert and Euler refined Newton's explanation of the precession of the equinoxes [d'Alembert 1749, Euler 1749b] to the extent that they could also account for the newly discovered nutation of the earth's axis, a subtle perturbation in the earth's orbit announced by the British Astronomer Royal James Bradley in 1748.

The three-body problem continued to pose a monumental hurdle to further progress in celestial mechanics. Most of the planets do not interact in any significant way with any body in the solar system other than the sun, so they may be treated as though they are part of a two-body system. Newton had solved the two-body problem and shown that in such a situation, his inverse square law implies Kepler's laws—this was one of the central triumphs of the *Principia*.

The earth is different. Other planets either have no satellites at all, or have multiple satellites with masses insignificant when compared to their own. Because the earth has a single satellite of significant mass, neither earth-sun nor earth-moon may be considered in isolation. The intractability of the general three-body problem means that an analytic solution to the motion of the moon is actually impossible, although arbitrarily good approximations can be made. Developing the mathematical tools for these approximation techniques occupied the Continental community throughout the 18th century and beyond.

Another significant three-body system in our solar system consists of Jupiter, Saturn and the Sun. When these enormous planets are near conjunction, their mutual attraction perturbs their orbits, which otherwise conform quite well to the rules of a two-body sun-planet system. The Paris Academy selected this as the topic for its 1748 Prize problem, asking entrants to come up with "a Theory of Saturn and Jupiter, by which one may explain the Inequalities which these two Planets appear to cause in one another, particularly at the time of their Conjunction" [Euler 1749a, Introduction]. As members of the Academy, neither d'Alembert nor his rival Clairaut, arguably the best theoretical astronomer of the period, were eligible to compete. It should come as little surprise, then, that the prize should fall to Euler, who concluded that neither the observed motion of Jupiter and Saturn nor that of the Moon could be explained entirely by Newton's Inverse Square Law.

The prize was awarded during a very cordial period in the Euler-d'Alembert correspondence, and d'Alembert could hardly wait to give his colleague the good news. He opened his letter of 17 June 1748 by saying

> It has been a very long time since I received any news from you, and from my end I have had so much to do recently that I have not been able to find the time to have the honor of writing you. Mr. Clairaut took it upon himself to inform you that you have won our prize, and your paper is most deserving. Some of our commissioners judged that you ought to have proved fundamental propositions, and to have expounded further on the details, and for little more than this, which is not a good reason, the awarding of the prize might have been postponed. However, this injustice seemed so particularly flagrant to me that I declared to the commissioners that I would not sign the decree should they assume that position, and Mr. Clairaut was also of a like mind in awarding to you. I flatter myself that you will also win the prize in two years, due to the fact that you have such a head start on your competitors, so that it will be extremely difficult for them to catch up to you. [Euler 1980, p. 287]

D'Alembert's posturing notwithstanding, it is a fact that Euler's paper constituted only a partial solution, and the committee clearly had reservations about awarding the prize. It frequently happened in 18th-century scientific prize competitions that none of the entrants were deemed to have adequately solved the problem. Typically in this case the problem was reassigned. Two years was the usual turn-around time for prize competitions, giving entrants a year to prepare their entries, and the judges a year to deliberate. It is a curious situation that although the Paris Prize for 1748 was awarded as scheduled, the same topic was set again for 1750.

It is also interesting to note that d'Alembert apparently advocated for Euler in this case. When the Berlin Prize for 1750 was postponed for lack of a suitable entry, d'Alembert was bitterly disappointed. Later on he was told by Grischow, one of the judges, that he had been the front runner and only Euler stood between him and the prize. This alleged slight was the reason that d'Alembert angrily broke off his correspondence with Euler in 1751. [Bradley 2007]

D'Alembert and Clairaut were also hard at work on the three-body problem as this competition was taking place. Hankins [Hankins 1970, p. 32] reports that Clairaut was already working on a lunar theory, and the three-body problem in general, as early as 1745. He continues:

> The next year, d'Alembert attacked the same problem so that in 1747 both men were working in secret, giving parts of their theories to the [Paris] Academy and depositing uncompleted portions with the secretary in the form of sealed *plis cachetés*. The greatest possible surprise occurred on 15 November 1747, when Clairaut, at a public session of the Academy, announced in rather pompous phrases that the Newtonian theory of gravity was false! [Hankins 1970, p. 32]

The text of Clairaut's announcement is in the volume of the *Mémoires* of the Paris Academy for 1745–49 [Clairaut 1747]. Hankins goes on to speculate that Euler's essay on Jupiter and Saturn may have given Clairaut the courage to challenge the Newtonian doctrine [Hankins 1970, p. 32]. For although the Paris Prize was not awarded until June

Alexis Clairaut (sculptor: Cathelin)

1748, Clairaut had the opportunity as a member of the Academy to see it much sooner. Indeed, he opens his letter to Euler of 11 September 1747 by saying "I have just avidly looked through your piece on Saturn, for I frankly acknowledge that I recognized you from the first glance." He goes on to admit that although this was no difficult feat as Euler had written it in his own hand, nevertheless he was convinced that there was nothing Euler could have done to keep Clairaut from recognizing him [Euler 1980, p. 173]. He soon turned to the motion of the lunar apsides:

> I was delighted to see that you think as I do on the Newtonian attraction. It seems to have been demonstrated that it does not suffice to explain the phenomena, but the distinctive characteristic of the moon that you have given seems to me to be less striking than the one that I have noticed. Instead of looking at what the distance ought to be, I have examined what the motion of the apogee ought to be. And in finding barely half of what actually exists in Nature, it seems this has given me the proof of the utter insufficiency of the Law of Squares. ... I think rather that the general agreement of the system requires that the general law be as $\frac{1}{\text{dist}^2}$ + a small function of the distance, significant enough at small distances like the Moon's, but almost nothing at greater distances. [Euler 1980, p. 173-174]

Thus Clairaut, like Newton before him, could account at this time for only half of the precession of the lunar apsides using the inverse square law. His solution is to posit a higher order term (or terms) in the law of gravitation. Two months later, when he delivered his controversial conclusion to Paris Academy, he specifically suggested that the force of varies as

$$\frac{c}{r^2} + \frac{d}{r^4} \quad \text{and not as} \quad \frac{c}{r^2},$$

where r is the distance between the bodies, the fourth degree term becoming insignificant in the interplanetary range; see [Smith 1999, p. 263], summarizing [Clairaut 1747].

By the time Clairaut made this announcement, both Euler and d'Alembert had reached the same conclusion, the former in his as-yet-unpublished essay on Jupiter and Saturn, and the latter in a sealed note (*plis cacheté*) deposited with the Secretary of the Paris Academy earlier the same month [Hankins 1970, p. 32]. In a letter to Clairaut of 6 January 1748, Euler shared the calculations that had led him to his conclusion, but ceded priority for the discovery of the insufficiency of the inverse square law to Clairaut, "because I am convinced that you have more thoroughly deepened our understanding of this matter than I." [Euler 1980, p. 181]

Notwithstanding the above, all three men continued to seek a lunar theory that was based solely on the inverse square law. Clairaut was the first to find the correct solution to the problem, and retracted his original claim in another announcement to the Academy on 17 May 1749 [Clairaut 1749]. D'Alembert also found his way to the same conclusion at about the same time, and wrote to Cramer on 12 May 1749, expressing his embarrassment at having doubted Newton's Law [Hankins 1970, p. 34].

Smith gives the following account of how Clairaut reached his initial conclusion in 1747 and his subsequent revision in 1749 [Smith 1999, p. 263–264]. In 1747, when Clairaut was calculating the mean precession of the apsides, he had made certain simplifying assumptions, believing that these would not significantly affect the accuracy of his conclusions. Specifically, he modeled the moon's orbit as an ellipse revolving about the earth, believing he could neglect the perturbing effect of the sun's force on the orbital shape without harming the accuracy of his results. When he later reworked this calculations without this simplifying assumption, taking into account the solar deformation of the ellipse, he found that there were higher order terms, involving the square and cube of the eccentricity of the orbit, and that these significantly altered the value of his approximate solutions. In his earlier calculations, Clairaut, like Newton before him, had considered only linear terms in the eccentricity.

5   The Dual Moon Hypothesis

During the period between Clairaut's 1747 announcement and his 1749 retraction, both Euler and d'Alembert discussed the insufficiency of the Newtonian hypothesis in their letters, and yet both were diligently looking for ways to save the hypothesis and still account for the phenomena. Perhaps the most creative thinking along these lines was expressed by d'Alembert in his letter to Euler of 20 January 1748:

> Tell me also, Sir, whether you believe that the differences between the real movement of the apsides of the moon and that which we find by the Theory necessarily prove that the force of attraction does not exactly follow a law of the inverse square of the distance. It seems to me that the only thing one ought to conclude is that the force that draws the center of gravity of the moon towards the earth is not as the square of the distance, but it seems to be that this would be the case if the moon were not a spherical body, and composed of concentric homogeneous layers. Since this planet always shows us the same face, it is certainly possible that its figure, and the mutual arrangement of its parts, are quite irregular. I've considered what would have to happen to the moon, under the hypothesis that it is separated into two globes A and B, held together by a rod, which turn about their center C, at the same time that the center C revolves around the earth, and I have found that CA would need to be $1/30$ of AT in order that the apsides be $1°\frac{1}{2}$ of revolution. This, compounded with the solar force that would also apply, would give a total of $3°$, as all observations indicate. If we assume for the moment that the system of globes A, B is covered by some sort of crust, which is hollow inside or at most filled with a very rarefied substance, this body might represent the moon, whose figure is entirely unknown to us, as we have only ever seen one of its faces. I would not claim to anyone else that the moon has this shape, but it seems to me that this suffices to show how irregularities in its figure and its density might account for the observed phenomenon. I have also found that under this hypothesis, the swinging motion of the moon would be very small, and if the phases of the moon more or less follow the law of the versed sines of the elongation, one need only assume that the anterior piece is more or less spherical. [Euler 1980, p. 277–278]

D'Alembert included simple line drawings to illustrate his hypothesis, similar to the ones in figure 3; see [Euler 1980, p. 277] for reproductions of the originals. Both d'Alembert and Euler, in [d'Alembert 1743] and [Euler 1736] respectively, had studied systems consisting of a finite number of point masses connected by rigid immaterial rods, and so were

Figure 3. D'Alembert's hypothesis

familiar with their dynamics. In proposing such a configuration for the body of the moon, d'Alembert is suggesting a scheme in which the precession of the apsides can be explained without altering the inverse square law. Accepting that the sun's pull on the moon accounts for only 1.5° of the precession, d'Alembert uses the additional "swing" of the moon in this two-piece configuration to explain the other 1.5°. This distribution of mass allows d'Alembert to maintain the Newtonian hypothesis while altering neither the total mass of the moon nor the distance from its center of mass the earth. The effect can be made as large as one wishes, simply by adjusting the distances between each of the bodies A and B and their mutual center of mass.

In his response of 15 February 1748, Euler presumably included a line drawing of his own, although only a modern schematic rendering is reproduced in the *Opera Omnia* [Euler 1980, p. 279]. Euler refers to the center of mass of the two bodies of the moon as L instead of C, but otherwise his notation in the quoted passage below is consistent with figure 3.

He begins by observing that because the shape of the earth is not spherical, "its force of gravity does not exactly follow the law of inverse squares of the distance, but it is as

$$\frac{\alpha}{zz} + \frac{\beta}{z^4} + \frac{\gamma}{z^6} + \text{etc.},$$

where z denotes the distance." [Euler 1980, p. 279] We note the similarity to Clairaut's hypothesis of higher order terms in the law of gravitation, but observe that this is meant to be a consequence of the inverse square law in light of the oblate spheroidal shape of the earth, and is not meant to apply universally. Euler then addresses the dual moon hypothesis:

> But if the body the moon were elongated, this force would undergo a double ir-regularity, and to assure myself of this latter disturbance, I have, like you, also considered the body of the moon as if it were composed of two globes A and B, joined by an immaterial rod AB, with the center of gravity at L. Supposing that the direction of the rod AB always lies more or less along the line LT, drawn towards the center of the earth T, as long as the motion of the point L, sometimes slower and sometimes quicker, does not produce any declination, I have found, like you, that the movement of the point L more or less follows an ellipse, but one in which the line of the apsides precesses. Further calculations furnished me with the follow-ing rule: that the mean motion of the moon would be to the motion of the apogee as LT^2 is to $6LA \cdot LB$, and therefore this figure of the moon should necessarily cause a progressive motion of the apogee. Now, since according to observations, the mean motion of the moon is to the motion of the apogee as 1 is to 0.0084473, while the theoretical value, based on the attraction of the sun accounts for only 1 to 0.0041045. So there is missing from the motion of the apogee the difference 0.0043428, which I set equal to the effect now found to be $6LA \cdot LB/LT^2$. Now, letting $LA = LB$ and assuming LT to be 60 times the radius of the earth, we have $LA = LB = 1\frac{1}{4}$,[2] from which AB is $2\frac{1}{2}$ times the radius of the earth, or the longi-tude of the moon AB surpasses the diameter of the earth. This seems to me, as you have remarked, to be untenable. [Euler 1980, p. 279–280]

---

[2]There appears to be an inconsistency here. From the given figures one calculates $LA = 1\frac{3}{5}$. Alternately, if Euler had meant $10LA \cdot LB$ instead of $6LA \cdot LB$ then $LA = LB = 1\frac{1}{4}$.

6 Conclusion

Clairaut's announcement of November 1747 was controversial, and in particular led to a heated debate with Buffon [Hankins 1970, p. 33]. Newton's inverse square law was elegant and attractive, and the Continental scientific community seemed, by and large, to want to preserve it. Even Clairaut, Euler and d'Alembert, who all concluded in 1747 that the preponderance of evidence argued against the Newtonian hypothesis, continued to work at preserving it if at all possible.

The idea that the shape of the moon might account for its special status could have occurred to a number of astronomers, providing the extra "swing" in the apsidal line for a purely dynamical reason. However, the calculations showed d'Alembert and Euler that a simple elongation in the direction of the earth would not suffice: anything remotely spherical would not add the required 1.5° of precession. A division of the mass into disjoint bodies was the only realistic possibility that could account for the phenomenon.

Although they disagree by a significant factor on the distance separating the two bodies, both Euler and d'Alembert entertained the same hypothesis and were in broad agreement on its mathematical consequences. There seems to be a significant difference, however, in their willingness to consider the hypothesis as a possible description of reality. Euler unequivocally declares it to be "untenable," because of the great distance between the bodies implied by the model. Although he attributes the same opinion to his correspondent, d'Alembert most decidedly does not dismiss the hypothesis out of hand. He does not explicitly declare himself one way or another on the matter of plausibility, although his concern for his public reputation is evident when he tells Euler "I would not claim to anyone else that the moon has this shape." What seems most revealing in d'Alembert's account is the amount of detail he adds to the abstract mathematical model of two spheres and an immaterial rod. With his speculation about a hollow crust enclosing the two bodies, it seems as though he is trying to lend an air of plausibility to the model that Euler had rejected. Perhaps in the privacy of his own imagination, d'Alembert sincerely entertained the possibility of a two-bodied moon.

Acknowledgements: Translations from the Euler-d'Alembert correspondence were done jointly with John Glaus of the Euler Society. Other translations are by the author.

References

[d'Alembert 1743] D'Alembert, J., *Traité de dynamique*, Paris: David, 1743.

[d'Alembert 1749] ———, *Recherches sur la précession des équinoxes, et sur la nutation de l'axe de la terre dans le systême newtonien*, Paris: David, 1749.

[Bradley 2007] Bradley, R. E., "Euler, d'Alembert and the Logarithm Function," in *Leonhard Euler: Life, Work and Legacy*, R. E. Bradley and C. E. Sandifer, eds, Amsterdam: Elsevier, 2007.

[Clairaut 1747] Clairaut, A., "Du dystème du monde dans les principes de la gravitation universelle", *Mémoires d l'Académie royale des Sciences*, (1745/49) 1749, p. 329–364.

[Clairaut 1749] ———, "Avertissement de M. Clairaut au sujet des Mémoires qu'il a donnés en 1747 et 1748 sur le système du Monde dans les principes de l'attraction", *Mémoires d l'Académie royale des Sciences*, (1745/49) 1749, p. 578–579.

[Cohen 1999] Cohen, I. B., A Guide to Newton's Principia, in [Newton 1999], 1–370.

[Euler] Euler, L., *Opera Omnia*, Basel: Birkhäuser, 1911– .

[Euler 1736] ——, *Mechanica sive motus scientia analytice exposita*, 2 vols., St. Petersburg: Acad. scient. Imper., 1736. Also in [Euler], series II, vol. 1 and 2.

[Euler 1749a] ——, *Recherches sur la question des inégalites du mouvement de Saturne et de Jupiter*, Paris: Acad. Royale Sci., 1749. Also in [Euler], ser. II, vol. 25, 45–157.

[Euler 1749b] ——, "Recherches sur la précession des équinoxes," *Mém. Berlin*, **V** (1749) 1751, 289–325. Also in [Euler], ser. II, vol. 31, 92–123.

[Euler 1980] ——, *Opera Omnia*, Series IVA, volume 5 (correspondence with Clairaut, d'Alembert and Lagrange), eds. A. P. Juškevič, R. Taton, Basel: Birkhäuser, 1980.

[Gregory 1702] Gregory, D., *Astronomiae Physicae & Geometricae Elementa*, Oxford, 1702.

[Hankins 1970] Hankins, T., *Jean d'Alembert: Science and the Enlightenment*, Oxford: Clarendon, 1970.

[Newton/Cohen 1975] Newton, I., Cohen, I., Isaac Newton's Theory of the Moon's Motion (1702) . . . introduction by I. Bernard Cohen, Folkestone: Dawson, 1975.

[Newton 1999] ——, *The Principia: Mathematical Principles of Natural Philosophy*, a new translation by I. B. Cohen and A. Whitman, Berkeley, University of California Press, 1999.

[Smith 1999] Smith, G., "The Motion of the Lunar Apsis," in [Cohen 1999], 257–264.

"The fabric of the universe is most perfect": Euler's research on elastic curves[1]

Lawrence D'Antonio

Introduction

Euler's work on elastic curves is a landmark in the theory of mathematical elasticity. In the current paper we focus on the genesis and influence of Euler's 1744 work *De Curvis Elasticis*, published as an appendix to Euler's monumental treatise on the calculus of variations E65, the *Methodus Inveniendi Lineas Curvas* [14].

For Euler, the elastic curve (or elastica) is the curve which, among the set of all curves of a given length, with given tangents at the endpoints, minimizes the value of $\int ds/R^2$, where ds is the element of arclength and R is the radius of curvature.

This use of a variational principle in studying the elastica was suggested to Euler by Daniel Bernoulli in a letter of October 20, 1742. Bernoulli obtained an expression for the potential energy of a bent rod and hypothesized that the rod will assume the shape that minimizes this energy (or *vis viva* as Bernoulli calls it). That the universe should so happily conform to such a principle is the idea behind the quote from Euler used in the title of the present paper.

This paper will consider the different forms of the elastic curve as enumerated by Euler, the introduction of the concept of the bending moment, the related study of the buckling load of a column, and the connections to Euler's work on elliptic integrals.

To conclude, we examine Euler's influence on a variety of later work in elasticity. Some examples of Euler's influence are the theory of the cantilever beam developed by Coulomb, Navier and Kirchhoff; 19th-century engineering, especially bridge construction; research into the function of size and shape in biology, including the height of trees and the shape of the spine. A more recent example of Euler's influence is the very active research into minimum energy models of the shape of the DNA molecule. This research, known as the

---

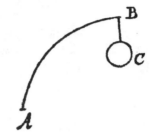

Figure 1. Bernoulli's Elastic Rod

elastic model of DNA, illustrates how Euler remains just as vital in the 21st century as he was in the 18th.

The problem of the elastica (also called the elastic rod or band) can be stated in several forms. The original version of the problem is to find the shape of an elastic rod when deflected by some force, see Figure 1, taken from an article of Jakob Bernoulli [5]. The version stated by Daniel Bernoulli and eventually solved by Euler is to find the curve of a given length that minimizes $\int \frac{ds}{R^2}$ or $\int \kappa^2 ds$ (R the radius of curvature, κ the curvature). More generally, the problem is to minimize $\int (\kappa^2 + \beta)ds$ (β a constant). Another way to look at the problem is to find the curve of given length between two points such that when revolved about that line, it generates the greatest volume.

Examples of other mechanical curves studied at this time:

Catenary The curve hanging between two points with the lowest center of gravity.

Velaria The figure of a perfectly flexible cord loaded by a uniform normal pressure.

Linteria The form of a cylindrical cloth filled with water.

Early History

The first discussion of the elastic rod can be found in the 13th-century work *De Ratione Ponderis* of Jordanus de Nemore [28]. Book 4 considers the problem of the shape of weighted rods. Proposition 13 states that "When the middle is held fast, the end parts are more easily curved." This proposition is accompanied by the illustration in Figure 2.

As for the shape of the bent rod, Jordanus hypothesizes (incorrectly)

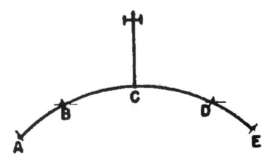

Figure 2. Bent rod of Jordanus

"And so it comes about that since the ends yield most easily, while the other parts follow more easily to the extent that they are nearer the ends, the whole body becomes curved in a circle." [28, p. 223]

In the seventeenth century there were several works devoted to the study of the bending or breaking of beams supported at one end and having a weight attached at the other. Prominent among the seventeenth century researchers who worked in this area prior to the Bernoullis are Galileo, Huygens, Hooke, Mariotte, and Leibniz. Other than Hooke's Law, none of this research seems to have had a significant influence on Euler's work. See the work of Timoshenko [45] or Truesdell [46] for a thorough discussion of this time period. The first significant work on the elastic curve was the article *Curvatura Laminae Elasticae* (On the Curvature of Elastic Bands) by Jakob Bernoulli, published in the *Acta Eruditorum* in June 1694 [5]. A discussion of this article can be found in Truesdell [46, pp. 88–96]. In the very complicated Figure 3, the elastic band has perimeter $AQRSTyV$. The one end,

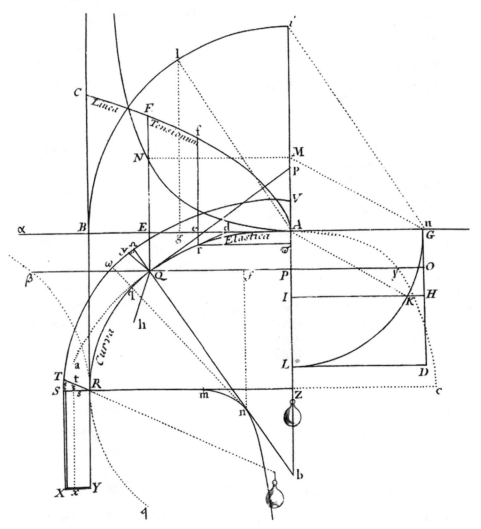

Figure 3. Bernoulli's Elastic Curve

RS, is fixed and the other end AV has the weight Z attached to it, which has caused the band to bend into the shape of a rectangular elastica, each end being on lines perpendicular to the other. The curve AFC is called *linea tensiorum* or the "line of elongation."

To understand the role of the *linea tensorium*, consider a point Q and its corresponding cross section Qy of the band. Q has abscissa $x = PQ$ and ordinate $y = AP$. Note that the variable y is different from the point y.

Bernoulli imagines a lever with fulcrum placed at Q and having as lever arms the segment Qy and curve AQ. The weight Z pulls down point A and hence lifts up point y. Thus the side of the band SyV is stretched compared to the unweighted band. The amount of stretching is what is measured by the *linea tensorium*.

Bernoulli indicates this stretching by placing a spring at point y in the figure. This spring is barely discernible but a corresponding spring may be seen more clearly at point S. The stretching force on point y depends on x, since the larger the abscissa of Q, the longer is the lever arm AQ. So that the elongation at any point of the elastica is a function of the abscissa x. The actual shape of AFC depends on the nature of this function. Bernoulli specifically considers elongations proportional to some power x^m.

Define $c = Qy, b = AR, a^2 = bc$. The quantities a, b, c are constants. Let t be the elongation function, the area under the "line of elongation" is written as $S = \int t(x)dx$.

Bernoulli states that "I can no longer deny to the public the golden theorem" for the radius of curvature at Q,

$$\frac{1}{r} = \frac{t}{bc} = \frac{t}{a^2},$$

here r is the radius of curvature and $1/r$ the curvature. Therefore the radius of curvature at any point is proportional to the elongation function. But also the radius of curvature has the formula,

$$\frac{1}{r} = -\frac{ddy}{dxds}$$

Equating these expressions for the curvature and integrating with respect to x, Bernoulli obtains

$$a^2dy = -Sds \Rightarrow a^4dy^2 = S^2dx^2 + S^2dy^2.$$

Bernoulli considers elongation functions of the form $t \propto x^m$. In particular, values for which $m > 1$ correspond to nonlinear elasticity. This paper is perhaps the earliest consideration of nonlinear elastic forces, i.e. forces that do not obey Hooke's Law. When $m = 1$, we obtain the equation for the rectangular elastica

$$dy = \frac{x^2 \, dx}{\sqrt{a^4 - x^4}}. \tag{1}$$

We now recognize this as an example of an elliptic integral. Bernoulli comments

> "I have serious cause to believe that the construction of our curve depends neither on the quadrature nor on the rectification of any conic section."

Euler's Work on Elasticity

The work of Jakob Bernoulli helped pave the way for the efforts of Euler, who was also strongly influenced by the work of Daniel Bernoulli, the nephew of Jakob and the son of

Euler's mentor Johann Bernoulli. Euler's research on elasticity occupied him for several decades. His work on the oscillations of an elastic ring, E831 [21], was likely written in 1727 while he was still in Basel. The very significant series of three papers on the buckling of columns was published in 1780 (see [17, 18, 19]). Over the course of half a century and many publications (most of which can be found in the *Opera Omnia*, Series 2, Volumes 10, 11, and 17) Euler truly established the discipline of mathematical elasticity.

Euler on elastic curves

Euler first considered elastic curves in the paper of 1728, E8 *Solutio problematis de invenienda curva, quam format lamina utcunque elastica in singulis punctis a potentiis quibuscunque sollicitata* (Solution of the problem of finding the curve formed by an elastic band loaded by arbitrary forces at each of its points), [14]. In this paper, which Euler seems to have started while in Basel, he attempts a unified treatment of several curves. He finds a differential equation that describes the elastica, the catenary, the velaria, and the linteria.

The highlight of Euler's research in elasticity is *De Curvis Elastica* published in 1744. In this work Euler analyzes the deformation of a thin elastic rod under a terminal load. As significant as Euler's work may be, it has been frequently overlooked by later researchers.

Outline of *De Curvis Elastica*

Below is an outline of Euler's appendix on elastic curves. I refer to the section numbers in the original. There is an English translation of this work by Oldfather [42].

§1 Metaphysical introduction

§§2-4 Curvature of uniform elastica, derived through final causes (variational method)

§§5-13 Curvature of uniform elastica, derived through effective causes (equilibrium of forces)

§§14-36 Enumeration of species of elastic curves

§37 On the force necessary to buckle a column

§§38-40 Determination of "absolute elasticity" by experiment

§§41-46 Curvature of nonuniform elastica

§§47-54 Curvature of naturally curved elastica

§§55-60 Curvature of elastica due to several forces

§§61-62 Curvature of elastica under its own weight

§§63-64 Oscillations of elastic curves: Introduction

§§65-79 Oscillations of elastic curves: clamped at one end

§§80-90 Oscillations of elastic curves: free at all points

§§91-93 Oscillations of elastic curves: clamped at both ends

§§94-97 Oscillations of elastic curves: fastened to a wall at both ends

Metaphysics

Euler begins the *De Curvis Elastica* with a discussion of certain metaphysical principles. Those who know Euler solely through his work in mathematics may be surprised to learn the level of interest that Euler had in metaphysical disputes. Euler engaged in discussions concerning action-at-a-distance, monads, the principle of least action, and final causes. A good survey of Euler's metaphysics can be found in [47].

Final causes are ultimate purposes, what a thing is for. Final causes involve teleological explanations and as such were generally banished from scientific thought in the Enlightenment. On the other hand, Euler sees the universal applicability of the methods of maxima and minima as a sign of the Creator's purposes.

> "For since the fabric of the universe is most perfect and the work of a most wise Creator, nothing at all takes place in the universe in which some rule of maximum or minimum does not appear." [42, p. 76]

Euler distinguishes effective causes from final. Effective causes are ones that derive from physical principles such as forces or moments. For example, for a body to be held in equilibrium it is necessary to equate certain moments. This is a method of analysis that Euler frequently uses and he does not want to abandon this method for one solely based on variational principles.

> "Wherefore there is absolutely no doubt that every effect in the universe can be explained as satisfactorily from final causes, by the aid of the method of maxima and minima, as it can from the effective causes themselves. ... Since, therefore, two methods of studying effects in Nature lie open to us, one by means of effective causes, which is commonly called the direct method, the other by means of final causes, the mathematician uses each with equal success." [42, p. 77]

Euler illustrates the difference between effective and final causes with the following example. Effective causes are identified with the analysis using gravitational forces while final causes correspond to the principle that a hanging chain should have its center of gravity at the lowest possible point, in comparison to other curves of the same length and endpoints.

> "Thus the curvature of a rope or of a chain in suspension has been discovered by both methods; first, *a priori*, from the attractions of gravity; and second, by the method of maxima and minima, since it was recognized that a rope of that kind ought to assume a curvature whose center of gravity was at the lowest point." [42, p. 77]

Euler's contemporaries were not always impressed by his metaphysical writings. For example, D'Alembert wrote in a letter to Lagrange from August 1769,

> "You are right to say that for the sake of his honor he should not have had this work printed [*Letters to a German Princess*]. It is unbelievable that so great a genius as he in geometry and analysis should be in metaphysics so inferior to the least schoolboy, not to say so dull and absurd, and it is a case of the saying that the gods do not shower all gifts to the same man." [33, vol. 13, p. 147] as translated in [47, p. 401]

Daniel Bernoulli

Daniel Bernoulli

Euler's work on the problem of the elastic curve is motivated by a series of letters between Daniel Bernoulli and Euler. Bernoulli sets the problem for Euler and encourages him until the problem is solved.

Euler acknowledges the contributions of Daniel Bernoulli in the introduction to the *De Curvis Elastica*.

"[T]he most illustrious and, in this sublime fashion of studying nature, most perspicacious man, Daniel Bernoulli, pointed out to me that the entire force stored in the curved elastic band may be expressed by a certain formula, which he calls the potential force, and that this expression must be a minimum." [42, p. 78]

The motivation for Euler's research in elastic curves can be traced to a letter from Daniel Bernoulli.

"Find among all isoperimetric curves having the same endpoints, the one that minimizes or maximizes $\int r^m ds$ where r is the radius of curvature."
Letter to Euler, May 24, 1738 [25, Vol. II, pp. 446–448].

As is apparent from the following quote, Daniel Bernoulli initially considered solving the problem of the elastic curve himself.

"[T]he elastica, as I can show, is of such a nature that $\int \frac{ds^3}{r^2 d\xi^2}$ = maximum or minimum. I will send my reflections on this another time."
Letter to Euler, November 8, 1738. Quoted in [46, p. 173]

Euler responded to this letter by agreeing that the problem is finding a curve that gives a maximum or minimum total curvature.

"For superficially, I see that these curves [elasticae] have a maximum or minimum in the course of bending."
Letter to D.B., December 23, 1738. Quoted in [46, p. 173]

In his next letter to Euler, Bernoulli enunciated a principle that is reminiscent of Maupertuis' Principle of Least Action. In the next decade there arose a fierce debate over the significance and claims of priority for this priniciple. This debate is known as the Koenig affair and involved many of the leading scientists of the day. Bernoulli also states his intention of writing a paper on the subject.

"I think that an elastic band which takes on of itself a certain curvature will bend in such a way that the live force will be a minimum, since otherwise the band will move of itself. I intend to develop this idea in a memoir; but in the meantime I wish to know your impression of this hypothesis."
Letter to Euler, March 7, 1739. [25, Vol. II, pp. 453–457]

Again, Euler assented to Benoulli's observation, but without giving any further discussion of method. It is also clear that at this point Euler views this problem as Bernoulli's area of research.

"That the elastic curve must have a maximum or minimum property I do not doubt at all . . . I am eager to learn from the piece your Worship has promised."
Letter to D.B., May 5, 1739. Quoted in [46, p. 174]

After a gap of three years Bernoulli wrote a letter that challenges Euler to solve the problem. Bernoulli seems to have ceded the field to Euler.

"I should like to know if your Worship could not solve the curvature of the elastic band . . . Since no one has perfected the isoperimetric method as much as you, you will easily solve this problem of rendering $\int ds/r^2$ a minimum."
Letter to Euler, October 20, 1742 [25, Vol. II, pp. 499–507].

We don't have Euler's intervening letter, but Euler seems to have given some sign of interest.

> "I am glad that you are so pleased with my principle for finding the elastica by the isoperimetric method."
> Letter to Euler, December 12, 1742 [25, Vol. II, pp. 508–514].

Bernoulli knew that Euler was finishing the *Methodus Inveniendi Lineas Curvas* and in a letter to Euler, April 23, 1743 [25, Vol. II, pp. 521–528], proposed that Euler add an appendix on the elastic curve problem.

In the letter to Euler of September 4, 1743 [25, Vol. II, pp. 529–538], Bernoulli stated that he had received Euler's "Isoperimetric Additions." This would indicate that Euler finished the appendix in the summer of 1743. Thus, Euler's appendix on elastic curves was completed several months before Maupertuis' presentation of the Principle of Least Action to the Paris Academy on April 15, 1744 [37]. This would imply that Euler had some right to claim priority for this principle, although he never put forth such a claim. See the discussion in Terrall's biography of Maupertuis [44, Ch. 9].

Elastica using final causes

In determining the equation of the elastica, Euler used two methods, final causes and effective causes. The method of final causes uses variational principles which Euler has previously worked on. In the appendix on elastic curves Euler applies a general variational technique described in detail in E99, [15]. This method is in turn based on an earlier work on variational methods published in 1741, *Curvarum maximi minimive proprietate gaudentium inventio nova et facilis* (New and easy method of finding curves enjoying a maximal or minimal property), [13]. This paper set the groundwork for the *Methodus*.

In the appendix on elastic curves, Euler uses the variational method in §§1–4 to find the equation describing the elastic curve. The goal is to minimize $\int ds/R^2$ with the constraint that $\int ds$ is fixed. Then we have that

$$\int \frac{ds}{R^2} = \int \frac{q^2 dx}{(1+p^2)^{5/2}} = \int Z\,dx.$$

The constraint equation has the property that

$$\int ds = \int \sqrt{1+p^2}\,dx = \text{const.}$$

From the minimization and isoperimetric conditions, Euler infers that

$$\alpha \frac{d}{dx} \frac{p}{\sqrt{1+p^2}} = \frac{dP}{dx} - \frac{d^2Q}{dx^2},$$

where α is a constant. $P,\ Q$ are defined by

$$P = \frac{-5p\,q^2}{(1+p^2)^{7/2}},\ Q = \frac{2q}{(1+p^2)^{5/2}}.$$

This leads to the defining equations for the elastica,

$$\alpha\sqrt{1+p^2} + \beta p + \gamma = Z - Qq$$
$$dy = \frac{(\alpha + \beta x + \gamma x^2)dx}{\sqrt{\alpha^4 - (\alpha + \beta x + \gamma x^2)^2}}$$

Before attempting to solve this equation, which is an elliptic integral, Euler will check that the method of effective causes leads to the same answer. Euler has previously encountered elliptic integrals in, for example, the work of Jakob and Johann Bernoulli on the elastica. Euler's major work on elliptic integrals was to await his discovery in December 1751 of the works of Count Fagnano.

Elastica using effective causes

Next in the appendix on elastic curves, Euler computes the form of the elastica using effective causes. Namely, he will consider the equilibrium of forces that determine the shape of the elastica. Euler states "In order that this agreement be placed more clearly before the reader, I shall investigate also *a priori* the nature of the elastic curve." [42, §5]

Consider Figure 4. An initially straight elastic band AB is clamped at end B and a rigid rod AC of length c is attached at point A. A load of weight P is attached at point C and is shown hanging down to D. The end of the rod at A is deflected downwards. Let $AP = x$, $PM = y$ (so P is being used ambiguously to represent a weight and a point). The moment at M generated by the load P is $P \cdot (c + x)$. The bending moment at M is Ek^2/R, where E and k^2 are constants depending on the properties of the elastica and R is the radius of curvature at M. The constant E is related to the stiffness of the elastica and is today called Young's modulus. This constant is named after the 19th-century British scientist Thomas Young, but was frequently used by Euler, first appearing in a paper of 1732 [12], and even earlier in the unpublished work E831 [21]. The constant k^2 is related to the diameter of the

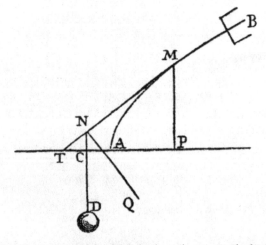

Figure 4. Euler's representation of the elastica using an attached weighted rod

elastica. Equating these two moments and using

$$R = -\frac{ds^3}{dx\,dy^2}$$

Euler obtains after integration,

$$dy = \frac{-P\,dx(\frac{1}{2}x^2 + cx + f)}{\sqrt{E^2k^4 - P^2(\frac{1}{2}x^2 + cx + f)^2}}.$$

This agrees with the result obtained by the variational method.

Enumeraton of elastic curves

Newton had made an enumeration of cubic curves, i.e., curves of the form

$$ay^3 + bxy^2 + cx^2y + dx^3 + ey^2 + fxy + gx^2 + hy + kx + l = 0.$$

Here we may assume that the coefficients are rational. Euler makes reference to Newton's enumeration in the *Methodus*. It is clear that he views his enumeration of elastic curves as following in the footsteps of Newton.

A significant difference between the classification of Euler and Newton is that Newton uses intrinsic properties of cubic curves in his classification scheme, e.g. the number and types of branches and characteristics of asymptotes. On the other hand, Euler bases his classification on a parametrization of the elastic curve. The parametrization is defined as follows in §§15-23.

The following equations use the notation in Figure 5. Euler derives the formulae for the elastica

$$dy = \frac{(a^2 - c^2 + x^2)dx}{\sqrt{(c^2 - x^2)(2a^2 - c^2 + x^2)}} \tag{2}$$

$$ds = \frac{a^2dx}{\sqrt{(c^2 - x^2)(2a^2 - c^2 + x^2)}}. \tag{3}$$

These are elliptic integrals, which cannot be evaluated by elementary methods. Instead, Euler expands the integrands into series and integrates for x going from 0 to c to arrive at,

$$AC = f = \frac{\pi a}{2\sqrt{2}}\left(1 + \frac{1^2}{2^2}\cdot\frac{c^2}{2a^2} + \frac{1^23^2}{2^24^2}\cdot\frac{c^4}{4a^4} + \cdots\right) \tag{4}$$

$$AD = b = \frac{\pi a}{2\sqrt{2}}\left(1 - \frac{1^2}{2^2}\cdot\frac{3}{1}\cdot\frac{c^2}{2a^2} - \frac{1^23^2}{2^24^2}\cdot\frac{5}{3}\cdot\frac{c^4}{4a^4} - \cdots\right). \tag{5}$$

He parametrizes these solutions using the following angles

$$\alpha = \angle PAM, \quad \beta = \angle DAM, \quad \sin\alpha = \cos\beta = 1 - \frac{c^2}{a^2}.$$

The angle α is measured with the horizontal axis AE, while β is measured with the vertical axis AB.

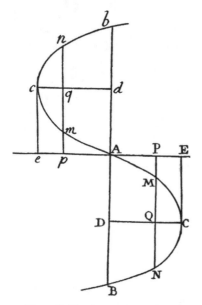

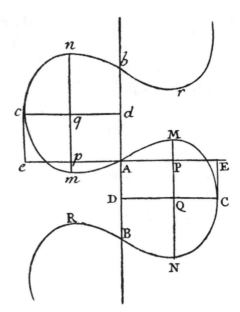

Figure 5. Elastic curve: species 1   Figure 6. Elastic curve: species 4

In this notation the load on the curve is given by

$$P = \frac{2Ek^2}{a^2}.$$

Euler distinguishes nine species of elastic curves. The first species of curves is the case when $c^2/a^2 = 0$. In this case the angle $\beta = 0°$. This seems to imply that the curve is a straight line. In fact this case corresponds to the situation where the force on the elastica is the minimum needed to bend it from vertical. The equation for dy may be written as

$$dy = \frac{a\,dx}{\sqrt{2(c^2 - x^2)}}.$$

This can be integrated and gives a sinusoidal shape for the elastic curve,

$$y = \frac{a}{\sqrt{2}} \arcsin(x/c).$$

Note that this shape is valid only on the assumption of a very small deflection. Since the curve is only infinitesimally deflected, $AD = AC$ in Figure 5, with both equal to

$$f = \frac{\pi a}{2\sqrt{2}}.$$

This leads to the Euler buckling load, namely the minimum force needed to deflect the elastica:

$$P_{\text{crit}} = \frac{2Ek^2}{a^2} = \frac{\pi^2}{4} \cdot \frac{Ek^2}{f^2}.$$

This critical load will be the object of further study when Euler investigates the buckling of columns.

The remaining species are also determined by the value of c^2/a^2.

Species two is defined by

$$0 < \frac{c^2}{a^2} < 1 \Rightarrow 0 < \beta < 90°.$$

In this case the series defining f converges.

Species three is the rectangular elastica. This occurs when $a = c$, so that $\beta = 90°$. For this case Euler states the identity

$$4bf = \pi a^2.$$

This identity first appeared in a letter to Johann Bernoulli of December 20, 1738. He did not provide a proof of this identity until a paper of 1782 [20].

Species four (Figure 6) has $a < c, b > 0$. In this case the angle $\beta > 90°$. As will be seen in the next species we also have $\beta < 130°41'$. As $b \to 0$, the points A and B approach one another.

Starting with this species Euler redefines the angle α. Previously α was measured clockwise from the x-axis AE. Now it will be measured counterclockwise so that $\sin \alpha = \frac{c^2}{a^2} - 1$. Euler does not make any further reference to $\angle DAM$, although we will continue to use this angle.

Species five (Figure 7) is characterized by $a < c, b = 0$. In this case, the curve has the property that $AD = 0$. As can be seen, the curve is now self-intersecting with points A and B now coincident. Substituting $v = \frac{c^2}{2a^2}$ into the series for AD, Euler obtains an equation for v

$$1 = \frac{1 \cdot 3}{2 \cdot 4}v + \frac{1 \cdot 1 \cdot 3 \cdot 5}{2 \cdot 2 \cdot 4 \cdot 4}v^2 + \frac{1 \cdot 1 \cdot 3 \cdot 3 \cdot 5 \cdot 7}{2 \cdot 2 \cdot 4 \cdot 4 \cdot 6 \cdot 6}v^3 + \cdots.$$

Using "methods familiar to everyone" [42, §29], Euler finds limits for the solution of this equation, $0.824 < v < 0.828$. Substituting the limits into the above series Euler concludes that

$$v = 0.825934 \Rightarrow \frac{c^2}{a^2} = 1.651868.$$

Euler then computes $\alpha = \angle PAM$

$$\sin \alpha = \frac{c^2}{a^2} - 1 = 0.651868 \Rightarrow \alpha = 40°41'.$$

The angle β then measures $130°41'$ counterclockwise from the vertical axis AB.

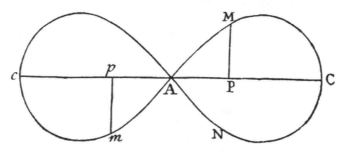

Figure 7. Elastic curve: species 5

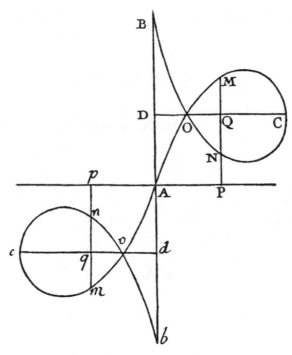

Figure 8. Elastic curve: species 6

Species six (Figure 8) has $1.651868 < \frac{c^2}{a^2} < 2$. For this curve $40°41' < \angle PAM < 90°$ as Euler is measuring the angle. As c^2 approaches $2a^2$ the points A and B move farther apart.

Species seven (Figure 9) has $\frac{c^2}{a^2} = 2$. Something very interesting has occurred in this case. The points A and B have moved infinitely far apart and the line AB is now an asymptote of the elastic curve. Substituting $c^2 = 2a^2$ in Equation (5) results in the following divergent series for f,

$$AC = f = \frac{\pi a}{2\sqrt{2}}\left(1 + \frac{1^2}{2^2} + \frac{1^2 \cdot 3^3}{2^2 \cdot 4^2} + \frac{1^2 \cdot 3^2 \cdot 5^2}{2^2 \cdot 4^2 \cdot 6^2} + \cdots\right).$$

Euler gives no explanation of why the series diverges, but the series may be shown to majorize the harmonic series [23, p. 228].

Euler is confronted with the following dichotomy. If $a = c = 0$ then the above series is not a valid representation of AC. In this case the length f will still be finite, but then the applied force $P = 2Ek^2/a^2$ is infinite. The other possibility is that $a \neq 0$ and the curve is indeed infinitely long and $c = DC$. In this case Equation (2) for the curve becomes

$$dy = \frac{(a^2 - x^2)dx}{x\sqrt{2a^2 - x^2}}.$$

This may be integrated to obtain the equation for the curve

$$y = \sqrt{c^2 - x^2} - \frac{c}{2}l\left(\frac{c + \sqrt{c^2 - x^2}}{x}\right).$$

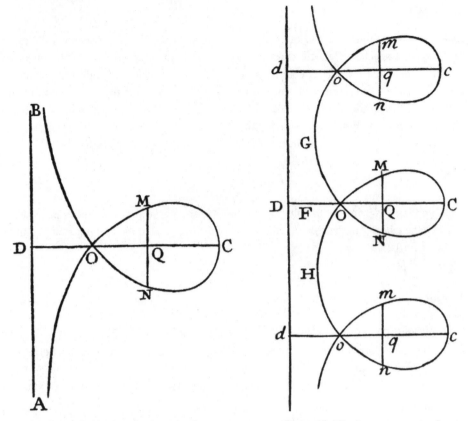

Figure 9. Elastic curve: species 7   Figure 10. Elastic curve: species 8

In this formula l is Euler's notation for the natural logarithm.

Referring back to Figure 9, Euler is using $x = DQ$ and $y = QM$. So at the double point O the ordinate is zero. Euler performs an impressive calculation to find that at O

$$\frac{x}{c} = 0.2884191.$$

He also computes the angle MON at the double point to be $112°56'48''$.

Species eight (Figure 10) has $\frac{c^2}{a^2} > 2$. Euler writes $c^2 = a^2 + g^2$. In this case the curve has vertical tangents at the points $G, H, \ldots$ and at c, C, c.

Species nine occurs in the limit as $g \rightarrow c$. Euler describes the curve as "reduced, vanishing into space." Writing $g = c - 2h$ and letting $c \rightarrow \infty$, Euler obtains the differential equation

$$\frac{dy}{dt} = \frac{t}{\sqrt{h^2 - t^2}},$$

the solution of which is a circle.

In this enumeration we have seen the possible shapes of the elasticae vary from the barely deflected rod through various bent shapes, finally ending in elastica bent into a circle.

Columns

Euler discussed columns in §37 of *De Curvis Elastica*. His analysis is essentially the same as in the first species of elastic curve. The problem is to determine the minimum force needed to buckle a cylindrical column of a given height. When the height of the column is much greater than its diameter, this problem is no different from that of determining the minimum force needed to bend a vertical elastic rod of a given length. Just as with the elastic rod problem, Euler is considering the column to be weightless.

In §25 Euler had calculated the critical load for bending an elastic rod to be

$$P_{\text{crit}} = \frac{\pi^2}{4} \cdot \frac{Ek^2}{f^2}.$$

Euler applies this principle to columns. In the situation where the column has just started to bend, the length l of the column equals $2f$. This gives rise to the familiar Euler column buckling formula,

$$P_{\text{crit}} = \pi^2 \frac{Ek^2}{l^2}.$$

This formula is valid for an elastic column where the height is much greater than the diameter.

Coulomb's 1773 essay on statics [10], with a translation by Heyman [27], is one of the first significant works influenced by Euler's research in elasticity. Coulomb criticizes the buckling load formula as not being correct for masonry columns. Euler appears to have already known this for he ends the section on columns with the following observation,

> "This principle can, therefore, be applied in the case of wooden columns, since they are subject to bending." [42, p. 103]

In E238, *Sur la force des colonnes* (On the strength of columns) [16], Euler advances his previous work by considering the critical load for both uniform and nonuniform column stiffness. Previously Euler had not clearly indicated the end conditions on the column, but in E238 the column has its top and bottom pinned (so the top and bottom are not free to move). Euler also considers the problem of finding the maximum height that a column of given proportions can reach before buckling under its own weight. He was unable to solve that problem in E238, but it became the primary theme of E508–E510.

Euler discusses an interesting paradox in E238. For a horizontal elastic rod any force whatsoever is sufficient to deflect it from the horizontal. On the other hand, for a vertical elastic rod it is necessary, in order to bend the rod, to apply a force at least as large as the critical buckling load derived in *De Curvis Elastica*. To Euler this appears to contradict the so-called "law of continuity" [16, §§X–XI]. This law states that when in nature an object passes from one state to another, it will also pass through all intermediate states. The law of continuity was widely held to be true in the 18th century and Euler appears to be deeply puzzled by the fact that his research on columns seems to have contradicted it. He believed that his theory of columns was correct, but also believed that the law of continuity was valid. In [16, §§XII–XVIII] Euler attempts to find a mathematical explanation for the apparent contradiction.

Referring back to Figure 5, we let $\theta = \angle DAM$ be the angle of deflection for the column. When the force applied to the column is greater than its critical load then $\theta > 0$

and the column will bend. When the applied force is exactly equal to the critical load, i.e., the column is just starting to bend, then $\theta = 0$. If we accept the law of continuity then what should be the correct value of θ for forces less than the critical load? Euler proposes a rather astonishing solution. He attempts to prove that in the case of a force insufficient to bend the column, the angle of deflection will be imaginary!

How does Euler arrive at this conclusion? He shows that in the case of small deflections then the applied force satisfies the following equation [16, §XVII],

$$P = \pi^2 \frac{Ek^2}{l^2} \sqrt{1 + \theta^2}.$$

As Fraser has pointed out [23], the final term should be $(\theta/2)^2$, but this does not interfere with Euler's argument. As can be seen in this formula, when the applied force is precisely the critical load $\pi^2 \frac{Ek^2}{l^2}$ then the angle of deflection must be 0. As the force increases beyond this critical value, the angle of deflection increases. Finally, when the applied force is less than the critical load then $\sqrt{1 + \theta^2} < 1$ which implies that θ must be imaginary.

Euler wrote a series of three additional papers on the theory of columns: E505 was presented to the St. Petersburg Academy in 1757 [17], and E509, E510 were both presented to the St. Petersburg Academy in 1778 [18, 19]. In these papers Euler considers the problem of determining how tall a column may be until it buckles under its own weight. In E508 Euler finds that the maximum possible height of a column is related to the diameter of the column by the relationship $h_{\text{crit}} \propto D^{2/3}$.

Euler's work on columns was a starting point for the research of Lagrange, whose paper *Sur la figure des colonnes* [32] considers the shape of the strongest column of a given height and volume. The work of Euler and Lagrange is the beginning of a long period of research on the shape of a strongest column. Clausen first found the correct shape for a column with circular cross-sections [9], whereas Lagrange had previously given an incorrect solution to the problem. Assuming that the cross-sections of the column are convex, what is the shape of the strongest column? Keller in 1960 [30] found that the strongest such column is tapered (being thicker in the middle) and has equilateral triangle cross-sections.

Later Developments

Euler's research on elasticity has had a continuing influence on many areas of research such as the theory of cantilever beam, applications to the size and shape of organisms, later work on the elastica, and the consideration of the DNA molecule as an elastic curve.

Cantilever beam

Several advances in engineering in the 19th century have their origins in the work of Euler. A cantilever beam is a horizontal beam anchored at one end. Such beams play an important role in the theory of bridge building. The Industrial Revolution saw the need for bridges that were strong enough to support locomotive traffic. The analysis of the bending and breaking of such beams is critical to engineering practice.

The fundamental equation in this area is called the Euler-Bernoulli beam equation. Euler's use of variational methods in studying problems in elasticity was a direct influence on Coulomb's very significant paper of 1773, [10]. Coulomb's work in turn led to Navier's study of cantilevers [40]. An excellent history of the development of engineering theory can be found in the book of Charlton [8].

Later work on the elastica

Euler's work on elastic curves was later developed in several directions. One such example is Kirchhoff's work on three dimensional elastic curves. Central to Kirchhoff's theory is the Kirchhoff analogy [31] which is a remarkable mathematical metaphor. This analogy states that for a thin bar, acted on only by end forces and producing small deflections, the equations of the elastica are equivalent to the equations of motion of a rigid body about a fixed point. For planar elastica, the analog is the pendulum. For elastica in space, the analog is the gyroscope. Using this metaphor, Kirchhoff finds the equations of equilibrium for the three dimensional elastic curve, but he does not write down a closed form solution to these equations.

Saalschütz, in his 1880 treatise *Der belastete Staab* [43] determined the first closed solution for the elastica. He used elliptic functions extensively in his solution. The most complete discussion of the classical elastic curve can be found in Max Born's dissertation [6].

More recently there has been a great deal of research in extending the work of Euler and Kirchhoff to non-Euclidean spaces. For example, in their hallmark paper [35], Langer and Singer generalized Euler's work to closed elastic curves on the sphere. At the same time, Bryant and Griffiths analyzed closed elastic curves in hyperbolic manifolds [7]. A paper of Jurdjevic [29] gives a unified approach to elastica in the Euclidean plane, the sphere, and the hyperbolic plane.

Size and shape in biology

The elastic constraints that determine the maximum height of a column also apply to biological organisms. In 1881 A.G. Greenhill wrote a groundbreaking paper on the maximum height possible for a tree of given proportions [26]. Specifically the problem is to find the greatest height that may be attained by a cylindrical tree of a given diameter and a constant density.

Greenhill finds the maximum height possible for a tree of given dimensions

$$h_{\text{crit}} = 1.26 \left(\frac{Ea^2}{w} \right)^{\frac{1}{3}}.$$

A tree of any greater height would start to buckle under its own weight. Here $2a$ is the diameter of the tree, E is Young's modulus and w is the cross-sectional density of the tree. This formula, known as the Greenhill formula, indicates that the maximum stable height of trees goes as the two-thirds power of the diameter, just as Euler found for columns in E508. This relationship has been confirmed empirically for a variety of tree species [41].

The derivation of the Greenhill formula closely follows Euler's paper E509 (perhaps we should call it the Euler-Greenhill formula). This work has been the starting point for later research on the bending of palm trees in a strong wind [48], the curvature of the spine [39], the mechanics of insect wings [49], and the maximum size of the torso [38].

DNA

C. J. Benham has extended Euler's work on elastic curves to study elastic properties of the DNA molecule, [2, 3]. He considers the DNA molecule as a symmetric elastic rod. Unstressed DNA has the form of a double helix with a twist angle of $\approx 34°$. Deviations from this conformation give rise to elastic restoring forces.

If one end of the DNA molecule is twisted, an elastic strain will be induced. Suppose one end of the molecule is twisted, connected to the other end to form a circular molecule and then released. The elastic strain will cause the molecule to attempt to untwist and move towards some equilibrium configuration, e.g., a figure eight. Such a configuration is called DNA supercoiling and is currently a major area of research [2, 3, 24, 34].

Conclusion

There are several significant innovations in *De Curvis Elastica*, including the use of variational methods to solve a physical problem, the application of elliptic integrals, the analysis of column buckling as a bifurcation problem, and the construction of a mathematical model for elasticity having predictive force. We continue to see the influence of Euler in current research. There are many areas of mathematics today that show the handiwork of Euler, but perhaps nowhere is the connection so direct as in the field of elasticity. As Stuart Antman wisely observed [1, p. 286]

> "There is unfortunately a voluminous and growing literature devoted to doing poorly what Euler did well.... It would help if this literature were confined to some newly founded journal, perhaps to be called *Regressions in Applied Mathematics*."

References

[1] Antman, S.S., "The Influence of Elasticity on Analysis," *Bull. Amer. Math. Soc.*, 9 (1983), pp. 267–291.

[2] Benham, C., "Elastic Model of Supercoiling," *Proc. Nat'l. Acad. Sci. USA* 74 (1977), 2397–2401.

[3] ——, "An Elastic Model of the Large-Scale Structure of Duplex DNA," *Biopolymers*, 18 (1979), 609–623.

[4] Bernoulli, Jakob, "Additamentum ad Problema Funicularium," appears at the end of "Specimen alterum Calculi differentialis in dimetienda Spirali Logarithmica, Loxodromiis Nautarum, & Areis Triangulorum Sphaericorum: una cum Additamento quodam ad Problema Funicularium, aliisque", *Acta Eruditorum*, June 1691, pp. 282–290.

[5] ——, "Curvatura Laminae Elasticae," *Acta Eruditorum*, June 1694, pp. 262–276.

[6] Born, M., *Stabilität der elastischen Linie in Ebene und Raum*, Göttingen, 1906.

[7] Bryant, R. and P. Griffiths, "Reductions for constrained variational problems and $\frac{1}{2} \int k^2 ds$," *Amer. J. Math.*, 108 (1986), pp. 525–570.

[8] Charlton, T.M., *A history of theory of structures in the nineteenth century*, Cambridge University Press, Cambridge, 1982.

[9]   Clausen, T., "Über die Form architektonischer Säulen," *Bull. physico-math. Acad. St. Petersburg*, 1 (1849-1853), pp. 279–294.

[10] Coulomb, C.A., "Essai sur une application des règles de statique, relatifs à l'architecture," *Mémoires de Mathématique & Physique, présentés à l'Académie Royale des Sciences par divers Savans*, 7(1773), 1776, pp. 343–382.

[11] D'Alembert, J., *Traité de dynamique*, Paris, 1758.

[12] Euler, L., "Solutio problematis de invenienda curva, quam format lamina utcunque elastica in singulis punctis a potentiis quibuscunque sollicitata" (E8), *Comm. acad. sci. Petro.*, 8 (1728), 1732, pp. 70–84, reprinted in *Opera Omnia*, Series 2, Vol. 11, pp. 1–16

[13] ——, "Curvarum maximi minimive proprietate gaudentium inventio nova et facilis" (E56), *Comm. acad. sci. Petro.*, 8, 1741, pp. 159–190, reprinted in *Opera Omnia*, Series 1, Vol. 25, pp. 54–80.

[14] ——, *Methodus inveniendi lineas curvas maximi minimive proprietate gaudentes, sive solutio problematis isoperimetrici lattissimo sensu accepti* (E65), 1744, reprinted in *Opera Omnia*, Series 1, Vol. 24.

[15] ——, "Solutio problematis cuiusdam a Celeberrimo Daniele Bernoullio propositi" (E99), *Comm. acad. sci. Petro.*, 10, 1747, pp. 164–180, reprinted in *Opera Omnia*, Series 1, Vol. 25, pp. 84–97.

[16] ——, "Sur la force des colonnes" (E238), *Mémoires de l'académie des sciences de Berlin*, 13 (1759), pp. 252–282, reprinted in *Opera Omnia*, Series 2, Vol. 17, pp. 89–118.

[17] ——, "Determinatio onerum, quae columnae gestare valent" (E508), *Acta acad. sci Petro.*, (1778), 1780, pp. 121–145, reprinted in *Opera Omnia*, Series 2, Vol. 17, pp. 232–251.

[18] ——, "Examen insignis paradoxii in theoria columnarum occurentis" (E509), *Acta acad. sci Petro.*, (1778), 1780, pp. 146–162, reprinted in *Opera Omnia*, Series 2, Vol. 17, pp. 252–265.

[19] ——, "De altitudine columnarum sub proprio pondere corruentium" (E510), *Acta acad. sci Petro.*, (1778), 1780, pp. 163–193, reprinted in *Opera Omnia*, Series 2, Vol. 17, pp. 266–293.

[20] ——, "De miris proprietatibus curvae elasticae sub aequatione $y = \int \frac{xx\,dx}{\sqrt{1-x^4}}$ contentae" (E605), *Acta acad. sci. Petro.* 1782, 1786, pp. 34-61, reprinted in *Opera Omnia*, Series 1, Volume 21, pp. 91–118.

[21] ——, "De oscillationibus annulorum elasticorum" (E831), *Opera Postuma* 2, 1862, pp. 129–131, reprinted in *Opera Omnia*, Series 2, Vol. 11, pp. 378–383.

[22] ——, *Opera omnia*, B.G. Teubner, Berlin, 1911–.

[23] Fraser, C.G., "Mathematical Technique and Physical Conception in Euler's Investigation of the Elastica," *Centaurus*, 34 (1991), pp. 211–246.

[24] Fuller, F. Brock, "The Writhing Number of a Space Curve," *Proc. Nat. Acad. Sci.*, 68 (1971), pp. 815–819.

[25] Fuss, P.H., *Correspondance mathématique et physique de quelques célèbres géomètres du XVIIIème siècle, précédé d'une notice sur les travaux de Léonard Euler, tant imprimés qu'inédits et publiée sous les auspices de l'Académie impériale des sciences de Saint-Pétersbourg*, l'Académie impériale des sciences, Saint Pétersbourg, 1843.

[26] Greenhill, A.G., "Determination of the greatest height consistent with stability that a vertical pole or mast can be made, and the greatest height to which a tree of given proportions can grow," *Proceedings of the Cambridge Philosophical Society*, 4 (1881), pp. 65–73.

[27] Heyman, J., *Coulomb's Memoir on Statics: An Essay in the History of Civil Engineering*, Imperial College Press, London, 1997.

[28] Jordanus de Nemore, *De Ratione Ponderis*, translation in *The Medieval Science of Weights*, ed. E.A. Moody and M. Clagett, University of Wisconsin Press, Madison, Wisconsin, 1960.

[29] Jurdjevic, V., "Non-Euclidean Elastica," *Amer. J. Math.*, 117 (1995), pp. 93–124.

[30] Keller, J.B., "The shape of the strongest column," *Arch. Rat. Mech. Anal.* 5 (1960), pp. 275–285.

[31] Kirchhoff, G., "Über das Gleichgewicht und die Bewegung eines unendlich dünnen elastischen Stabes," *J. Reine Anglew. Math. (Crelle)*, 56 (1859), pp. 285–313.

[32] Lagrange, J.L., "Sur la figure des colonnes", *Miscellanea Taurinensia*, 5, 1770–1773, reprinted in *Oeuvres*, Vol. 2, pp. 125–170.

[33] ——, *Oeuvres de Lagrange*, ed. Serret, Gauthier-Villars, Paris, 1867–92.

[34] Le Bret, M., "Twist and Writhing in Short Circular DNAs According to First-Order Elasticity," *Biopolymers*, 23 (1984), 1984, pp. 1835–1867.

[35] Langer, J. and D.A. Singer, "The Total Squared Curvature of Closed Curves," *J. Diff. Geom.* 20 (1984), pp. 1–22.

[36] Maupertuis, P.L. de, "Loi du repos des corps", presented February 20, 1740, *Mém. Acad. Sci. Paris*, (1740), 1742, pp. 170–176.

[37] ——, "Accord de différentes lois de la nature qui avaient jusqu'ici paru incompatibles," presented April 15, 1744, *Mém. Acad. Sci. Paris*, (1744), 1748, pp. 417–426.

[38] McMahon, T., "Size and Shape in Biology," *Science*, 179 (1973), pp. 1701–1704.

[39] Meakin, J. R., D. W. L. Hukins and R. M. Aspden, "Euler Buckling as a Model for the Curvature and Flexion of the Human Lumbar Spine," *Proc. Roy. Soc.: Biological Sciences*, 263 (1996), pp. 1383–1387.

[40] Navier, C.L., *Résumé des leçons données à l'Ecole des Ponts et Chaussées sur l'application de la méchanique à l'établissement des constructions et des machines*, Carilian-Goueury, Paris, 1826.

[41] Niklas, K., "Interspecific allometries of critical buckling height and actual plant height," *Amer. J. Botany*, 81 (1994), pp. 1275-1279.

[42] Oldfather, W.A., C.A. Ellis and D.M. Brown, "Leonhard Euler's Elastic Curves," *Isis*, 20 (1933), pp. 72–160.

[43] Saalschütz, *Belastete Stab unter Einwirkung einer seitlichen Kraft*, Teubner, Leipzig, 1880.

[44] Terrall, M., *The man who flattened the earth : Maupertuis and the sciences in the enlightenment*, University of Chicago Press, 2002.

[45] Timoshenko, S., *History of Strength of Materials*, McGraw-Hill, New York, 1953.

[46] Truesdell, C., *The Rational Mechanics of Flexible or Elastic Bodies 1638–1788*, in *Opera Omnia*, Series 2, Vol. 11, part 2, Orell Füssli, Zurich, 1961.

[47] Wilson, C., "Euler on action-at-a-distance and fundamental equations in continuum mechanics," in *The Investigation of Difficult Things: Essays on Newton and the History of the Exact Sciences in Honour of D. T. Whiteside*, ed. P. Harman, A. Shapiro, Cambridge Press, Cambridge, 1992, pp. 399–420.

[48] Winter, D.F., "On the Stem Curve of a Tall Palm in a Strong Wind," *SIAM Review*, 35 (1993), pp. 567–579.

[49] Wootton, R.J., "Geometry and Mechanics of Insect Hindwing Fans: A Modelling Approach," *Proc. Roy. Soc.: Biological Sciences*, 262 (1995), pp. 181–187.

The Euler Advection Equation

Roger Godard

Abstract. Among the prestigious mathematical models of the 18th century, there is the forgotten advection equation. In 1755, Euler found the equations of fluid motion. At the same time, he derived the advection equation for conservative systems. The advection equation is a consequence of a linearization process of the continuity equation. Our purpose is to present the Eulerian continuity equation, and then to comment on the methods for the solution of the advection equation, and particularly the method of characteristics.

1 Introduction

In 1755, during his golden years in Berlin, Leonhard Euler published, from our point of view, his most important work on the theory of the motion of fluids. Euler was so pleased, so enthusiastic about his equations that he wrote in "Continuation des recherches sur la théorie du mouvement des fluids" (E227) [Euler, 1755b]:

> Quelques sublimes que soient les recherches sur les fluides, dont nous sommes redevables à Mrs. Bernoullis, Clairaut & d'Alembert, elles découlent si naturelle-ment de mes deux formules générales: qu'on ne saurait assés admirer cet accord de leurs profondes méditations avec la simplicité des principes, d'oú j'ai tiré mes deux équations, & auxquels j'ai été conduit immédiatement par les premiers axiomes de la mécanique... Quoiqu'il ne soit pas souvent à propos de donner à nos recherches une trop grand étendue, de peur qu'on ne tombe dans un calcul trop compliqué, dont on ne puisse faire application aux cas les plus simples, il arrive précisément ici le contraire: puisque mes équations, quelques générales qu'elles soient, ne laissent pas d'être assés simples, pour les appliquer aisément à tous les cas particuliers: & par cela même elles nous présentent des vérités universelles, que notre connaissance en tire les plus grands éclaircissements, qu'on puisse souhaiter.

Euler's French is so clear, so illuminating, that all quotations will be presented in their original language. Theoretical fluid dynamics will make enormous progress during the 18th century with Daniel Bernoulli (*Traité des fluides*, 1744), d'Alembert (*Résistance des fluides*, 1749), Clairaut (*Théorie de la figure de la Terre tirée des principes de l'hydro-dynamique*, 1743), Euler (1752, 1755a, 1755b), and later with Lagrange. The resistance of fluids was the 1748 subject of the Berlin Academy for the 1750 prize. In 1749, Jean d'Alembert submitted his "Essai d'une nouvelle théorie de la résistance des fluides," which was published in 1752. However, even though the 1750 prize was not awarded, we are stricken by the ambitions of the geometers of the 18th century.

In 1752, Euler wrote his first memoir about the motion of fluids. Later, in his 1755 memoir: "Principes généraux du mouvement des fluids" [Euler, 1755a], Euler studied the general principles of the motion of fluids in three dimensions. In the introduction, Euler said explicitly:

> Il s'agit donc de découvrir les principes, par lesquels on puisse déterminer le mouvement d'un fluide, en quelque état qu'il se trouve, & par quelques forces qu'il soit sollicité.
>
> On doit aussi supposer, que l'état du fluide dans un certain tems soit connu, & que je nommerai l'état primitif du fluide,… et le mouvement qui leur aura été imprimé…
>
> En troisième lieu, il faut compter parmi les données les forces externes, à la sollicitation desquelles le fluide est assujetti: je nomme ici les forces externes…

Euler had in mind to study the fluid flow around a vessel! It was a very clearly written article, *la merveille* for historians of fluid mechanics, and an important contribution in the Age of Enlightenment. Euler's idea was to describe the motion of a perfectly inviscous fluid subject to any kinds of forces, by mathematical equations. He derived one of the earliest systems of first-order partial differential equations in mathematical physics. Euler ended up with a system of four equations in five unknowns: pressure, three velocity components and density. He overlooked an equation for temperature, the link between density and pressure, but in 1755 this seemed to be insignificant.

Euler had these ideas when the calculus of partial differential equations was first being developed. The new analysis had started in the 1740's with contributions by d'Alembert, Euler and Clairaut. [Kline, ch. 22, 1972, Demidov, 1982, 1989, Youschkevitch, 1989, Paty, 1998] The only mathematical tool available to Euler was the concept of total differentials. This is why Euler wrote explicitly the following warning:

> On comprend aisément que cette matière est beaucoup plus difficile, & qu'elle renferme des recherches incomparablement plus profondes, de sorte que s'il y reflète des difficultés, ce ne sera pas du côté de la mécanique, mais uniquement du côté de l'analytique…

Euler's 1755 article is one of the best examples of geometrical and diagrammatic deduction. We are struck by its simplicity in both proofs and reasoning. Euler had mentioned some difficulties from "l'analytique" (the mathematics). By this, Euler meant that he had derived the governing equations but that analytical solutions were difficult to find except in certain simple cases. In his conclusion, Euler complains "l'analytique n'est pas assez cultivée."

It is not our purpose to discuss and to present here the Euler equations. They have been well described elsewhere. [Salas, 1988, Truesdell, 1954, 1955, 1968, 1984, Visher, 1987, Wilson, 1992]

While working on the continuity equation, Euler derived another equation now called the advection equation. This equation arises from a linearization of the continuity equation and is important in meteorology and in fluid mechanics. This is the particular equation that we want to present. We would also like to describe certain mathematical tools still important in modern fluid dynamics. These include the elementary fluid element, the "eulerian" and "lagrangian" concepts of motion, the continuity equation, the total derivative, and Lagrange's solution of the advection equation.

2   The elementary fluid element

Because of the complexities of fluid motion, geometers of the 18th century decomposed the fluid into elementary fluid elements. In each elementary fluid element, the density of the fluid is assumed to be uniform. Like d'Alembert, Euler considered an infinitesimal parallelepiped carried by the fluid motion. This decomposition of the volume into parallelepipeds corresponds to a macroscopic description of matter in opposition to an atomistic description, even if Euler and Lagrange considered an infinite number of particles. Later, Navier [1822] will follow motions of "molecules," which was most unfortunate. This split between atomists and macroscopic modelers will have enormous consequences during the 18th century. Later, Stokes [1845] will clarify the motion of a fluid element and the definition of the velocity of a fluid, writing:

> In the first place, the expression "*the velocity of a fluid at any particular point*" will require some notice. If we suppose a fluid to be made up of ultimate molecules, it is easy to see that these molecules must, in general, move one another in an irregular manner, through spaces comparable with the distances between them, when the fluid is in motion. But since there is no doubt that the distance between two adjacent molecules is quite insensitive, we may neglect the irregular part of the velocity, compared with the common velocity with which all molecules in the neighborhood of the one considered are moving.

In Euler's article, u, v, and w are defined as three components of the velocity U at a point Z. The following figure (page 276a of the 1755 article) represents the path that will follow a hypothetical elementary fluid element:

Euler chose the Cartesian system of coordinates, and his fluid element is a parallelepiped. Euler expressed very clearly that we must know "l'état primitive du fluide," i.e., its initial values. During the time dt, the fluid element will move along its path (le chemin) from point Z to point Z' [Euler's figure seems incorrectly drawn, because the fluid path stays horizontal].

Hydrodynamics and meteorology make a clear distinction between two different approaches when considering the motion of fluids. In the first, an observer stays at the same position and observes the motion of the fluid from his position. This is called an eulerian approach. In the second approach, the so-called lagrangian approach, the observer moves with a fluid element along its path. Ironically, in this derivation, Euler chose the "lagrangian" scheme.

3   The continuity equation: the conservation of matter

The 18th and the 19th centuries are characterized by the refinement of the notion of the continuity of a function. Euler and d'Alembert were active participants in these developments.

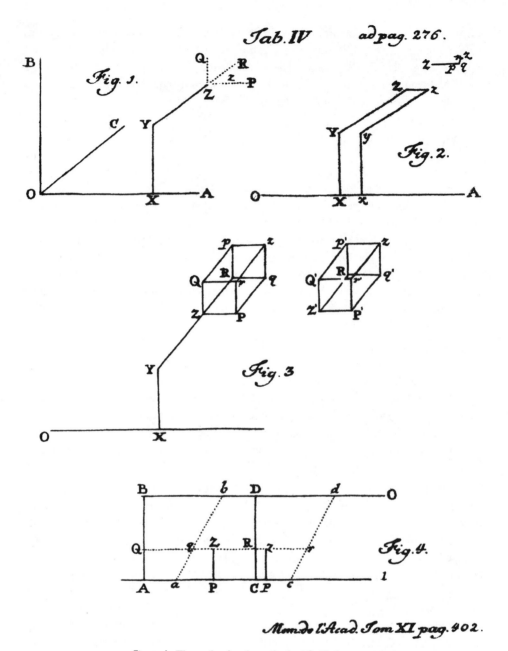

Figure 1. The path of an hypothetical fluid element

We can draw a parallel between the continuity of a function and the continuity equation for fluid motion. The basic idea is that the fluid motion must never be interrupted, and this was specifically Euler's idea of the continuity of a function. Euler succeeded in mathematizing the notion of continuity for fluids at a time when the notion of continuity for a function was not yet precisely defined.

Does the name of the continuity equation carry some ambiguity? The notion of eulerian "continuity" is too restrictive for the study of fluid motion because it requires differential calculus. Fluid dynamists preferred to refer to the continuity equation as the mass or matter conservation equation. However, Geometers of the 18th century were able to express the Leibnizian "law of continuity," "the labyrinth of the continuum" in mathematical formulas [Grant, 1991, Leibniz, 2001, Guénon, 2004]. For example, the second labyrinth is on the composition of the continuum, on time, place, motion, atoms, the indivisible and the infinite.

Fluids are divided into two categories: incompressible, compressible. Lagrange described water as an incompressible fluid, where the density q is constant inside a given volume; but air and steam are compressible fluids, where the density q is not a constant.

In 1750, d'Alembert derived a continuity equation for both compressible and incompressible flows. D'Alembert's reasoning was correct, "It is necessary that the infinitely small portion of the fluid included in the first parallelepiped be equal to that which shall fill the second." Unfortunately, d'Alembert had some difficulties in translating his reasoning into equations. We quote Lagrange: "But these equations did not yet possess all the generality and simplicity they could have." Euler, and also d'Alembert did not hesitate to use what Lagrange called "le circuit métaphysique des infiniment petits." Euler used the same symbols for partial derivatives as for ordinary derivatives.

Euler derived his continuity equation in a simple "lagrangian" way. In his equations, he established a link between the velocity components and a scalar function (the density q of the fluid). Euler remarked that at the initial time, the infinitesimal volume element is $dxdydz$ at the point Z. Because of the distortion of the different sides of the parallelepiped, the new elementary local volume at the point Z' is

$$dxdydz\left(1 + dt\left(\frac{du}{dx}\right) + dt\left(\frac{dv}{dy}\right) + dt\left(\frac{dw}{dz}\right)\right).$$

Here Euler ignores second order infinitesimals. If the fluid is incompressible, these two elementary volumes must be identical. It is called the conservation of volume because in an incompressible fluid the density is an invariant. Consequently,

$$\left(dt\left(\frac{du}{dx}\right) + dt\left(\frac{dv}{dy}\right) + dt\left(\frac{dw}{dz}\right)\right) = 0.$$

If we divide by dt, the continuity equation is:

$$\left(\frac{du}{dx}\right) + \left(\frac{dv}{dy}\right) + \left(\frac{dw}{dz}\right) = 0. \tag{1}$$

Lagrange later called this equation the incompressibility equation. It represents the rate of change of the volume. In the language of modern vector calculus, Equation 1 means that the fluid is divergence free so $\nabla \cdot U = 0$.

Euler also proved the continuity equation for the most general case of compressible, elastic flows, and for the density q of the fluid:

$$\left(\frac{dq}{dt}\right) + \left(\frac{d.qu}{dx}\right) + \left(\frac{d.qv}{dy}\right) + \left(\frac{d.qw}{dz}\right) = 0 \tag{2}$$

Lagrange called this mass continuity equation the "density equation" for compressible flow. The mass continuity equation shows a sort of symmetry between space and time. In a sense, the motion is doubly continuous in this combination of coordinates.

Using the modern notation of partial derivatives, Equation 2 can be rewritten as:

$$\frac{\partial q}{\partial t} + \nabla \cdot (qU) = 0 \tag{3}$$

Indeed, if the flow is incompressible, q is constant and Equation 2 becomes Equation 1.

The advection equation, the total derivative

After deriving the continuity equation, a relation between the velocity components and the density, Euler sought another relation drawn from considering forces. Taking P, Q, R to be accelerating forces acting on the fluid at point Z, Euler concludes that the fluid element is also affected by the pressure surrounding the fluid. Since Euler is considering a perfectly inviscid fluid, all forces act perpendicularly to the surface of the infinitesimal fluid element and there is no frictional tangential stress. Euler balanced all the accelerations, and he obtained a system of three partial differential equations.

The remainder of Euler's article concerns various discussions and linearizations on the possibility of solving these equations.

On page 300 of his 1755 article, Euler studied the Equation 4, describing the density q. It is is now called the advection equation or the convection equation. In order to simplify the problem, Euler linearized the equation of continuity Equation 2 for compressible flow. Because the continuity equation is non-linear, Euler assumed that the velocity $U = (u, v, w)$ was a constant and he took a, b, and c to denote the components of the velocity. Thus Euler obtained a simplified continuity equation with only one unknown, the density q:

Voilà une question analytique bien curieuse, par laquelle on demande quelle fonction de x, y & z doive être prise pour q, afin qu'il devienne:

$$\left(\frac{dq}{dt}\right) + a\left(\frac{dq}{dx}\right) + b\left(\frac{dq}{dy}\right) + c\left(\frac{dq}{dz}\right) = 0. \tag{4}$$

... Il est évident qu'après le tems t les coordonnées x, y & z, seront transformées par le changement $x - at$, $y - bt$, $z - ct$, d'oú nous concluons qu'on satisfera à notre équation en prenant pour q une fonction quelconque des trois quantités $x - at$, $y - bt$, $z - ct$.

Euler performed an intuitive argument. A function $q = q(x - at, y - bt, z - ct)$ possesses a differential:

$$dq = L(dx - a\,dt) + M(dy - b\,dt) + N(dz - c\,dt)$$

with

$$L = \frac{dq}{dx}, \quad M = \frac{dq}{dy}, \quad N = \frac{dq}{dz}.$$

Consequently:

$$\frac{dq}{dt} = -aL - bM - cN.$$

In meteorology, Equation 4 is called the advection equation. In other contexts, the advection equation is also called a one-sided wave equation. We can draw a parallel with the 1746–1749 d'Alembert solution for the vibrating string. The advection equation is a first order partial differential equation, but it belongs to the family of hyperbolic systems. Truesdell briefly mentioned the advection equation in the *Opera Omnia*. He just said that the solution must have the form $q = q(x - at, y - bt, z - ct)$, with a perfect symmetry among the three space variables. The solution is even reversible in time if the velocity $U \to -U$. Euler considered that the solution is "fonction quelconque," i.e., an arbitrary function. Engelsman [1980] gave an explanation of the origin of Euler's terminology:

> According to Euler the integration of an equation of order n is complete if the integral contains n arbitrary functions. In Euler's view partial differential equations are just like ordinary differential equations, in that the role of the arbitrary constant is taken over by an arbitrary function.

This concept of an arbitrary function became a hot topic in mathematics for the vibrating string equation and also later with Fourier's heat equation [Youschkevitch, 1989]. Curiously, the advection equation didn't attract the attention of historians of mathematics the way the string equation did, although it belongs to the prestigious class of mathematical models of the 18th century involving partial differential equations. In order to illustrate more clearly the advection equation, we shall use a more modern notation. The total derivative, also called the material, transport, or convective derivative of a scalar quantity (the temperature or the density) is defined as:

$$\frac{Dq}{Dt} = \frac{\partial q}{\partial t} + \frac{\partial q}{\partial x} \cdot \frac{\partial x}{\partial t} + \frac{\partial q}{\partial y} \cdot \frac{\partial y}{\partial t} + \frac{\partial q}{\partial z} \cdot \frac{\partial z}{\partial t}$$
$$\frac{Dq}{Dt} = \frac{\partial q}{\partial t} + \frac{\partial q}{\partial x} u + \frac{\partial q}{\partial y} v + \frac{\partial q}{\partial z} w. \tag{5}$$

The velocity is defined as $U = (u, v, w) = (a, b, c)$. We can write:

$$\frac{Dq}{Dt} = \frac{\partial q}{\partial t} + U \cdot \nabla q. \tag{6}$$

If the system is invariant, then $\frac{Dq}{Dt} = 0$. This first order partial differential equation is the advection equation. It implies that information is conserved along the trajectory of a fluid element. In other words, the rate of change of a scalar quantity with respect to time is compensated by the advection term $U \cdot \nabla q$.

If the scalar quantity is temperature or pressure, and if the velocity is U at some point Z, the information is simply translated along the path (le chemin), and rough weather forecasts become possible.

Figure 2 illustrates the motion of translation of a cloud (or rain) along its path. Without realizing it, Euler had in fact, all the theory necessary to produce short term weather forecasts using the advection equation, and he could have contributed to the solution of the 1746 problem of the Berlin Academy!

Lagrange and the method of characteristics

Some 26 years after Euler's article of 1755, Lagrange (1736–1813) published his Mémoire sur la théorie des fluides [1781]. There he writes,

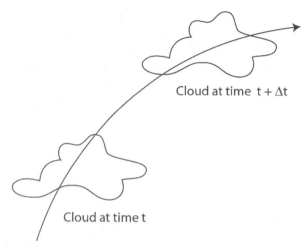

Figure 2. Translation of a cloud along its path

> Depuis que M. d'Alembert a réduit à des équations analytiques les vraies lois du mouvement, cette matière est devenue l'objet d'un grand nombre de recherches qui se sont répandues dans les Opuscules de M. d'Alembert, & dans les Recueils de cette Académie & de celle de Pétersbourg (i.e., Euler's work).

Lagrange will be more explicit in his book *Analytical Mechanics* [1881], where he made an historical review of the principles of hydrodynamics:

> Euler was the first to give the general formulas for the motion of fluids, based on their laws of equilibrium and presented in the simple and clear notation of partial differences ... Unfortunately, these equations are so difficult to integrate that it was not possible, until now, to solve them with the exception of a few limited cases.

Perhaps in deliberate contrast to Euler's geometrical reasoning and detailed steps, Lagrange uses no figures or mechanical arguments. We find only algebraic operations subject to a regular and uniform procedure.

In his 1781 article, Lagrange was interested in solving the channel problem. He had to consider the problem of the free boundary condition at the surface of the fluid. Let $A(x, y, z, t) = 0$ be the equation of the surface bounding the fluid. Lagrange explained that we must have the same type of equations at the walls (another boundary condition). From the motion of the fluid, the spatial coordinates (x, y, z) of a given particle becomes: $(x + u dt, y + v dt, z + w dt)$, while the time moves from t to $t + dt$. The equation for A becomes $A(x + u dt, y + v dt, z + w dt, t + dt) = A + \frac{dA}{dt} dt = 0$. The condition on A becomes:

$$\frac{dA}{dt} + u\frac{dA}{dx} + v\frac{dA}{dy} + w\frac{dA}{dz} = 0. \tag{7}$$

In other words, the total derivative of A is zero. Equation 7 is of the same type as Equation 4, the advection equation. Lagrange finds that this equation is integrable by the general method, he described in 1779 [Lagrange 1779]. This "Lagrange method" was the beginning of enormous progress in the solution of first order partial differential equations. Demidov [1982] has distinguished two stages in the development of the partial differential equations of the first order during the 18th century. The first one, the so-called formal-analytic period, lasted to the end of the 1760s or the beginning of the 1770s and was linked to d'Alembert and Euler. The second stage started with Lagrange, with the participation of Charpit. Lagrange wrote several memoirs on the theory of the first order partial differential equations in 1774, 1776, 1779 and 1787 [Kline, 1972, Engelsman, 1980, Fraser, 1991].

The next important step was made by Monge in 1787. Lagrange proposed to solve his Equation 7 by the method he described in his 1779 memoir (page 152). In this method, he replaces the partial differential Equation 7 with a system of four ordinary differential equations [1781, page 161]:

$$dx = udt, \quad dy = vdt, \quad dz = wdt, \quad dA = 0. \tag{8}$$

To explain the geometrical aspects of the method of characteristics, we have borrowed some information from a standard textbook [Stavroulakis and Tersian, 1999]. Let us consider a partial differential equation of the first order:

$$a(x, y, A)\frac{\partial A}{\partial x} + b(x, y, A)\frac{\partial A}{\partial y} = c(x, y, A). \tag{9}$$

A solution defines an integral surface $S: A = A(x, y)$. The normal to this surface at the point $P(x, y, A)$ is the vector $\vec{\eta}_p\left(\frac{\partial A}{\partial x}, \frac{\partial A}{\partial y}, -1\right)$ and let $\vec{v}_P$ be the vector $\left(a(x, y, A), b(x, y, A), c(x, y, A)\right)$. The scalar product $\vec{\eta}_P \cdot \vec{v}_P$ is zero and the vector $\vec{v}_P$ is tangent to the surface. We define as characteristic curves:

$$\begin{cases} x = x(t) \\ y = y(t) \\ A = A(t) \end{cases} \tag{10}$$

The integral curves of the characteristic system are given by:

$$\frac{dx}{dt} = a(x, y, A), \qquad \frac{dy}{dt} = b(x, y, A), \qquad \frac{dA}{dt} = c(x, y, A). \tag{11}$$

The solution of the partial differential equation is replaced by the solution of a non-linear system of ordinary differential equations. For example, if we solve the straightforward one-dimensional linear Euler advection equation $\frac{\partial A}{\partial t} + a\frac{\partial A}{\partial x} = 0$, the characteristic lines are straight lines, and the information u is constant along these lines.

4   Conclusion

At this step, we would like to link the Euler equations and the advection equation to natural philosophy. In 1822, Joseph Fourier published *The Analytical Theory of Heat*. The introduction to his work and the natural philosophy implied there deserve some comment. Fourier himself wrote:

> Les causes primordiales ne nous sont point inconnues, mais elles sont assujetties à des lois simples et constantes que l'on peut découvrir par l'observation, et dont l'étude est l'objet de la philosophie naturelle... Fourier adds later: L'étude approfondie de la nature est la source la plus féconde des découvertes mathématiques.

Non seulement cette étude, en offrant aux recherches un but déterminé. A l'avantage d'exclure des questions vagues et les calculs sans issue; elle est encore un moyen assuré de former l'analyse elle-même ...

The great mathematical models of the 18th and 19th centuries, the theory of potential, the vibrating string, the study of tides, the theory of gravitation, the theory of heat, the Euler equations in fluid dynamics, etc. were great stimuli in mathematical analysis. Among these equations, the non-linear system given by Euler equations was the most difficult to solve. The basic idea was the linearization of the problem, leading to, for example, the advection equation in fluid dynamics. Even if viscosity effects were neglected, fluid dynamics remained a very complex field to study. Because of their non-linearity, it was tempting to solve them numerically. The first numerical simulation in fluid dynamics appeared in England in 1922, when Richardson tried to do numerical weather forecasts. He tried to integrate the "primitive equations," i.e., the Euler equations of motion. Curiously, a simple advection equation is a most stimulating equation to study numerically. The advection equation is a typical example where central differences, which are supposed to have smaller truncation errors, engender more numerical instabilities than forward time differences, which are always computationally stable. It means that each category of time dependent problems needs special algorithms. The techniques of "upwind" differencing are now classical for the discretization of the advection (convection) terms. In these methods, the derivation is done in the direction of the wind carrying the information, i.e., in the "lagrangian" way.

References

Demidov, S.S., 1982. The study of partial differential equations of the first order in the 18th and 19th centuries, *Archive for History of Exact Sciences*, 26, 325–350.

——, 1989. D'Alembert et la naissance de la théorie des équations différentielles aux dérivées partielles. In *Jean d'Alembert, savant et philosophe*, Éditions des archives contemporaines, Paris, 333–350.

Engelsman, S.B., 1980. Lagrange's early contribution to the theory of the first-order partial differential equations. *Historia Mathematica*, 7, 7–23.

Euler, L., 1752. Principes généraux de l'état d'équilibre des fluides (E225), *Histoire de Acad. Roy. Sci. et Belles-Lettres de Berlin*, 11, pp. 217–273. (Berlin: Haude et Spener, 1757). *Opera Omnia* Series II vol. 12 pp. 2–53. On the web at `www.bbaw.de/bibliothek/digital/index.html` and at `EulerArchive.org`.

——, 1755a. Principes généraux du mouvement des fluides (E226), *Histoire de Acad. Roy. Sci. et Belles-Lettres de Berlin*, 11, pp. 274–315. (Berlin: Haude et Spener, 1757). *Opera Omnia* Series II vol. 12 pp. 54–91. On the web at `www.bbaw.de/bibliothek/digital/index.html` and at `EulerArchive.org`.

——, 1755b. Continuation des recherches sur la théorie du mouvement des fluides (E227), *Histoire de Acad. Roy. Sci. et Belles-Lettres de Berlin*, 11, pp. 316–361. (Berlin: Haude et Spener, 1757). *Opera Omnia* Series II vol. 12 pp. 92–132. On the web at `www.bbaw.de/bibliothek/digital/index.html` and at `EulerArchive.org`.

Fraser, C., 1991. The Emergence and Consolidation of Lagrange's Analysis 1770–1776, *Proceedings of CSHPM*, 4, 123-129.

Guénon, R., 2004. *The Metaphysical Principles of the Infinitesimal Calculus*, Sophia Perennis, Hillsdale, NY. Originally published in French in 1946.

Grant, H., 1991. Leibnitz—Beyond the Calculus, *Proceedings of CSHPM*, 4, 155–168.

Kline, M., 1972. *Mathematical thought from ancient to modern times*, Chap. 22, Partial Differential Equations in the Eighteenth Century, Vol. 2, 502–543.

Lagrange, J.L., 1781. Mémoire sur la théorie du mouvement des fluides, *Nouveaux Mém. Acad. Roy. Sci. et Belles-Lettres de Berlin*. On the web at `www.bbaw.de/bibliothek/digital/index.html`.

——, 1779. Sur différentes questions d'analyse relatives à la théorie des intégrales particulières, *Nouveaux. Mem. Acad. Royale des Sci. et Belles-Lettres*, Berlin. On the web at `www.bbaw.de/bibliothek/digital/index.html`.

——, 1881. Analytical Mechanics, translated from the *Mécanique analytique, nouvelle édition*, 1811, Kluwer Academic Press, Dordrecht.

Leibniz, G.W., 2001. *The labyrinth of the continuum: Writings on the continuum problem, 1672–1686*, edited by R. T. W. Arthur, Yale University Press.

Navier, M., 1822. Mémoire sur les lois du mouvement des fluides, *Mémoires de l'Académie Royale des Sciences de l'Institut de France*, 389–439.

Paty, M., 1998. *D'Alembert ou la raison physico-mathématique au siècle des lumières, Les belles lettres*, Paris.

Salas, M.D., 1988. Leonhard Euler and his contributions to fluid mechanics, AIAA paper 88-3564-CP, 98–103.

Stavroulakis, I. P. and Tersian, S. A., 1999. *Partial differential equations*, World Scientific, New Jersey.

Stokes, G.G, 1845. On the Theories of the Internal Friction of Fluids in Motion, and of the Equilibrium and Motion of Elastic Solids, *Trans. Cambridge Phil. Society*, 287–319.

Truesdell, C., 1954. Rational fluid mechanics 1687–1765, *Leonhardi Euleri Opera omnia*, ser.II., vol. 12, IX–CXXV.

——, I. 1955. The first three sections of Euler's treatise on fluid mechanics (1766), III. Rational fluid mechanics (1765–1788), *Opera omnia*, Ser. II, Vol. 13, VII–CXVIII.

——, 1968. *Essays in the History of Mechanics*, Springer-Verlag, New York.

——, 1984. *A first course in rational continuum mechanics, Vol.1, General Concepts*.

Visher, D., 1987. Daniel Bernoulli and Leonhard Euler: the advent of hydrodynamics, *Hydraulics and Hydraulic Research: a Historical Review*, 145–156.

Wilson, C., 1992. Euler on action-at-a-distance and fundamental equations in continuum mechanics, in *The investigation of difficult things: essays on Newton and the history of the exact sciences in honor of D.T. Whiteside*; edited by P.M. Harman, Alan E. Shapiro, 399–420.

Youschkevitch, A.P., 1989. D'Alembert et l'analyse mathématique, in *Jean d'Alembert, savant et philosophe*, Actes du Colloque de 1983, éditions des archives contemporaines, Montreux.

LEONARD EULER.

E. Handmann, pinx.   T. Cook, sculp.

Published by W. Bent, London, 1787.

Leonhard Euler
Engraving by T. Cook from a painting by E. Handmann. Published by W. Bent, London, 1787.

Euler Rows the Boat

C. Edward Sandifer

Abstract. It is widely known that Euler won the Paris Prize for his 1726 essay on the masting of ships. Two of his major works, the two-volume *Scientia navalis* of 1749 and his last book, *Théorie complète de la construction et de la manoeuvre des vaisseaux* of 1773, also dealt with ships and shipbuilding. It is less well known that Euler wrote two papers on the propulsion of ships when there is no wind. In a 1748 paper, Euler shows how a perpetual motion machine for propelling ships proposed by Jakob Bernoulli could not work. Then in a 1752 paper, also a Paris Prize paper, he gives four of his own ideas. Some of his ideas were, at best, bizarre, but one closely resembled a screw-type propeller. His ideas were apparently ignored, since the "official" inventor of the screw propeller was John Ericsson, who patented it in 1838, 86 years after Euler won the Paris Prize for the idea.

Long before there were Fields Medals or Nobel Prizes, the great scientific academies of Europe regularly proposed problems, with lucrative cash prizes for the best solutions. There has been an ironic change in the order of events for prizes over the last three centuries. Then, the Academies would meet and decide which questions were important. They would announce the problems, and savants around Europe would make their best efforts. Winners would be announced in a big ceremony, and the losers' entries would be "burned before the assembled Academy."

The Paris Prize was the most coveted of these. In the early and mid 1700s, the Paris problems often involved ships and navigation. For 1727, they posed a problem on the masting of ships, how many masts to use and where in the ship to position the masts. A nineteen-year-old Euler wrote his essay in 1726, and when the results were published in 1728, he won second prize. This sparked a lifetime off-and-on interest in Euler in mathematical and physical problems involving ships and navigation. Euler wrote only about a dozen papers on the subject, but he wrote two major books, including his last book, *Théorie complète de la construction et de la manoeuvre des vaisseaux*, published in two volumes in 1773.

An illustration from his paper for the 1727 Paris Prize is shown in Figure 1. It shows part of Euler's analysis of how the force of the wind on a mast will tilt a ship.

We digress for a brief history of the Paris Prize. The prize was founded with a bequest of 250,000 livres[1] by Rouillé de Meslay, a *conseiller* in Parliament who died in 1715. Half

---

[1] It is hard to know exactly what this would be worth now, but some sources suggest that 250,000 livres would be worth something like $100 million today.

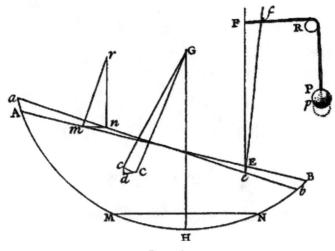

Figure 1.

of the income from this bequest went to the prize itself, while the other half went for the costs of administering the prize and to the Academy itself. The first prize was for the year 1720. After that, there were prizes almost annually from 1724 to about 1760, and then biennially until the dissolution of the Academy in 1793.

Some years, like 1724, either there were not enough entries, or the Academy thought that none of the entries were worthy. Then, they would re-open entries, double the prize, and extend the question two years. Thus, the question of 1724, on the collision of inelastic bodies, was asked again for 1726.

Occasionally, there were two or more winners, as with the doubled prize of 1739–1741 on capstans, which was split four ways. It seems that doubled prizes were most likely to be shared. Although most of the losing papers were "burned before the assembled Academy," some papers were spared, deemed "*accessit*," what we would now call "honorable mention." Euler's paper mentioned above actually earned an *accessit*. I suspect that the *accessit* was sometimes used as a political prize, as for the prize on the nature of fire for the years 1736–1738. Euler won the prize, but there were an unprecedented four *accessits* awarded to important people, Lozeran du Fiesc, the Compte de Crequy, the Marquise du Châtelet and Voltaire.

One year, 1760, there were two prizes. One was a special prize, funded anonymously, on the manufacture of glass without imperfections, presumably for use in telescopes and microscopes.

Every several years, the Academy bound and published volumes of the winning essays. There were nine such volumes through 1776. After that, winning essays were published annually in the *Mémoires* of the Academy. We give a table below, summarizing the topics and the winners through 1772, as summarized in the introduction to the ninth volume of winning essays. Some information there is missing or ambiguous. For example, sometimes it is not clear which Bernoulli is meant.

We return to Euler and his fifth paper on nautical topics, E137, *Examen artificii navis a principio motus interno propellendi*, (A study of propelling ships by the principle of internal motion), written in 1748 and published in 1750. Jakob Bernoulli's collected works

Year	Winner	Topic
1720	Crouzas Massy	Motion of a pendulum at sea
1724/26	Maclaurin Johann Bernoulli Maziere	Collision of inelastic bodies
1725	Daniel Bernoulli	Action of water clocks and hourglasses at sea
1727	Bouguer	Masting of ships (*accessit* by Euler)
1728	Bulefinger	Cause of gravity
1729	Bouguer	Measuring the elevation of stars
1730	Johann Bernoulli	Orbits and Aphelions of planets
1731	Bouguer	Declination of the compass
1732/34	Bouguer	Inclination of the orbits of planets
1733	Poleni	Measuring the path of a ship at sea
1735/37	Johann Bernoulli Daniel Bernoulli Poleni Tresaguet	Anchors
1736/38	Euler	Nature of fire
1739/41	Four winners	Capstan (three more *accessits* including Euler)
1740	Maclaurin Euler Daniel Bernoulli Cavalleri	Flux and reflux of the sea
1742	?	
1743	Daniel Bernoulli Euler	Inclination of a magnet
1744/46	Euler du Four D. & J. Bernoulli	Magnetism (a rare 18th century co-authored paper)
1745/47	Daniel Bernoulli four anonymous papers	Finding time at sea
1748	Euler	Irregularities in the orbit of Saturn
1749	?	
1750	?	
1750	Daniel Bernoulli	Currents
1752	Euler	Irregularities in the orbit of Jupiter
1753	Daniel Bernoulli	Propulsion of a ship without wind (*accessit* by Euler and Mathon de la Cour)
1754	?	

Year	Winner	Topic
1755	Chauchot	Pitch and roll
1756	Euler	Irregularities of the Earth (shape or orbit?)
1757	Bernoulli	Pitch and roll
1758	?	
1759	Broignard Euler	Pitch and roll
1760	d'Antic	Making glass without imperfections
1760	Charles Euler	Variations in the mean motions of planets
1761	Euler l'Abbe Bossut	On the loading of ships
1762	l'Abbe Bossut	Resistance of the ether (accessit to J.A. Euler)
1764	Lagrange	Motion of the moon
1766	l'Abbe Bossut Bourde de Villehuet Groignard anonymous	Loading of ships
1766	Lagrange	Irregularities in the motions of Jupiter and Saturn
1768/70	L. & J.A. Euler	Theory of the Moon (co-authored)
1772	Euler Lagrange	Theory of the Moon

appeared in 1744, and Euler noticed there an article where Bernoulli proposed a perpetual motion machine to propel a ship. The key idea is illustrated in Figure 2.

Bernoulli proposed to erect a wall near the bow of the ship and to suspend a heavy weight from the top of the wall at the point marked A. He would lift the ball to the point B and let it drop. It would swing through M, strike the wall at C, and propel the boat forward. At the same time, he hoped, the ball would bounce back to B, from which it would fall again and propel the boat forward again. Obviously, Bernoulli never actually tested his design. It would have been a rough ride.

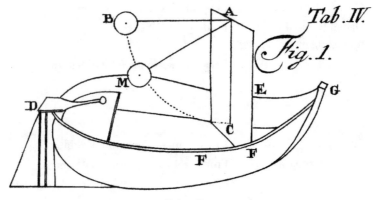

Figure 2.

Euler didn't build the boat, either, but in this article he works through some calculations to show why it couldn't work.

Now let's move on to Euler's seventh nautical paper, E413, written in 1752 for the 1753 Paris Prize, but not published until 1771. It was titled "De promotione navium sine vi venti", or "On the movement of ships without the force of the wind." Euler's son Johann Albrecht published a French version of this same paper in 1766. In typical essay form, Euler proposes five successively more sophisticated ideas for propelling ships. His first idea, illustrated in Figure 3, seems almost goofy:

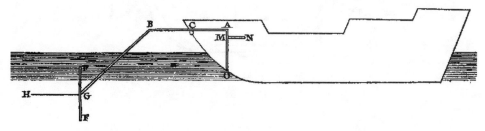

Figure 3.

Here, we have a vertical surface, FF, attached to a bent support $ACBG$ and suspended from the front of the boat. Workers inside the boat pull the system along the path MN, then lift it out of the water, push it forward and lower it back in to the water. It works kind of like a hoe. Euler decides it isn't really a very good idea.

Euler's next idea, shown in Figure 4, isn't very good, either. He proposes attaching paddles, FGF, to both sides of the ship and attaching the paddles to a shaft $DABCCBAD$. Workers on the deck can then turn the shaft and mechanically row the boat. It may seem as if Euler is wasting his time on these silly ideas, but as he studies them, he is developing some equations of energy and fluid resistance that are quite useful.

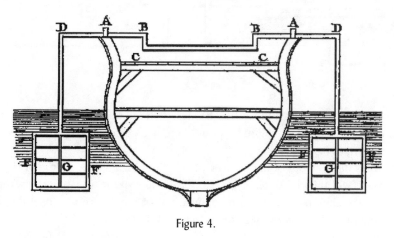

Figure 4.

Euler's third idea is a modification of the one-paddle system we just described. He arranges four paddles around the shaft, instead of just one, and he gets a reasonable amount of energy by designing a system of cranks, all labeled M in Figure 5. This is almost a 19th-century paddle wheel.

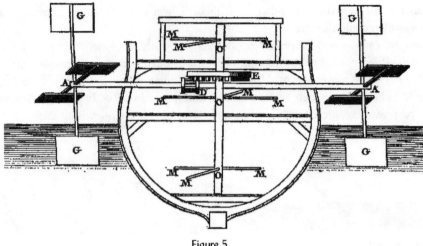

Figure 5.

Euler's fourth idea also would not prove useful until the 19th century. Shown in Figure 6, he proposed extending a kind of fan in front of the ship, then turning it with the same kind of mechanism that he had used for the paddle wheel. This idea was patented in 1838 by the Swedish inventor John Ericsson. Ericsson had in mind that the propeller would be turned by a steam engine.

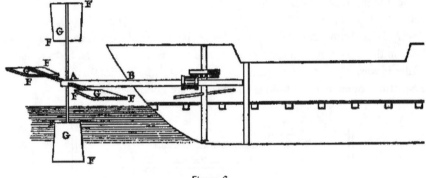

Figure 6.

Euler's final idea is almost futuristic. His idea, pictured in Figure 7, is to try to harness the motion of waves to move a ship. He proposes to put a trough, $AEFB$ just above water level in the stern of the ship.

The idea is that the tops of the waves will be a little higher than the rim of the trough, and the trough will fill with water. Then, since the water in the trough is above the water level around the ship, the water can be drained out of the trough to propel the ship. In principle, the plan should work, but the effect would be very subtle, and there may be problems keeping the ship steady enough to make it work. However, in the 20th century, electrical power generators were designed and built along the same principles, and they work just fine.

It seems that nobody tried to actually construct a ship that used any of Euler's ideas for propulsion. That is probably just as well, since, as he described them, they almost certainly

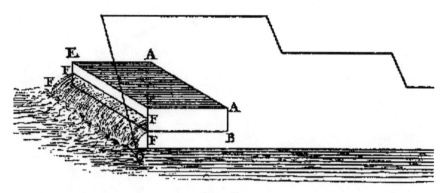

Figure 7.

would not have worked any better than Bernoulli's wall-striking idea would have worked. It is tempting to say, on the basis of these ideas, that Euler deserves credit for "inventing" the paddle wheel boat, the screw propeller and the wave-activated power systems. Not only would that be unfair to Fulton and Ericsson, who designed and built steam boats and screw propellers that actually worked, but to credit Euler would be an anachronistic view of history. Euler was using 18th-century ideas to try to solve 18th-century problems. His ideas didn't work. He had no reason to expect that, a hundred years later, steam engines would make ideas similar to his practical, and even important. There is apparently no evidence that Ericsson or Fulton knew of Euler's ideas. They had to re-discover them to solve their 19th-century problems.

References

[Ericsson] John Ericsson— www.pt5dome.com/JohnEricsson.html.

[E4] Euler, L., "Meditationes super problemate nautico," *Pièce qui a remporté le prix de l'académie royale des sciences* 1727, 1728, pp. 1–48, reprinted in *Opera Omnia* I.20, pp. 1–35. This and the other works by Euler are available online at www.EulerArchive.org.

[E94] ——, "De motu cymbarum remis propulsarum in fluviis," *Commentarii academiae scientiarum Petropolitanae* 10, 1747, pp. 22–39, reprinted in *Opera Omnia* I.20, pp. 83–100.

[E413] ——, "De promotione navium sine vi venti," *Pièce qui a remporté le prix de l'académie royale des sciences* 1753, 1771, pp. 1–47, reprinted in *Opera Omnia* I.20, pp. 190–228.

[Islay] Islay Wave Power Station— news.bbc.co.uk/1/hi/sci/tech/1032148.stm.

[Lalande] La Lande, Joseph-Jérôme, *Recueil des pièces qui ont remporté les prix de l'Académie Royale des Sciences depuis leur fondation en M. DC. XX. Tome Neuvième*, Paris, 1777.

[Maindron] Maindron, M. E., Les fondations de prix à l'Académie des Sciences, *La Revue Scientifique*, Deuxième Série, Tome XVII, pp. 1107–1117, Librairie Germer Bailière, Paris, 1879.

Lambert, Euler, and Lagrange as Map Makers

George W. Heine, III

Abstract. In the eighteenth century, cartography and analysis briefly coincided in a series of papers by Lambert, Euler, and Lagrange. These papers both founded the applied science of mathematical cartography and prepared the ground for Gauss' work on conformal mappings and differential geometry.

The symbiosis between mathematics and cartography was particularly fruitful in the notion of a conformal projection. The term *proiecto conformalis* was not introduced until 1789 [Youschkevitch, 1991, p. 746], but, as we shall see, the ideas were in place more than a decade earlier. In this survey, we take a brief glance at two important conformal projections known before 1700, then examine the contributions of Lambert, Euler, and Lagrange.

1   The Stereographic Projection

The stereographic projection, or planisphere (see Figure 1), may have been known in ancient Egypt [Keuning, 1955]. Synesius of Cyrene attributes its discovery to Hipparchus [Heath, 1981, p. 293]. Ptolemy's *Planisphaerum* describes its use, but in astronomy, not geography; in fact this projection seems to have been used exclusively for star charts and astrolabes until the Renaissance.

The planisphere has two appealing geometric properties. First, all circles on the sphere (both great circles and small circles) are carried into circles (or exceptionally into straight

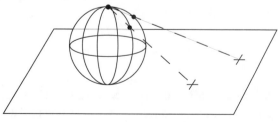

Figure 1. The stereographic projection. Every line formed by a point on the sphere and its image on the plane also meets the pole of the sphere.

lines) on the plane. This property, a simple consequence of Apollonius' work on subcontrary cutting planes (e.g., Book I, Prop. 5, of the *Conics*), was apparently known to Ptolemy, although he gave no general proof.

About 1500, the stereographic function began to be widely used and popular for geographic maps [Keuning, 1955]. Lagrange [Lagrange, 1778] states that "most modern Geographers" used it to construct their maps. This may have been because it was so easy to implement. Since all meridians and parallels were circles, one needed to find only (as Lagrange pointed out) three points on each to trace its entire curve.

The second property of the planisphere, unknown to Ptolemy, is that the projection preserves angular measure. That is, if two great circles on the sphere intersect at a given angle, then their images on the plane (which, by the first property, are circles or lines) intersect at the same angle. Edmund Halley (1656–1742) was the first to publish a proof, although Thomas Harriot proved the result in a manuscript from about 1614. (See [Pepper, 1968].)

2 Mercator's Projection

As the mariner's compass came into use in the late Middle Ages, ship captains began sailing out of sight of coastal landmarks, navigating by keeping their ships on a constant compass bearing (a constant angle between the ship's direction and the local meridian). Unless the direction is straight north, south, east, or west, the curve (called a *rhumb line* or *loxodrome*) traced out by a ship on a constant compass heading is represented on the globe by a line which spirals logarithmically toward each pole.

A loxodrome is not a great circle. Pedro Nuñez proved this in 1537 in his *Tratado de Esfera*. We do not know whether the Flemish mapmaker Gerard Mercator ever heard about the works of the Portuguese geometer, but by 1541, Mercator found a way to draw accurate loxodromes on a globe, and, eventually, to transfer them to straight lines on a sheet of paper. In 1569, he published his famous world map, with the title *A new and enlarged description of the earth, with improvements for use in navigation.* [1]

We do not know how Mercator actually constructed the map. He certainly used graphic instruments; tables of secants were not yet available, so that a direct computation such as equation (1) below would not have been possible. One plausible theory, advanced by Nordenskiöld [Keuning, 1955], was that Mercator divided the surface of the globe into zones of latitude ten degrees wide. While (graphically) transferring each zone to the plane, he scaled the length so that it matched the length of the equator, and then scaled the width of the zone by the same amount. On a globe of unit equatorial circumference, this would mean that a zone about the circle at latitude ϕ would need to be enlarged by $\sec\phi$, and the parallel would be represented by a straight line at constant ordinate

$$0.5 \cdot \sec\phi \cdot z + \sum_{\psi < \phi} \sec\psi \cdot z, \tag{1}$$

where z represents the width of each zone. Mercator used $z = 10$ degrees; by taking limits as z goes to zero, we get the Mercator projection M from a point at latitude ϕ, longitude λ

---

[1] "Nova et aucta orbis terrae descriptio ad usum navigantium emendatae accomodata"

on the sphere as

$$M_x(\phi, \lambda) = \lambda, \qquad M_y(\phi, \lambda) = \int_0^\phi \sec\phi \, d\phi = \ln\tan\left(\frac{\pi}{4} + \frac{\phi}{2}\right).$$

(Of course, on a real map, the planar coordinates M_x, M_y would be scaled and shifted in some appropriate fashion.)

For comparison, here is the formulation of the stereographic projection S in its "polar" aspect, that is, when projecting from the north pole to a plane tangent to the south pole. It is most simply expressed in polar coordinates (θ, ρ):

$$S_\theta(\phi, \lambda) = \lambda, \qquad S_\rho(\phi, \lambda) = \ln\tan\left(\frac{\pi}{4} + \frac{\phi}{2}\right).$$

If, like Riemann, we view the codomain of the stereographic projection as the Argand plane of complex numbers, then

$$S(\phi, \lambda) = \ln\tan\left(\frac{\pi}{4} + \frac{\phi}{2}\right) \cdot \exp(i\lambda).$$

The Mercator projection becomes

$$M(\phi, \lambda) = \lambda + i \cdot \ln\tan\left(\frac{\pi}{4} + \frac{\phi}{2}\right)$$

so that (modulo a reflection through the real axis), the Mercator projection is i times the complex logarithm of the stereographic projection.

3   Lambert

Sailors gradually discovered the advantages of Mercator's projection and came to use it exclusively for their nautical charts (in fact it is still used today). However, it was apparently not until the early eighteenth century that serious attention focussed on the problems of *terrestrial* cartography. Perhaps this came about in part because of the foundation of modern nation-states, with their need to map large areas accurately, both for taxation and for warfare. The invention of the telescope made accurate surveying possible.

As long sea voyages became common, travelers began to report that pendulum clocks consistently ran slow near the equator. In Book III of the *Principia*, Newton mentioned this phenomenon and suggested (Proposition 18) that perhaps the earth was not quite spherical; that it bulged slightly at the equator and thus the force of gravity was less there. The theory was confirmed after expeditions in the 1730s by Maupertuis to Lapland and La Condamine to what is now Ecuador.

Johann Heinrich Lambert published his *Notes and Comments on the Composition of Geographic and Celestial Maps* [2] [Lambert, 1772]. Lambert's work is considered the foundation of modern mathematical cartography. Lagrange gives Lambert credit as the first to characterize the problem of mapping from a sphere to a plane, while preserving a given

---

[2] *Anmerkungen und Zusätze zur Entwerfung der Land und Himmelscharten*

property, in terms of nonlinear partial differential equations. The technique was astoundingly fruitful, for he invented several whole families of conformal and equal-area projections, some of which are still in widespread use today. Lambert also seems to have been the first to take account of the ellipsoidal, rather than spherical, shape of the earth.

We shall look in some detail at his development of a projection now called Lambert's Conformal Conic, then briefly examine another projection called the Transverse Mercator.

In a section subtitled "More General Method to Represent the Spherical Surface so that All Angles Preserve their Size," Lambert begins:

> Stereographic representations of the spherical surface, as well as Mercator's nautical charts, have the peculiarity that all angles maintain the sizes that they have on the surface of the globe. This yields the greatest similarity that any plane figure can have with one drawn on the surface of a sphere. The question has not been asked whether this property occurs only in the two methods of representation mentioned, or whether these two representations, so different in appearances, can be made to approach each other through intermediate stages. Mercator represents the meridians as parallel lines, perpendicular to the equator...Contrastingly, in the polar case of the stereographic projection, the same straight meridians intersect at the proper angle. Consequently, if there are stages intermediate to these two representations, they must be sought by allowing the angle of intersections of the meridians to be arbitrarily larger or smaller than its value on the surface of the sphere. This is the way in which I shall now proceed. [Lambert, 1772, p. 28]

In other words, Lambert proposes to investigate conic projections. These have a history dating back at least to Ptolemy's *Geography*, which describes (more or less) an "equidistant" conic projection, where parallels of latitude appear as equally spaced concentric arcs. Conic projections preserve scale along paths of constant latitude, and thus are well suited for regions of the globe which extend east-west rather than north-south. In the eighteenth century, the equidistant conic was apparently rediscovered by Nicolas DeLisle, Euler's colleague at St. Petersburg, and used for the 1745 atlas of Siberia.

Lambert considers the representation M on the plane of a spherical point with colatitude ε. (The colatitude is the distance from a point on the sphere to the nearest pole.) Let P be the representation of the pole, μ be a point at the same latitude as M, such that the angle $MP\mu$ is "infinitely small." (See Figure 2.)

Since this is an angle between the representations of two meridians, and since there is assumed to be a constant ratio m between the angles of meridians on the sphere and their representations on the plane, we can also write this angle as m times the difference in longitudes $d\lambda$. Finally, let N be the representation of a point on the same meridian as M but with colatitude $\varepsilon + d\varepsilon$, and ν be the point which completes the trapezoid.

If $\mu M N \nu$ is to be similar to the spherical figure it represents, then it must preserve the same proportion of sides:

$$\frac{M\mu}{MN} = \frac{d\lambda \sin \varepsilon}{d\varepsilon}, \tag{2}$$

or, if we set $PM = x$, $MN = dx$, so that

$$M\mu = x \cdot \angle MP\mu = x m \, d\lambda,$$

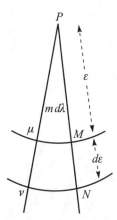

Figure 2. A copy of Lambert's original diagram. Some annotation added.

then (2) becomes

$$\frac{m\,x\,d\lambda}{dx} = \frac{d\lambda\sin\varepsilon}{d\varepsilon}, \quad \text{or} \quad \frac{dx}{x} = \frac{m\,d\varepsilon}{\sin\varepsilon}.$$

Lambert now integrates both sides to obtain

$$\ln x = m\ln\tan\varepsilon/2 + C.$$

If we now assume that x takes the value 1 when M represents a point on the equator (this is only a matter of scale), then the constant C must be zero, so that

$$x = \left(\tan\frac{\varepsilon}{2}\right)^m. \tag{3}$$

Lambert observes that the case $m = 1$ corresponds to the stereographic projection, and also argues, by expanding (3) in infinite series, that Mercator's projection is the limit as $m \to 0$. When m is strictly between 0 and 1, the result is a conic projection, known today as "Lambert's Conformal Conic". Figure 3(a) is a sample map, drawn by Lambert.

Later in the work, Lambert attempts to give the most general possible solution for the conformal condition. He considers the following system:

$$dy = M\,d\phi + m\,d\lambda \quad dx = N\,d\phi + n\,d\lambda$$

where M, N, m, and n are unknown functions of ϕ and λ. Geometric considerations, similar to those above, lead to the two conditions

$$M\cos\phi = n, \quad -N\cos\phi = m.$$

Lambert shows that the Mercator and stereographic projections fit this framework, but is unable to find a general closed-form solution. However, "since one eventually relies on infinite series using this procedure, I return directly to the two differential equations." Lambert produces x as a doubly infinite series in terms of $\cos k\phi$, and y as a doubly infinite series in terms of $\sin k\phi$. He then computes more than thirty of the coefficients, and gives an explicit formula for finding (recursively) all coefficients of terms involving the first five powers of λ.

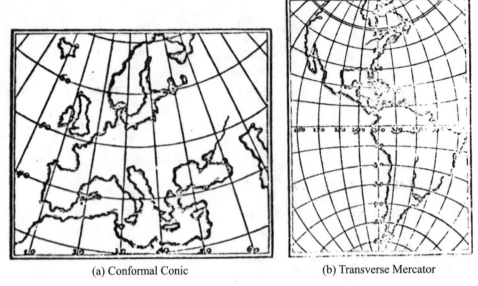

(a) Conformal Conic   (b) Transverse Mercator

Figure 3. Some of Lambert's Map Projections

The prodigious labor pays off when Lambert looks for a conformal map on which the equator and central meridian are both straight lines, and parallels intersect the central meridian at equal intervals. By manipulating the infinite series, and then "summing from below," he finds

$$x = \phi + \arctan \frac{\sin 2\phi \tan^2 \frac{1}{2}\lambda}{1 - \cos 2\phi \tan^2 \frac{1}{2}\lambda}$$

$$y = \frac{1}{2} \ln \left(\frac{1 + 2\tan \frac{1}{2}\lambda \cos \phi + \tan^2 \frac{1}{2}\lambda}{1 - 2\tan \frac{1}{2}\lambda \cos \phi + \tan^2 \frac{1}{2}\lambda} \right)$$

These are not simple, perhaps, but are at least in closed form. This is the sideways, or transverse, version of the Mercator projection, in which the circle of true scale is a meridian rather than the equator. See Figure 3(b) for Lambert's picture of a sample map in this projection. It does not map loxodromes to straight lines, and most circles on the globe become transcendental curves. Nevertheless, it has turned out to be enormously practical for maps of small regions, both because of good error control, and because adjacent regions north to south can be tiled together. The "Transverse Mercator," with adjustments for the ellipsodial shape of the earth (also given by Lambert) is today the most widely used projection for large scale maps in the United States.

4   Euler

Euler's contribution to mathematical cartography consisted of a series of three papers published by the St. Petersburg Academy in 1777:

- *On the representation of a spherical surface on the plane*; [Euler, 1778a] (E490).

- *On the geographic projection of the surface of a sphere*; [Euler, 1778b] (E491).

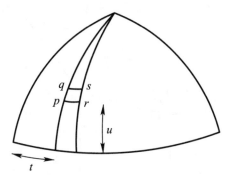

Figure 4. Copy of Euler's figure. Distances t and u added by the author.

- *On De Lisle's Geographic Projection and Its Use in the General Map of the Russian Empire* [Euler, 1778c] (E492).

We shall concentrate on the first of these three papers here. The second paper proves a number of results about the geometry of the image, under the Mercator and stereographic projections, of great circles and circles of latitude. The same topic was covered in greater generality by Lagrange. The third paper describes the equidistant conic projection used by Euler and DeLisle in their 1745 atlas of Russia.

The first paper is the longest and treats the subject in greatest generality. In the original, it consists of twenty-five pages with sixty numbered paragraphs.

Euler sets up the problem by considering a point p on the sphere at latitude u and longitude t. Please see Figure 4, a copy of Euler's original illustration.

He proposes to study the mapping by examining what it does to infinitely small variations du of latitude and dt longitude. To that end, he introduces a point q at longitude t, latitude $u + du$, a point r at longitude $t + dt$, latitude u, and a point s at longitude $t + dt$, longitude $u + du$. We look at the images P, Q, R, S under the mapping of the four points p,q,r,s. Please see Figure 5, again a copy of Euler's original.

Choose[3], arbitrarily, coordinate axes (in the figure, EF is the horizontal axis) and name x and y the coordinates of point P. Since P and Q are images of points p and q with the same latitude u, and P and R are images of points p and r with the same longitude t, the coordinates of the three points Q, R, and S are, respectively

$$Q: \quad EU = x + du\left(\frac{dx}{du}\right), \qquad QU = y + du\left(\frac{dy}{du}\right)$$

$$R: \quad EV = x + dt\left(\frac{dx}{dt}\right), \qquad RV = y + dt\left(\frac{dy}{dt}\right)$$

$$S: \quad EW = x + dt\frac{dx}{dt} + du\frac{dx}{du}, \quad SW = y + dt\frac{dy}{dt} + du\frac{dy}{du}.$$

The vectors PQ and RS each have an abscissa of $du(dx/du)$ and an ordinate of $du(dy/du)$. Thus the figure $PQRS$ is a parallelogram.

Euler remarks[4] that it is "obviously" not possible to represent a spherical surface exactly (preserving all distances and angles) on a plane. This would not have been a new or

---

[3] Paragraph 4 in [Euler, 1778a].
[4] Paragraph 7 of [Euler, 1778a].

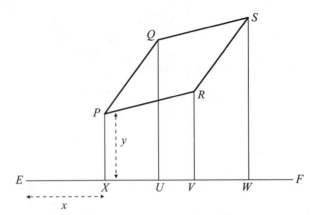

Figure 5. Copy of Euler's Figure. Distances x and y added by the author.

surprising result to his contemporaries. Lambert mentioned that such a mapping was not possible because the angles of a spherical triangle sum to more than 180 degrees. Even Ptolemy, in the *Geography*, seems to have recognized the impossibility. Euler's proof is still remarkable, though, as it uses purely analytic techniques. We examine this proof in more detail.

Suppose[5], says Euler, that we had functions x and y of the two variables u and t, giving the abscissa and ordinate, respectively, of the projected image of a point on the sphere at latitude u and longitude t. If these two functions preserved distance along meridians, then

$$\sqrt{\left(\frac{dx}{du}\right)^2 + \left(\frac{dy}{du}\right)^2} = 1, \quad \text{or} \quad \left(\frac{dx}{du}\right)^2 + \left(\frac{dy}{du}\right)^2 = 1. \tag{4}$$

Similarly, if the two functions preserved distance along a parallel at latitude u, then (because the circumference of this non-great circle is equal to $\cos u$ times the equatorial circumference),

$$\left(\frac{dx}{dt}\right)^2 + \left(\frac{dy}{dt}\right)^2 = \cos^2 u. \tag{5}$$

Finally, on the sphere, meridians and parallels always intersect at right angles. If this is to be true in an "exact" mapping, then (referring to Figure 5), the angle QPR must also be a right angle. But the line PQ forms an angle with the axis EF whose tangent is $(dy/du)/(dx/du)$, and the line PR forms an angle with the axis EF whose tangent is $(dy/dt)/(dx/dt)$. Thus [6],

$$\tan \angle QPR = \frac{\left(\frac{dx}{dt}\right)\left(\frac{dy}{du}\right) - \left(\frac{dx}{du}\right)\left(\frac{dy}{dt}\right)}{\left(\frac{dx}{du}\right)\left(\frac{dx}{dt}\right) + \left(\frac{dy}{du}\right)\left(\frac{dy}{dt}\right)}.$$

If QPR is a right angle, then its cotangent must be zero, and so, setting the denominator of this expression equal to zero, we arrive at the third condition, along with (4) and (5),

---

[5] The argument paraphrased here occupies paragraphs 5 through 9 of [Euler, 1778a]

[6] Euler does not say how he obtains this expression. But it can easily be derived from the trigonometric formula for the tangent of the difference of angles.

which a perfect map must satisfy:

$$\left(\frac{dy}{du}\right)\Big/\left(\frac{dx}{du}\right) = -\left(\frac{dx}{dt}\right)\Big/\left(\frac{dy}{dt}\right). \tag{6}$$

Euler now introduces a new function ϕ of t and u, satisfying

$$\left(\frac{dy}{du}\right) = \left(\frac{dx}{du}\right)\tan\phi. \tag{7}$$

In Figure 5, ϕ is the angle which the line PQ forms with the horizontal. With this definition, condition (6) implies that

$$\left(\frac{dy}{dt}\right) = -\left(\frac{dx}{dt}\right)\cot\phi. \tag{8}$$

Substituting (7) and (8) into (4) and (5), respectively, we obtain

$$\left(\frac{dx}{du}\right)^2 = \cos^2\phi, \text{ and } \left(\frac{dx}{dt}\right)^2 = \sin^2\phi\cos^2 u;$$

and therefore

$$\left(\frac{dx}{du}\right) = \cos\phi; \qquad \left(\frac{dx}{dt}\right) = -\sin\phi\cdot\cos u; \tag{9}$$

$$\left(\frac{dy}{du}\right) = \sin\phi; \qquad \left(\frac{dy}{dt}\right) = \cos\phi\cdot\cos u. \tag{10}$$

Now x and y are each functions of the two variables u and t, so we can write

$$dx = du\cos\phi - dt\sin\phi\cos u; \text{ and} \tag{11}$$

$$dy = du\sin\phi + dt\cos\phi\cos a. \tag{12}$$

Now comes Euler's critical insight. Since dx must be an "exact differential," the coefficients of du and dt in (11) must satisfy

$$-\left(\frac{d\phi}{dt}\right) = \sin u\sin\phi - \left(\frac{d\phi}{du}\right)\cos u\cos\phi. \tag{13}$$

Similarly, dy is an exact differential, so that

$$-\left(\frac{d\phi}{dt}\right)\cos\phi = -\sin u\cos\phi - \left(\frac{d\phi}{du}\right)\cos u\sin\phi. \tag{14}$$

If we multiply equation (13) by $\cos\phi$, equation (14) by $\sin\phi$, and add, we obtain

$$0 = \left(\frac{d\phi}{du}\right)\cos u, \text{ that is,} \qquad \left(\frac{d\phi}{du}\right) = 0,$$

which means that ϕ depends only on the variable t. On the other hand, if we multiply (13) by $-\sin\phi$ and (14) by $\cos\phi$, and add, this yields

$$\left(\frac{d\phi}{dt}\right) = -\sin u,$$

which means that $d\phi/dt$ depends on the variable u, a contradiction.

Since "perfect" mappings are impossible, what kinds of projections are possible under less stringent conditions? Euler spends the rest of the essay answering this question. He examines three sets of conditions:

I. The images of all meridians, and of all parallels, are straight lines, and each meridian intersects each parallel at a right angle. Today these are called *cylindrical* projections.

II. Angles are preserved, today called *conformal* projections.

III. Surface area is preserved, today called *equal-area* projections.

In keeping with our focus on conformal projections, we examine (II) in more detail[7]. Since a conformal projection preserves angles, the quadrilateral $PQSR$ in Figure 5 will be similar to the spherical figure it represents. Equations (4) and (5) do not hold, but if we set

$$\sqrt{\left(\frac{dx}{du}\right)^2 + \left(\frac{dy}{du}\right)^2} = m,$$

then, since the sides of the spherical figure are in the ratio $1 : \cos u$, the sides of the planar figure must be in the same ratio, i.e.,

$$\sqrt{\left(\frac{dx}{dt}\right)^2 + \left(\frac{dy}{dt}\right)^2} = m \cos u.$$

Invoking similarity again, QPR is a right angle, so that (6), and thus (7) and (8), still hold. Thus we can write:

$$dx = m \cos \phi \, du + m \sin \phi \cos u \, dt, \tag{15}$$

$$dy = m \sin \phi \, du - m \cos \phi \cos u \, dt \tag{16}$$

These are the conditions that a geographic projection must satisfy to be conformal.

Euler now looks at the purely analytical problem of solving (15) and (16). He suggests two different ways to proceed, a "methodus particularis" and a "methodus generalis." Neither yields a closed form solution. For the second method Euler approximates the solution using infinite series in the quantity

$$\ln \tan \left(\frac{\pi}{4} - \frac{\phi}{2} \right).$$

We saw that a similar expression appears in the formulas for both Mercator's and the stereographic projection. In fact, Euler shows that these projections are special cases of his general solution.

5   Lagrange

In response to the works by Lambert and Euler, Lagrange published two notes, together titled "On the Construction of Geographic Maps," appearing in 1779 in *Nouveaux Mémoires de l'Académie Royale des Sciences et Belles-Lettres de Berlin*. Of the three writers, Lagrange is perhaps the most accessible; he constantly works to interpret his symbols for the reader, and to make plausible his symbolic arguments; moreover his standards of rigour are reasonably close to contemporary ideas.

---

[7]Paragraphs 24–51 of [Euler, 1778a]. Euler entitles this section "Hypothesis 2. Qua regiones minimae in Terra per similes figuras in plano exhibentur."

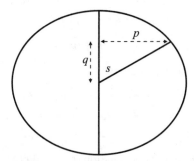

Figure 6. Lagrange's method for dealing with an ellipsoidal earth.

Lagrange begins by discussing Lambert's and Euler's work on conformal map projections, and complains that, although both have found a general solution to the system of differential equations, neither has yet exhausted the limits of the theories.[8] (This is not quite accurate in the case of Lambert, who invented several new families of map projections not considered by Lagrange.) The extension that Lagrange has in mind is the family of projections in which all meridians and parallels are mapped to lines or circular arcs. We shall examine some of the compact, intuitively appealing features in Lagrange's analysis, and mention some interesting geometric results.

We look first at how Lagrange accounts for the ellipsoidal shape of the earth. Lambert also dealt with this subject, but Lagrange's treatment is both simpler and more general. He assumes that the earth is a solid of revolution (the generating curve needs to be a differentiable function of the angular distance from the pole, measured at a central point on the axis of rotation; Lagrange was thinking of a slightly deformed circle.) Any point on the surface is determined by the angular distance t of its meridian from a designated central meridian, and by the perpendicular distance q between the point and the axis. (See Figure 6.) Let s be the angular separation, measured at the center of the axis, between the point in question and the nearer pole.

Lagrange introduces the quantity u satisfying $du/ds = 1/q$. On a sphere, $q = \sin s$, so that $du/ds = \csc s$, and $u = \ln\tan s/2$. If the cross-section of the earth is an ellipse of eccentricity ε, then Lagrange shows that for ζ satisfying

$$\tan\frac{\zeta}{2} = \tan\frac{s}{2}\left(\frac{1 + \varepsilon\cos s}{1 - \varepsilon\cos s}\right)^{\varepsilon/2},$$

the rest of the computations will carry through unchanged, using ζ in place of s. Lagrange produces a power series approximation in ε^2 and claims that the first two terms give "as much precision as one could desire." In fact, the eccentricity of the earth is about 0.007, so that two terms in Lagrange's formula yielded ample precision for the state of geodesy in the eighteenth century.

Next we examine Lagrange's search for general conditions of a conformal map. He denotes a projection as a pair of functions, x and y, of the longitude t and colatitude s. If the mapping is conformal, then any scale distortion m is the same in all directions, and we can write

$$dx^2 + dy^2 = m^2(ds^2 + q^2 dt^2).$$

---

[8]"...personne n'a enterpris de donner à ces Théories toute l'extension dont elles sont susceptibles."

Now, remember that $du/ds = 1/q$, and set $n = mq$:

$$dx^2 + dy^2 = n^2(du^2 + dt^2),$$

and since t and u are independent variables,

$$dx = n(\sin \omega \, du - \cos \omega \, dt) = \alpha \, du - \beta \, dt \qquad (17)$$

$$dy = n(\cos \omega \, du + \sin \omega \, dt) = \beta \, du + \alpha \, dt \qquad (18)$$

for some angle ω, where for convenience $\alpha = n \sin \omega$, $\beta = n \cos \omega$. Equations (17) and (18) are essentially the same as Euler's equations (15) and (16).

To solve them, Lagrange uses a technique similar to Euler's "methodus generalis," and, like Euler, fails to find a closed form solution. However, Lagrange goes on to apply his analysis to the geometry of the problem. He produces a function Ω, satifsying

$$m = \frac{1}{q\Omega} = (\Omega)^{-1}\left(\frac{du}{ds}\right) \qquad (19)$$

and shows that if r and ϕ denote, respectively, the radii of the osculating circles of the images of the meridian and parallel at a point in the plane, then

$$\frac{1}{r} = -\left(\frac{d\Omega}{dt}\right), \qquad \frac{1}{\rho} = \left(\frac{d\Omega}{du}\right).$$

Now consider what happens if we want the scale factor m to be constant along a circle of latitude on the globe. (This is the case with both the Mercator and the stereographic projections.) Then we want m to be a function of the latitude s only. By (19), Ω is a function of s only, so that $d\Omega/dt = 0$ and the radius of the osculating circle is infinite at all points on the image of the meridian. That is, the meridian must project to a straight line.

By further manipulation of Ω, Lagrange shows that if all meridians project to circles or lines, then the same is true of all parallels, and vice versa.

Having gone as far as he could with only the requirement that a map be conformal, Lagrange adds the condition that all meridians and parallels be circular arcs. He shows that it would be impossible to have the scale factor m be constant along all meridians (unless the earth were cone-shaped!). He produces a constant c which parametrizes the entire family of projections, taking on the special values $c = 0$ for the Mercator and $c = 1$ for the stereographic projection. The essay concludes with a detailed examination of the image of various critical points of the sphere, and a discussion of how to choose c to minimize errors for a chosen region of the earth (the criterion for minimizing errors is to minimize the variability of the scale factor m).

Lagrange's paper, though brilliant, illuminated a blind alley. The family of projections he discusses turns out not to be useful in modern cartography; nor, as far as this author knows, did Lagrange's ideas lead to any further development of mathematical thought. Nevertheless, Lagrange's paper is worth reading today, both for its clarity of exposition and its geometric insight.

Afterword

This paper was written with the hope that it might be useful to two audiences: those who will not read the original authors, but want a summary of the ideas, and those who do want to read the originals, and would like a guide to the main ideas. To the extent possible, I have tried to follow the original notation, with some minor concessions to make it easier on the modern reader, e.g., x^2 in place of xx, "ln" in place of "log", and so forth.

Our figures 2, 3(a), and 3(b) are copies of those in [Lambert, 1772]. Our figure 4 appears as Figure 1 on page 248 of [Euler, 1778a], and figure 5 appears as Figure 2 on page 249 of [Euler, 1778a].

In assessing the influence of each of the three authors, several remarks can be made. Lambert was the first to parametrize the problem, putting the Mercator and stereographic projections at opposite ends of a continuum and discovering what lay in between. As a former surveyor, Lambert was no doubt concerned about applications, and, in fact, it is the Lambert projections that have been most successful in applied cartography.

Euler extended Lambert's work with several new ways to parametrize the problem, He most thoroughly connected the study of map projections to the existing body of mathematics, in particular the study of functions and differential equations. Euler's work was likely influential on nineteenth century mathematics, when conformal mappings became a formal subject of study. Euler's work had practical significance, in improving the state of cartography in Russia. (See [Snyder, 1987] and [Calinger, 1996] for more details.)

Of the three works, Lagrange's seems the most contemporary in style, and perhaps most approachable to the modern reader. His geometric approach contrasts with Euler's more purely analytical style. However, Lagrange's work, though interesting and readable, apparently had less influence than either Lambert's or Euler's, on either mathematics or cartography.

Acknowledgments

Thanks to Janet Barnett, Waldo Tobler, William Dunham, and the reviewers for helpful comments. Thanks to Janet Beery for assistance in locating material on Thomas Harriot.

References

[Calinger, 1996] Calinger, R., Euler's first St. Petersburg years. *Historia Mathematica*, 23:146–147. Section B. Russian Cartography.

[Euler, 1778a] Euler, Leonhard, De repraesentatione superficiei sphaericae super plano (E490). *Acta Acad Sci Petrop*, 1777(1):38–60. Reprinted in [SSNH, 1894], pp. 248–275.

[Euler, 1778b] ——, De projectione geographica suerficiei sphaericae (E491). *Acta Acad Sci Petrop*, 1777(1):133–142. Reprinted in [SSNH, 1894], pp. 248–275.

[Euler, 1778c] ——, De projectione geographica De-Lisliana in mappa generali imperii russici (E492). *Acta Acad Sci Petrop*, 1777(1):143–153. Reprinted in [SSNH, 1894], pp. 248–275.

[Heath, 1981] Heath, S. T., *A History of Greek Mathematics, Volume II*. Dover, New York, 1981.

[Keuning, 1955] Keuning, J., The history of geographical map projections until 1600. *Imago Mundi*, 12:1–25, 1955.

[Lagrange, 1778] Lagrange, J.-L., Sur la construction des cartes géographiques. In *Oeuvres*, volume 4, 637–692.

[Lambert, 1772] Lambert, J. H., Anmerkungen und Zusätze zur Etwerfung der Land- und Himmelscharten, 1772. In [Tobler (tr), 1972].

[Motte (tr), 1995] Motte, A. (tr), *The Principia*. Great Minds Paperbacks. Prometheus Books, Amherst, New York, 1995.

[Newton, 1687] Newton, I., *Philosophiae naturalis principia mathematica*, 1687. In [Motte (tr), 1995].

[Pepper, 1968] Pepper, J. V., Harriot's calculation of meridional parts as logarithmic tangents. *Archive for History of Exact Sciences*, 4:359–413, 1968.

[Snyder, 1987] Snyder, J., *Map Projections—A Working Manual, USGS Professional Paper 1395*. United States Geological Survey, Washington, DC, 1987.

[SSNH, 1894] Societatis Scientarum Naturalium Helveticae, 1894. *Commentationes Geometricae volumen tertium*, volume 28 of *Opera omnia sub auspiciis Societatis Scientarum Naturalium Helveticae Series I*. Teubneri, Leipzig. Among volumes on mathematics, this is the 28th, and among those about geometry, this is the third.

[Tobler (tr), 1972] Tobler, W. (tr), *Lambert's Notes and Comments on the Composition of Terrestrial Maps*. Number 8 in Michigan Geographical Publications. University of Michigan Press, Ann Arbor, 1972.

[Wangerin (tr), 1897] Wangerin, A. (tr), Drei Abhandlungen über Kartenprojectionen von L. Euler. In *Ostwald's Klassiker der exakten Wissenschaften*, volume 93. Engelmann, Leipzig, 1897.

[Youschkevitch, 1991] Youschkevitch, A., Leonhard Euler. In *Biographical Dictionary of Mathematicians*, volume 1, pages 736–753. Scribner, 1991.

Index